"*Dark Refuge* appears in print for the first time since its original publication in 1938, presenting a world traveler's experiences with bohemian life in Paris in a novel that also serves (thanks to Rob Couteau) as a biography of Beadle's life.

Extensive annotated references link Beadle's experiences to his fictional representations, offering a literary backdrop for understanding both the atmosphere and progression of his fiction and its roots in reality.

Readers should be prepared for a sexual romp that is ribald, explicit, and thoroughly steeped in Beadle's personal experiences of the times.

Beadle's language is evocative, poetic, and dramatic: 'I simply slip through the other room of the café and out into the other boulevard, laughing to twist my guts. Nobody knows that I have a rendezvous. The coat and hat annoy me. How silly! I throw them away as I run, for I know it is late and I'm frightened that my beloved will not wait. God is crying harder than ever, and I suck in his tears. How funny it must be to weep!'

Whether exploring drug experiments and the revelations that follow them or descending into the sordid and colorful world of bohemian Paris, Beadle flavors all of his impressions with the same attention to flowery detail that makes his writing so timeless: 'Inexorably I was borne along up this staircase of Time as an express lift passes floors, glimpsing worlds where the highest form of life was apes chattering futilely in leagues of simian nations of their own; where vast beasts resembling tanks plunged through swamp and over prairie; where the sky was of steam and gas, and volcanoes burst like firecrackers on a Chinese New Year amid a seething sea; and on and on until there were no more worlds and naught seemingly but incandescent void.'

Pair this with the extensive notes and annotated references Couteau injects to not just explain but expand the story, for a sense of the unique literary and historical importance of this reappearance of Beadle's rare classic, which has been out of print for far too long.

Libraries seeking literary representations of the marriage between fiction and nonfiction will find *Dark Refuge* a fine example. The 200+ annotated notes come from previously unpublished letters and documents, combining with photos and historical reviews to represent a hallmark of not only literary fiction, but biographical research.

Dark Refuge deserves a place in any library strong in works of literature that represent the intersection between fictional devices and biographical inspection, whether or not there is prior knowledge of or interest in Beadle's works and importance."

– Diane Donovan, *Midwest Book Review*

The author of eight novels and dozens of short stories, CHARLES BEADLE was a world traveler who was born at sea in 1881. When he was eighteen years old he expatriated from England and spent a dozen years exploring South Africa, Rhodesia, Zambia, Uganda, the Congo, Mozambique, Borneo, and Morocco. In his mid-twenties he organized an expedition to Fez and traveled there disguised as a dancing girl to interview the sultan of Morocco. In the 1910s he lived in Montmartre, where he befriended his neighbor Beatrice Hastings, the mistress of Modigliani and translator of Max Jacob. Modigliani later portrayed Beadle in a drawing. During World War I he traveled to the United States, where he published his stories in *Adventure* and in the *International*, a cultural journal edited by Aleister Crowley. He returned to the City of Light in the fall of 1919, where he lived throughout most of the 1920s, eventually moving to the French Riviera.

In 1938 Jack Kahane's Obelisk Press published Beadle's last novel, *Dark Refuge*: an unrecognized modern masterpiece that quickly fell into obscurity. It contains thinly disguised portraits of Modigliani, Max Jacob, Beatrice Hastings, Léopold Zborowski, and various other figures who haunted the Parisian demimonde of this period. Beadle's brazen portrayal of drug fueled pansexual orgies prevented the chronicle from being distributed in the Anglo-Saxon world despite its literary merit and lyrical beauty.

In 1941 Faber and Faber published *Artist Quarter*, a nonfiction work pseudonymously coauthored by Beadle with Douglas Goldring, which is still considered to be the urtext of Modigliani biography.

Beadle is presumed to have died sometime in the 1940s, but the circumstances of his death remain a mystery.

ROB COUTEAU is a writer and visual artist from Brooklyn whose publications have been praised in *Midwest Book Review, Publishers Weekly, Evergreen Review, Witty Partition*, and the *New Art Examiner*. His work is cited in books such as *Ghetto Images in Twentieth-Century American Literature* by Tyrone Simpson, *Gabriel Garcia Marquez's 'Love in the Time of Cholera'* by Thomas Fahy, *Conversations with Ray Bradbury* edited by Steven Aggelis, and David Cohen's *Forgotten Millions*, a book about the homeless. His interviews include conversations with Pulitzer Prize-winning author Justin Kaplan, *Last Exit to Brooklyn* novelist Hubert Selby, Simon & Schuster editor Michael Korda, LSD discoverer Albert Hofmann, Picasso's model and muse Sylvette David, sci-fi author Ray Bradbury, film star and bibliophile Neil Pearson, and historian Philip Willan, author *Puppetmasters: The Political Use of Terrorism in Italy*. In 1985 he won the North American Essay Award, sponsored by the American Humanist Association. He has appeared several times as a guest on Len Osanic's Black Op Radio and on Monocle 24 in Europe.

A former writer-in-residence at MIT and a widely published poet, CHRISTOPHER SAWYER-LAUÇANNO is the author of *E. E. Cummings* (Sourcebooks), *The Continual Pilgrimage: American Writers in Paris, 1944-1960* (Grove), and *An Invisible Spectator, A Biography of Paul Bowles* (Weidenfeld and Nicolson). His translations include *Barbarous Nights: Legends and the Little Theater* by Federico Garcia Lorca, and *Concerning the Angels* by Rafael Alberti (both published by City Lights).

Dark Refuge

Charles Beadle

Edited with Annotations and an Afterword by Rob Couteau

Postscript by
Christopher Sawyer-Lauçanno

DOMINANTSTAR

This edition published in 2023 by Dominantstar LLC, New York.

ISBN 978-1-7360049-3-7

Thanks to Céline Cardon, Tanya Gaitanis, John Locke, Bobbie Marks, Neil Pearson, Geoffrey Pocock, Christopher Sawyer-Lauçanno, and Yongzhen Zhang for their unstinting generosity in sharing their time, resources, and enthusiasm. Céline's ability to ferret out data from the French municipal archives was truly extraordinary and led to a fuller understanding of the Beadle saga. John Locke, who has done so much to bring Beadle's fiction back into the public eye, was unflagging in his efforts to unearth additional info, and he even proofread my manuscript. Neil Pearson's brilliant writing in *Obelisk* whetted my appetite for *Dark Refuge*, and he also led me to Beadle's great-niece Patricia and her daughter Liz. Besides providing a living link to the author, Liz and Patricia shared copies of Beadle's letters, genealogical records, and photographic portraits, including the one featured on the cover of this book.

10 9 8 7 6 5 4 3 2 1

Contents

Portrait of Charles Beadle, courtesy of Beadle's great-niece Patricia and her daughter Liz. An inscription on the back identifies it as a Christmas gift from "your loving son." Circa 1899.

Preface

Four years after Jack Kahane's Obelisk Press published *Tropic of Cancer* he brought another controversial (and confessional) novel into print: one that was far more daring and provocative than Henry Miller's groundbreaking rhapsody to bohemian life in Paris. On the flyleaf of the new book, the legendary publisher penned a pithy summary of the text:

DARK REFUGE
BY
CHARLES BEADLE

> The conception of this book is so original that it takes a place of its own amongst contemporary novels.
>
> The story deals in the most outspoken language with the erotic relations of a group of individuals some of whom are drug addicts and some not. The scene is France for the most part and the characters consist of men of different worlds, their wives and their mistresses. By a curious device which it is probable has not before been used by novelists the reader is introduced into the minds of the various characters and is thus able to experience in the most clairvoyant manner their reactions, their unsuspected lusts and hatreds, their fears and passions. By this means the author arrives at astonishing deductions in the field of human sexuality both in its normal and abnormal manifestations.

> A most extraordinary book that can be confidently recommended to those readers who want something new, and totally different from the ordinary novel.

All of which is certainly true; yet the innovative and courageous publisher failed to mention several other intriguing aspects of the novel that, if they were more widely known, might have generated the sort of attention that a fresh creation needs in order not to fall quickly into obscurity. For one thing, the author (and principal protagonist), Charles Beadle, was a world traveler and British expatriate who paid an early visit to Paris in 1904; lived there during the 1910s; and settled in France through most of the 1920s and '30s. During this time he befriended fellow expat and neighbor Beatrice Hastings, who became Modigliani's mistress in 1914; and through her he met Modigliani, who later portrayed him in a pencil drawing. Beadle was a sensualist who participated in the decadent orgies of the Belle Époque and Roaring Twenties (Les années folles), and he depicts fictionalized versions of figures such as Hastings, Modigliani, Max Jacob, Léopold Zborowski, and several lesser known characters as they imbibe illicit substances such as hashish and cocaine and partake in the erotic adventures of this period. The language is at once explicit and poetic – a combination particularly disdained by the censors, since it renders the "obscene" with the dignity of high art – and as such, only Obelisk had the temerity to print what would have been banned elsewhere in the Anglo-Saxon world of 1938.

Which leads to another question regarding the fate of this unusual novel. In none of the material about Beadle that I've read so far have I found any reference to the fact that the composition of certain characters draws its inspiration from such well-known personalities. Why didn't Kahane mention

this on the dust jacket of the book in order to stimulate sales? I suspect that fear of litigation might have been the main reason that he didn't. Both Jacob and Hastings were still alive in 1938. Although Modigliani and his mistress Jeanne Hébuterne had already perished, their estates could certainly have raised objections. (And in 1941, when Beadle produced his Modigliani biography, he made a point of keeping the true identity of "The English Poetess" – Hastings – under wraps.) But as a result of such a guarded silence, modern-day readers may glide through the pages without ever realizing that *Dark Refuge* seems to be offering us an intimate look at the lives of such celebrated figures – and one engendered by a witness who was there and who participated with several of them in a quotidian manner.

Sadly, about a year after its publication, Kahane, already suffering from ill health, died on 2 September 1939. Perhaps his heart failure – due to alcohol consumption – was related to another incident that had just occurred: on 1 September the Nazis invaded Poland.* The day after he passed away, both France and England declared war on Germany, and the anticipated global conflict finally broke out. In the midst of this turmoil, *Dark Refuge* was forgotten. And until now, never revived.

Beadle later contributed to a book about Modigliani and the artists' scene in Paris, *Artist Quarter: Reminiscences of Montmartre and Montparnasse in the First Two Decades of the Twentieth Century*. Published in 1941 by Faber and Faber, it was pseudonymously coauthored by Beadle and the literary editor Douglas Goldring. *Artist Quarter* is now regarded as a seminal work on Modigliani and is cited in many of the biographies that followed. Even while complaining about its "gossipy" nature and occasional inaccuracies, contemporary art historians continue to rely upon

it. The text provides an engaging, informative read, and the gossip only serves to make for a spicier dish.

A prolific author of pulp fiction,† Beadle's production of both novels and short stories was steady and unmitigated throughout the decades. His last stories appeared in print in the mid-1940s; but then, no more was heard from him, and he seems to have vanished off the face of the earth. Even his death certificate has eluded the handful of researchers who have attempted to flesh out his biography.

***

In this edition of *Dark Refuge* British spelling has been Americanized and grammatical errors have been corrected. Textual changes involving anything more complex, such as inserting missing words or phrases, are indicated by brackets. The annotated footnotes and Afterword represent an attempt to further limn the portrait of this talented and elusive author. In the fashion of a roman à clef, I've included a "key" that may enable readers to more easily navigate through the tale, populated as it is with so many figures. But although it may be read as a confessional novel, I'm not suggesting that the characters in the book are identical replications of those that they may resemble in "real" life. Every novelist borrows from his experience, but once his effort is transformed into art the result transcends the source of its inspiration.

– Rob Couteau

---

* In his artfully rendered biography of Jack Kahane, author Neil Pearson calls him "one of the Second World War's first casualties." See *Obelisk: A History of Jack Kahane and the Obelisk Press*, Liverpool, UK: Liverpool University Press, 2007, p. 72.

Dramatis Personae Cum Clave

[Names in brackets: figures that the characters appear to resemble in "real" life.]

Sir Brandon Thorpe Bart (friend of Eddie Delorme)
Flossie Barton (opera singer mentioned by Vee)
Boys (and other figures) at the English boarding school:
  Clack
  Dexter
  Gratton
  Thorpe "Primus" (later identified in the chronicle as Sir Brandon Thorpe Bart, father of Brandy)
  Croft "Quintus"
  Phillips "Sextus"
  Boggy "Tertius"
  Pexton "Tertius"
  Nellie (the needlewoman)
Ceccilini ("Cecci") [Amedeo Modigliani]
Chauffeur who drives Vee home
Belle Delorme (Eddie's first wife, voluptuous strawberry-blonde dancer and theatrical singer. Eddie later divorces her and marries Dulcie)
Bertie Delorme (Eddie's brother)
Dulcie Delorme (Eddie's second wife, from Austria)
Eddie Delorme (husband of Belle and then of Dulcie)
Bill ("Beel") Farder, Sr. (narrator) [Charles Beadle]
Bill Farder's daughter [Jane Beadle]

Eve Farder (Bill's English wife) [Sylvia Grace Ellen Hornsby, daughter of Teresa Isabel Ashwell and Edmund William Hornsby]

Englishman (accompanies Bill to the medical students' ball)

Ferdie (romantically interested in Belle; he's also her financial backer)

Fifi (companion of Vee's chauffeur))

Francine (former French mistress of Bill; mother of Cecile, Madeleine, and of Bill's son, Bill Farder, Jr.)

Fred (Suzie's acquaintance, a butcher boy who's the son of her concierge)

Georgette (companion of Volodia, morphine addict and petty dope dealer)

Gerald (Vee's seventeen-year-old English lover)

German opera singer (Volodia's guest, whose companion is an Austrian contralto)

Isidore "Izzy" Ginsberg [Max Jacob]

Hermann (Volodia's Austrian boyfriend and fellow opium addict)

Hutchins (Arthur Manzen's chauffeur)

Jerry (Vee's former lover) [Alfred Richard Orage, editor of the *New Age*]

Leon (doctor friend of Theodosia)

Loulou (referred to as "Mother Loulou" by Vee's chauffeur)

Ludwig of the Berlin Opera (guest of Theodosia)

Magda (Cecci's mistress) [Elvira, aka "La Quique," a very young woman who was briefly living with Modigliani]

Maggie (Belle Delmorme's personal assistant)

Mamie (acquaintance of Suzie)

Max (pianist and homosexual lover of Theodosia's husband)

Betty Mommond (Belle Delmorme's lover)

Narantsoula (Romanian fortuneteller; seductress of Volodia)

Pauline (coquettish Italian housemaid of Eddie Delorme and Dulcie)
Smythe Price (businessman in the entertainment industry, interested in promoting Belle)
Bernard ("Boysie") Manzen (son of Vee and Sir Arthur Manzen) [rumored son of Beatrice Hastings]
Victoria ("Vee") Manzen [Beatrice Hastings]
Sir Arthur Manzen (Vee's husband) [Edward Chamberlain]
Smythe Price (theatrical producer; Belle's boss)
Professor (guest of Theodosia)
Serge [Léopold Zborowski, Modigliani's art dealer]
Silenus (Bill's gardener in Montmartre)
Suze (Cecci's romantic partner or "wife") [based either upon Simone Thiroux or Jeanne Hébuterne]
Theodosia's Japanese manservant
Tony (drug dealer who appears at an orgy attended by Cecci and Bill)
Monsieur le Baron de Volnier (Theodosia's homosexual husband)
Theodosia, Madame la Baronne de Volnier (wealthy sybarite, poetess, and self-identified "androgyne"; daughter of Monsieur le Comte de Bézues) [possibly based upon Natalie Clifford Barney, a wealthy blonde American lesbian known for her Parisian literary salons]
Volodia (Romanian violinist, morphine and heroin addict, and petty dealer)
Women in the sewing factory:
Flat Guts (forewoman of the factory)
Lolotte
Madeleine (Horse Face)
Pretty girl
Suzie

"Personally I have a theory that a writer should only use material which he has more or less actually lived. Anyway, I work on that principle."

– Charles Beadle, January 1920

Dark Refuge

La morfinomane (1887), a lithograph by the artist Eugène Grasset (1845 – 1917) portraying what was already a widespread problem in France. Grasset, a pioneer of the Art Nouveau style, was a Swiss expatriate who worked in Paris during the Belle Époque.

The street door of the house up on the hill was double locked; my room bolted. Through the long window was a view of a pine-feazed slope and an arc of lights. Occasionally arose the honks of cars; the gnashing of lorries; rarely, the important scream of a train.

Upon the walls were no pictures; nor any decoration perpetrated by ancient or modern. On a red-lacquered chest before a mirror-fumed censer at the alabaster foot of Ganesha,[1] the three-eyed elephant god, he of four arms, son of Siva. By the divan a brass tray contained a teapot, a cup, sugar, a bottle of colorless spirit and a phial of dark liquid. I have mixed a liqueur glass of alcohol with sweetened tea and a teaspoonful of the viscous matter. The taste was of saccharine and aloes. A native, shod in clogs, clattered down the cobbled lane. Lighting a stub

[1] Ganesha: A widely worshipped Hindu god. Deity of intellect and wisdom, and patron saint of writing (he is said to be the scribe of the *Mahabharata*), Ganesha is also associated with the overcoming of obstacles. As the Lord of Beginnings, he is invoked at the commencement of sacred rites and rituals (thus, it's appropriate that he appears here, at the beginning of the tale). Ganesha also corresponds with the Muladhara chakra of Tantric Buddhism (located at the base of the torso), the storehouse of "sexual vitality" (another fitting detail regarding *Dark Refuge*). In the narrative that follows, Ganesha's trunk is tentacular: it reaches out and extends into things, mirroring the author / protagonist's ability to penetrate into the psyche of various characters via the use of an omniscient first-person narrative. The phial of dark liquid is probably some form of opium.

of candle and a cigarette, I arranged the cushions comfortably, switched off the electric light, and reclined to await.

Late at night, when the local bloods are not celebrating the fall of the Bastille, or the rise of a demagogue, and the foreign colony has run out of credit for liquor, high dreaming has been done.

* * *

… A chameleon tongue of turquoise began to lick the side of the window. The candlelight became squalid in the wash of the moon. Beneath the kimono fairy hands caressed my body from brow to soles. The menacing rumble of a train developed into a whistle which hurtled through the window with the volume of a wireless siren; dashed about the room beating the wings of a trapped albatross; as suddenly was not, as a moth scorched by a flame. Hosts of centipedes; ice clawed, were scampering along my veins dumping plummets of anguish in my brain. Again the albatross shrieked in agony; the din of invisible wings droned into a tremendous rumble – roaring, moaning, into distance. My nerves unknotted. The balm of hush soothed.

Daring all, I opened my eyes. The walls had receded; the ceiling had risen, to the proportions of a temple.

Beatitude flooded my being. The marrow of my bones melted into exquisite lassitude. Down the long room was an enormous Chinese print such as a Hokusai might have painted, a symphony in blues from indigo and smoky marine to a polished turquoise welded by a masterline of fireflies. A waft of incense obscured the four arms and folded trunk of Ganesha. The middle eye moved; became fixed upon me. The other two continued their indifferent contemplation.

A sense of the approach of an epoch surged. The sacred serpent, coiled upon the paunch, was in labor. A blue egg,

streaked with cabalistic signs in yellow, was laid. Slowly the proboscis uncurled; meticulously placed that egg within the idol's mouth. The central eye shimmered. The lids closed in a portentous wink. Above the golden crown appeared a young snake. The chromatic skin scintillated as the sweet reptile writhed along a politely extended trunk. Tiny eyes drilled into my brain. Opened the mouth, green and yellow spotted as if with an obscure oriental disease, in a laugh that resembled the vibration of a sea roller on an Atlantean reef.

Then the snake glided from the trunk over a shoulder and around my neck, chuckling pleasedly, and inserted its head between my lips. I swooned through aeons of spatial ecstasy into an empurpled stellary night. A constellation quickened. Around a cornelian planet whirled the dark of a moon. Implacably I pursued her hidden charms until at last I gazed upon her face turned from her earth. The cryptic patterns thereon became a picture as seen through the wrong end of a telescope. Slowly they drew into focus.

On the peak of a vast mountain was balanced a triangular rock which bowed to me courteously amid a whooshing wind. The mountain shook and creaked with the sound of the crackling of tissue paper; yet the uproar of the landslide was louder than a war barrage. The scarlet ocean boiled. Arose the three-sided rock upon telescopic legs dripping gouts of blood.

Like flights of flamingoes the spume flew as the trunkless being waded towards me. Appalled, I stared. Arms, which shot out and in, were joined to metal thighs at the base of an isosceles head where hung the sex. A gargantuan frog's mouth expanded in a laugh exposing rotting teeth which were cathedrals – Chartres, Albi, Westminster, Bourges, Milan,

Auxerre; and among the upper ones I distinguished amazedly St Mark's, St Sofia, Winchester, St Paul's, Cologne, Rouen.[2]

Instantly I recognized, as had Jeanne d'Arc the Archangel Gabriel, that he was the Hashish God! Then an icy gust of wind, which was the sacred breath, smote me. I was frozen to brittle nullity.

[2] In 1931 three of Beadle's poems ("Hashish," "Voyage," and "Small Body") were included in the literary anthology, *Readies for Bob Brown's Machine*, Cagnes-sur-Mer: Roving Eye Press, 1931. This was a prestigious accomplishment, as his fellow contributors include the likes of Kay Boyle, Paul Bowles, James T. Farrell, Gertrude Stein, Ezra Pound, and William Carlos Williams. Some of the lines from these poems closely presage the foregoing passage in *Dark Refuge*. The poem "Hashish" begins: "Three eyes four arms elephanted headed buddha bellied alabaster body bathed in pool blue light + + Ganesha son of Siva + + + serpent on lapis lazuli bosom in labor orgiastically + + lays yellow blue eggs chosen meticulously by divine trunk." Toward the end of the poem Beadle pens his first reference to teeth and cathedrals: "bodyless god triangular head three eyes + + sex beneath chin like superlative necktie + + laugh exposes decayed teeth + + + whirls near nearer + + cathedrals Chartres Albi Westminster Bourges Milan Auxerre + + recognition throbbing thrills + + upper teeth upside down cathedrals + + Saint Marks Saint Sofia Winchester Cologne Rouen + + + unknown cathedral among molars + +." Therefore Beadle was composing in a literary mode and attempting to incorporate Ganesha as a subject as early as 1931.

Beadle's third poem in the Brown anthology, "Small Body," contains the phrases "conjugal" and "duty"; and it expresses all the dire emotional associations these words conjure for him, i.e., his terribly unhappy marriage to a Victorian prude and the domineering British mother-in-law that he became saddled with. (The wife and mother-in-law portrayed later on in *Dark Refuge* seem to be modeled upon these figures.) See Craig J. Saper and Eric B. White, eds., *Readies for Bob Brown's Machine: A Critical Facsimile Edition*, Edinburgh: Edinburgh University Press, 2020, pp. 105-110.

Within a dank grave I stirred, soundlessly crying against the wire-hot worms consuming me. A prick upon the back of the neck like that of a hypodermic needle,[3] evoked a tenuous sensation of warm comfort. Gradually through a sanguine mist loomed that grotesque form no bigger than a thumbnail. Greenly glowed this strange being; seemingly had bluish tints, yellow, even purple; yet was none of these, nor any combination; was of a hue unknown and indescribable.

The twin lower eyes gazed with the sublime indifference of Ganesha, the alabaster Buddha; only the center orb was alive; and that twinkled so benevolently that fear was rubbed out.

Apperceptibly I perceived by a dim light that came from what suggested a fo'c'sle lantern,[4] that we were within a circular chamber. The spongy walls oozed bright blood. The domed roof had a pattern resembling a dead man's view of daisy roots. Objects swam in a red mist seemingly in the interior of a submarine. On one side was a complicated system of gadgets – gauges, thermometers, dials, tiny bulbs, and tubes.

Some of the first contained white of egglike fluids. The largest gauge was a sullen scarlet which rose and fell with the regularity of a minuscule tide. Apparently there were no wheels, nor levers of control, which seemed odd.

On the other side in the bloodshed twilight I became aware of a kind of furniture composed of a similar spongy matter as the

[3] The needle anticipates the drug addiction of several characters in the narration that follows.

[4] "Fo'c'sle": Variant of "forecastle," the forward part of a ship's upper deck. Beadle's short story, "The Better Man," published in the March 1913 issue of *The London Magazine*, features several scenes that occur in a ship's fo'c'sle. The story revolves around a love triangle consisting of two brutish itinerant sailors and an equally coarse washerwoman. Beadle authored numerous sea stories that contain details based on actual experiences.

walls. As I approached I discovered that they had no substance. I was moving through them. But they were still there to sight solid: bladderish. My fumbling fingers sank into an ectoplasmic medium, an unpleasant sensation. A slimy envelope recoiled exposing a tapeworm-like mass. Curiosity compelled me to raise a portion with a fingernail; grasp it. A mild nausea, such as that produced by a too rapidly descending lift, preceded a vision:

... I am amusedly watching a drabbish face resembling an overstuffed stool, puffy around the neck. The indefinite eyebrows are slightly contracted; the rather full lips pursed as he observes a young girl laughing as she enters from the street on the arms of two young men, who are even more hilarious than she. Her fur coat is open, revealing her naked belly on which is painted an interrogation mark, using the navel as the beginning of the crescent. Around her loins is a brief skirt, bearing the inscription: "Quo Vadis?"[5]

"Disgusting!" mutters my friend.

"Well, I warned you that this was a medical students' ball[6] which would singe your British prejudices!" I tell him. "Come

[5] "Quo Vadis": Where are you going?

[6] The infamous Bal de l'Internat ("internat" referring to a medical resident or *interne* as well as the boarding house where they lived): A well-established Parisian saturnalia, first celebrated as a banquet in 1852. This annual ball was held in either September or October, after the final day of exams. Both the Bal de l'Internat and the equally notorious Bal des Quat'z Arts (the art students' ball, which was celebrated in the spring) were held at the Salle Wagram, near the Etoile.

Beadle was no doubt aware of Brassaï's much talked about *Paris de nuit*, a collection of sixty photos and accompanying essays, which was published in 1933, just five years before the appearance of *Dark Refuge*. (Later published in translation as *The Secret Paris of the 30's*.) One of Brassaï's photo essays portrays these ribald medical and art

on, let's go in – unless you're going to funk! Open your coat to pass muster."

I had invited this chap on a mischievous caprice, and curiosity to see how a hundred per cent respectability would react. He is clad in a sheet knotted over one shoulder and list slippers, a costume improvised at the last moment. The effect isn't at all bad – rather suggests an overfed Roman pleb at the tail end of the Decadence, or an early Christian being driven into the arena.

"An English doctor!" I introduce him mendaciously to the grinning entrance committee as I hand an invitation card for two people. We leave our overcoats at the cloak room and enter the huge ballroom. On the threshold he balks as if he didn't like the look of the lions. I laugh, enjoying him vastly; reflecting that if we hadn't dined pretty freely I'd never have got him here at all.

A hundred or more men and women are dancing and prancing. Most of the women are young and nude. A few wear sketchy bathing costumes, or a shawl; a Hawaiian skirt made out of straw; a single girdle of colored beads. One tall man sports a highlander's kilt around his shoulders, and the bonnet is attached to a belt; an athletic fellow, a bunch of fig leaves.

Along one vast wall is a drawing of a colossal phallus which a gargantuan comic nurse is about to cut off with scissors; on the opposite side is a gigantic pyramid on the steps of which is a sculptural mass of men and women in nearly all the conceivable sexual positions; at the far end of the hall red curtains represent an enormous vagina into which guests as they go to, and come from, the lavatory, dive and pop.

---

student balls. The book also includes a brief photo essay about Brassaï's visit to a Parisian opium den. *Paris de nuit* was widely displayed in Parisian bookshops and includes a text by the popular French author Paul Morand.

"Oh, I say!" bleats respectability, "that's a bit too thick really, what?"

"You shouldn't have come," I retort impatiently, "if you must carry the Albert Memorial on your back!"

The shock seems to have sobered him a bit. He turns quite indignantly.

"D'you mean to tell me, William, that this sort of thing is tolerated by the authorities in this country? Why, in England –"

"In England," I catch him up, "this sort of thing is done in secret. Not with such a crowd, I admit, for you'd have to go through London with a tooth comb to find a few hundred who are sufficiently free from taboos as not to take sex too seriously."

"But it's absolutely obscene!" he snorts.

"It's your mind that sees it obscenely. For these people, it's merely a Rabelaisian frolic! You English – or we English, if you like – would snicker over a smutty photograph, or even pay to go to a voyeur show. What your Anglo-Saxon mind can't stand is that all this is done in the open – almost public. I'll bet that you and I are about the only Anglo-Saxons present. They have a sainted horror of British prudery, and the sponsor gets hell if any of his guests make asses of themselves."

"But the women? What are they? Prostitutes?"

"No. Mostly models, and – free women. Although it's understood that any woman who comes must obey the rules of the game!"

"Oh, my God! disgusting! Look at that!"

A band of half-naked youths are carrying a nude girl on their uplifted hands. Close to us is a canvas and wood affair, a property gypsy van. Through a large window a satyr with a beard of rope yarn and horns on his head receives the living offering to Eros, and bangs the window shut. The band go off, joyously chanting a Rabelaisian song.

"Oh, that's a jolly sight too thick!" exclaims my British specimen. "I've had enough!"

"All right," I agree irritably. "Go to the devil if you like. I'm going to join in the fun. Ta-ta, old boy!"

I laugh as I imagine the stories he will tell when he gets back to shock his fellow clubmen, no matter how indignant he pretends to be. I wager mentally that he won't be able to drag himself away as I plunge into the throng.

There is a crowd in a corner watching something with the absorbed interest of people observing the digging up of a drain pipe in a London street. As I make my way towards them a man with a girdle of nasturtium twitches the tucked-in fold of a sarong I am wearing which falls to my ankles. As I stoop, someone pulls my testicles. Bystanders giggle and laugh. I reach the crowd hunched together. As I am taller than most of them I can see over their shoulders or heads. On the floor, held [by] two young men, is a girl. Another strapping fellow is performing cunnilingus while two others suck her breasts. She squirms and sighs prodigiously. Presently she moans, the lids flutter; the eyes recede as with an animal cry she reaches the orgasm; goes limp. The crowd cheer[s].

"And you, Madame?" says the operator, lifting his dewy mouth.

I look up. Seated above us on a staircase is the handsomest woman I've ever seen.

"No, thank you, Monsieur!" says she, smiling amusedly.

She is an ash blond with cerulean eyes. Scandinavian, I imagine. Drop diamonds glitter on either side of a jowl sensual and determined; as masculine as the shoulders. An Indian shawl of brick red and black envelops like a sheath a lithe body: small pouting breasts. One magnificent nude thigh and leg are exposed; boyish. On each side of her is a tall cavalier. Their trunks are clad in leopard skins clasped on each left shoulder by

a single large diamond. One man has long jet-black hair cut in the Assyrian manner; the other is white haired with a youngish face. Both are handsome and insolent.

"Theodosia!" I mutter, "with her favorite centurion and the Court poet!"[7]

As the girl victim, who has suffered the pleasurable sacrifice, dances away the spectators break up in search of other amusements. My gaze follows "Theodosia" as she stalks off. Her companions walk at each shoulder like an Imperial bodyguard. She is nearly as tall as they; slender; supple as a Praxiteles nymph. I wonder who she is. Breeding and wealth are stamped on every gesture. Either she is known and respected exceptionally, or her regal manner and her escort scare off marauding packs. I speculate, with a pang of jealousy, regarding their relations as they make for another stairway leading to a balcony which runs across the ballroom.

A very pretty kid, of perhaps sixteen, in a green bathing suit, is dancing with a black-bearded man. On a sudden they are surrounded by a whooping band. The girl is lifted bodily. Her partner makes no objection. Evidently that is part of the game. She is laid on the floor. The leader calls loudly for scissors. No one has even a knife, as everybody is practically naked. Deftly he tears up a leg of the costume; runs his hand up; then cries:

"A virgin! Name of God, a virgin!"

Instantly she is released. As half scared, but laughing gamely, she is helped to her feet, the crowd shout: "A kiss! A kiss!" Giggling with relief she blindly kisses faces thrust at her. The bearded partner claims her; they dance away as if nothing had happened.

I have not, I muse, detected a single case of jealousy nor ill temper during these libertine frolics. Nor a glimmer of shame;

[7] "Theodósia": feminine form of Theodósius; from the Greek *theós* ("god ") + *dósis* ("a giving"): given by God.

nor prudishness; neither normal coupling. Only that one form of sexuality was permitted by some unwritten law. Why, I couldn't quite grasp. Of course what went on in the gypsy van, or private rooms, or in the corridors, was just nobody's business.

A wild shouting attracted my attention. A tall fellow, with his body made up to look like a skeleton, is rattling a wooden scalpel in a douche can. Around his waist upon an apron are painted the words: The Quick and the Dead.

Carried on the shoulders of two chunky men, clad in a fig leaf apiece, follows an elderly, scraggy woman with shrunken breasts and wrinkled belly. She is shrieking with laughter as she waves her skinny arms. Upon her gray head is a gilded cardboard crown bearing the inscription:

"Sic transit –"[8]

Around her dance joyously a band of nude young girls. Amid shouts and laughter the procession makes the tour of the hall; comes to a halt beside the gypsy van. The window opens; appears the gorilla-satyr of the rope yarn beard. Into his arms she is tossed. A pandemonium of yells is drowned by the band striking up a syncopated version of: Just a little bit of love.

More or less orthodox dancing is resumed. I look for my puritan friend. Apparently I have lost my bet. Evidently Luther has chased him away from temptation. Someone slaps me on the bottom. I turn. He is the young surgeon who procured the coveted invitation for me. He is clad in an apron made of wooden surgical instruments of all sorts which swing wildly as he prances.

"Perfect, old man!" says he, laughing a bit drunkenly as he refers to my costume, a scarlet silk sarong. "On s'amuse! Quoi! And your English prude, he amuses himself, too?"

[8] "Sic transit gloria mundi": A phrase spoken at papal coronations, meaning "Thus passes the glory of the world."

"Oh," I tell him, "I think he's run away with his morals shattered."

"All the better!" declares the surgeon. "That's why we don't let in foreigners, unless they've had their cerebral vermiform appendices removed!"

Two nude girls seize him around the waist and the neck, and they go galloping down the hall. As I happen to glance up at the balcony I catch a glimpse of blond hair and diamond earrings, surrounded by a band of men. I ascend the stairs cluttered with couples, male and female, and both sexes. A young girl still panting breaks through perspiring bodies. My regal Theodosia has been presiding at a lesbian sacrifice, for the operator this time is a woman of shingled hair and mostly clad in jewels.

A party of young men rush[es] down the stairs into the hall. Attended closely by the leopard-clad escort she rises; they lean over the rail. The pack below look up for orders. She indicates a slip of a girl dancing near the gypsy van. Uttering cries and howls like hounds giving tongue they dash upon the selected victim. Bearing her high on their hands triumphantly they bring her before "Theodosia" who, smoking a cigarette in a long amber holder, interestedly watches the performance. The wide sensitive nostrils, the haughty aquiline nose and rather high cheekbones, the amusedly contemptuous smile of the sensuous lips, one bare leg crossed insolently over the other, provoke me: my ideal woman!

I wonder how I can get to know her. No earthly chance of making her acquaintance as she dances with no one. The bodyguard never shifts from her sides. The longer I regard her the more obviously excited I become. Then I rush off to look for my surgeon friend. He may be able to help me. At first I cannot find him. Hidden in some alcove, I reflect indignantly. Peering about I perceive a familiar bald head. I've won my silly bet! He is posted in a corner behind a pillar. His face is apoplectic; his

eyes almost goggle as he watches greedily as a cat a mouse hole, the gypsy caravan where the same traffic is going on with the satyr. I creep up behind him and slap him on the stern. He turns bellicosely.

"Oh, it's you!" he says scowling.

"Why, I thought you'd gone home!" I laugh.

"Incredibly disgusting!" he states indignantly. "Why, I've counted seventeen naked girls who have been shoved into the caravan thing!"

"You look as if you had!" I retort, "and you're furious because you haven't been invited inside!"

"Don't be a damned fool!" he snorts. "The place is nothing but a brothel. It shouldn't be allowed!"

Write to *The Times*, old chap!" I advise. "They would be interested!"

"It's a disgrace to France! It wouldn't be tolerated in any civilized –"

"Oh, shut up and have drink!" I invite him, taking an arm.

He holds back, fascinatedly watching another girl being put through the window.

"But, I say," he demands, "do they really –?"

I laugh derisively.

"But, I say," he repeats, unable to drag his gaze away, "there's only room for one man in there and eighteen girls one after another –"

"You're jealous!" I tease him, choking with laughter. "Why, they take turns, of course, each putting on the makeup for the role!"

"Disgusting!" he mutters, reluctantly following. "These French are degenerate, and –"

We have to struggle to get near the bar. Someone smacks his portly belly below the belt. He glares around.

"Don't be a bloody fool!" I admonish him angrily. "You shouldn't have stayed if you can't stand a mild joke. You're having the time of your life, but you won't admit it!"

"Nothing of the sort!" he growls. "I merely stayed out of a sense of duty to see actually how far they would go, and –"

But I have dived forward to get the drinks. He manages to join me. His face has resumed the normal expression of Anglo-Saxon complacency. I hand him a glass to stop his mouth, for I divine what is coming.

"I must say, William," he begins in his musty office voice, "that when I asked you to show me a bit of Paris life I never imagined that anything so obscene existed –"

"And Roman orgies?" I query.

"Oh – er – but that's a long time ago," he defends, "and the Roman Empire was decadent, and we've progressed since then."

"Oh, have we?" I retort flippantly, "Chin-Chin!"

I take a violent dislike to the man. His whole personality jars. I regret having brought the fool. Then I catch sight of my surgeon friend. I gulp my drink.

"See you again!" I tell my obnoxious specimen and start to elbow my way.

"No, no, we'll go immediately," he announces pompously.

"You may go to hell, if you like!" I call back, fighting a passage to the other end of the bar where my quarry is standing with a couple of men and three girls.

"Listen," I tell him, "I want you to do me a great favor!"

He laughs as if I were trying to be funny. I seize an arm and pull him out of the bar. The others are too busy laughing and talking to notice my friend's protests, and he is too tight, and too good-humored, to resist effectively. I pilot him to the middle of the hall.

"See, up on the balcony that linen blond smoking?" I inquire eagerly. "D'you know her?"

"That one with a fellow glued to each shoulder?" he queries. "Seen her around," he adds shrugging. "Nice piece of flesh, too!"

"Don't be stupid!" I reprimand him, offended for the moment. "She's not a model. Who can she be?"

"Who knows!" he retorts. "Either a chicken or a grande dame. There's nothing between here tonight!"

"Thanks, old man!" I say disappointedly, letting him go. I stand staring up at the balcony as he weaves back to his pals. Evidently she is still occupied with her strange Diana sport. I can't resist. Again I mount the cluttered staircase where the couples are becoming more riotous. Fascinatedly I watch her playing High Priestess over the lesbian rites. Once more as if she exudes an erotic aura, I become randy. After the last orgasmic quiver of the victim "Theodosia" raises her eyes; her regard meets mine for an instant. Involuntarily I spend ...

* * *

Only highlights of this experience remained. I had totally forgotten my specimen of genus Brittanicus. But "Theodosia" I recollect vividly. I had never found out who she was; never saw her again; but for years I had dreamed of her as my ideal woman.

This strange bladderish contraption must be an organ of memory, I reflected, tending to prove, as some psychologists and physiologists maintain, that every emotion, act, sound, color, is registered in a lobe of the brain, the subconscious, as on a disc which, except under powerful stimuli, such as hypnotic suggestion, or external shock, is repressed by the taboos of the conscious. Maybe the drooling of age, I mused, was the individual, deprived of a future and the active present,

pathetically fumbling in this queer spool of memory in an endeavor to live over again.[9]

My quaint illuminated hobgoblin was there observing me with that twinkle of the middle eye, the frog's mouth twisted in an enigmatic smile.

Mildly resentful of what I considered an ill-timed flippancy I realized that I was no bigger than he; and, almost simultaneously, the significance of my weird surroundings: *the circular chamber of spongy red was the interior of my own skull!*

With this seemingly occult knowledge came an immense relief; supernatural qualities of this unknown god vanished as did, consequently, all dread of him. So I was not in the least startled when a telescopic hand pointed to some object behind me. Turning, I perceived upon the level of the floor two oval windows, like ports, the panes of which appeared to be frosted, having in the centers tiny opalescent corneas. Intrigued I knelt to peer through one and looked upon:

* * *

A garden, roses climbing over pergolas, nasturtium assaulting poles; hollyhocks lining a wall like grenadiers convoying prisoners in gay uniforms – foxgloves, cosmos and wallflower. Beyond a low parapet are a few mossy roofs; below, an army of chimneys marches into misty distance splotched with twin towers and domes.[10] Arises a murmur resembling a far off surf

[9] This paragraph encapsulates two key themes of the novel: the role and mysterious faculty of the unconscious; and the narrator's focus on delving into unanswered questions about the past (viewed not only through his eyes but through the eyes of others).

[10] This description tallies closely with Beadle's portrait of the garden in his nonfiction chronicle about Modigliani, *Artist Quarter: Modigliani, Montmartre and Montparnasse* (coauthored with the

English editor Douglas Goldring and originally published in 1941 by Faber and Faber under the portmanteau pseudonym Charles Douglas). There, referring to the poet Beatrice Hastings in the opening sentence, Beadle writes:

> The English poetess and I had one great interest in common. We were both keen gardeners and both of us tried to grow English flowers in our respective plots. In mine I had planted hollyhocks, roses, nasturtiums, wall-flowers, and so on, and she had done the same in hers. As was natural between neighbors with a similar hobby, we were continually discussing our horticultural successes and disasters. The latter predominated in my case, as my garden was exposed, on the verge of the Butte, and the wind caused much havoc, particularly among the hollyhocks and trellises of nasturtium. Hers was walled on three sides, the fourth being occupied by the cottage.
>
> However, if my studio garden was exposed, the view from it was superb. I could see, over the tops of a few old houses, almost the whole of Paris as far as the distant hills of Meudon.

An entire chapter is devoted to Hastings (née Emily Alice Haigh), who remains unnamed to protect her actual identity (or perhaps to protect the authors from litigation), titled "The English Poetess." See Charles Douglas, *Artist Quarter: Modigliani, Montmartre and Montparnasse*, London: Pallas Athene, 2018, p. 225.

On 30 Oct 1916 when Beadle embarked from Cadiz, Spain to sail for the United States, he listed Hastings in the ship's declaration form under the column "closest friend living in country of departure," noting her address as 13, rue Norvins, Paris: a cottage in Montmartre that she would later share with Modigliani, located near the rue Gabrielle residence of Max Jacob. According to a notice that he placed in *Adventure* magazine (3 December 1919 issue, p. 188), upon his return to France in November 1919 he lived at 7, place du Tertre,

synchronizing with the melancholy skirts of seabirds. A tall gaunt man with a battered gargoyle face, dressed in blue overalls, whom I recognize as Silenus,[11] the gardener of my one-time garden in Montmartre, is watering.

"Bon jour, mon vieux!" I exclaim, forgetting that I am trying to shout at a man who is long dead.

Meditatively he turns the ghostly hose towards me. Then as if mocking my illusion come gusts of laughter from behind a trellis of wisteria.

Lounging in a garden chair with elegantly shod tiny feet upon the parapet wall, is Eddie. On the chair arm, draping herself as if she were a rare tapestry, is his wife, Belle, laughing to show her perfect small teeth as she raises a glass of cherry brandy. On cushions set on a stone bench against the studio wall, sprawls a rodent eyed young man in a waisted coat and white spats. Beside him is that type of girl, overblued of eyelids and scarlet of mouth, who is attractive through the haze of a barroom after the fifth cocktail. Testing a cane chair to capacity is an uddered young woman, handsome in a shouty way. Opposite to her is the official lover; fair, smoky-blue eyes, smallish, slender of hips, and lips of a shy young girl, Volodia. Sitting on the parapet which divides the garden from the one window, is Vee.[12] She wears a pink cotton dress and a cloche hat with black lace partially shading eyes of a child born old; generally she looks and writes as if someone had told her all about the Brontë sisters. At her feet squats cross-legged, with the dignity of an unshaven Roman senator in brown corduroys and a red scarf, a swarthy fellow whose marble teeth gleam in a stray sunbeam as

---

where he continued to reside until at least 1920. Beadle's flat was only about 270 meters southeast of Hastings home.

[11] In Greek myth Silenus was a comrade of Dionysus.

[12] Beatrice Hastings' nickname was "Bea."

he talks.[13] In the doorway of the studio a tall girl, supple, with a rare length of limb and, I noticed detachedly, a curious erotic quality of flesh, bears a tray of liqueurs and coffees.

So strong is the charm of my quondam mistress, Francine,[14] that resuscitated passion drags me into the maelstrom of

[13] This character, whom the narrator later refers to as "Ceccilini" or "Cecci," is clearly based upon the artist Amedeo Modigliani (1884 – 1920), who regularly visited Beatrice Hastings' home during their romantic involvement. Beadle's *The Esquimau of Montparnasse* (1928) utilizes the author's intimate knowledge of the Parisian bohemian scene during the 1910s and Roaring Twenties. In one passage the "Esquimau" protagonist, seated in a café, salutes "a swarthy man in corduroys who had the features of an unwashed Roman senator." The man has "bright" eyes (from having imbibed too much alcohol and / or other intoxicants) and is identified in dialogue as "One of the few painters left in the Quarter" (a reference to Modigliani). Twenty-three years later, on page 205 of *Artist Quarter*, Beadle describes Modigliani's "charming smile, now beginning to be slightly twisted into a sneer, and the still liquid eyes in that handsome face, resembling a Roman senator's," which "continued to fascinate women of every class." In this passage in *Dark Refuge* Beadle also mentions Modi's trademark scarf. This accoutrement was more than merely decorative; it protected the tubercular artist from catching a cold. Thus, *Dark Refuge* – replete with such signature details – often reads like a Roman á clef. For this reason I have provided a "key" in this edition that provides information on the various characters that may have been modeled upon actual historical figures.

[14] On page 226 of *Artist Quarter* Beadle describes a visit to Hastings' rue Norvins home while accompanied by his partner: "... my girl-friend, who was tall and slender, and had a rather swanlike neck, though nothing approaching Modi's ideal." He later mentions her by name: "Suze." On the next page Beadle writes that around this time Modigliani made a drawing of Beadle, titled "Le Pelèrin" (The Pilgrim), which was later stolen from the author:

> One evening, after dinner at my studio, Modi, who was full of drink and drugs, suddenly took it into his head that he wanted to draw me. He did so, producing his usual purity of line with a hand that was as steady as a machine. The sketch finished, he just toppled over and passed out. The drawing was one of the most curious I have ever seen by him. As usual with Modi's portraits, there was no physical resemblance to the sitter whatever; rather what another poet friend termed "the splendor of the soul." I don't know anything about the splendor of my soul – if it has any. But it was odd that he entitled the portrait "Le Pelèrin," and represented me in shorts, open shirt, and bare arms, with a Tirai hat on my head and the head of a hunting dog protruding between my thighs. I am practically certain he couldn't have known that I had spent many years in Central Africa, but his poetess friend always insisted that he was a medium. Some years after Modi's death the drawing was on show at Zborowski's gallery – just before the latter's death – and was stolen.

I conducted an online search for this piece on 9 June 2022 and discovered the following. According to Christie's website, a pencil drawing by Modigliani titled "Le jeune pelèrin" (The Young Pilgrim), dated from 1916 – 1917, was sold at auction on 18 June 2007 for $55,636.20. (Beadle was in New York by November 1916 and remained in the States till at least October 1918; so the dating for the drawing would more likely be 1914 – 1916, when Beadle's friend Beatrice Hastings was involved with Modigliani.) The drawing measures 18¼ x 12 in. (46.6 x 30.8 cm.), and it closely resembles Beadle's description of the piece featured in the 1941 edition of *Artist Quarter*. The provenance trail mistakenly indicates that the first owner was Crozer F. Martin (instead of Beadle), of Philadelphia, and that the drawing was later acquired by the Perls Galleries in New York, by 1951. The web site Artnet.fr mistakenly titles the piece "Le

apparent reality to greet her, a curious telescoping of time, the present ego barnacled with experiences reacting exactly as myself of that epoch. In my illusionary ardor I rush right through her. As I recoil in momentary horror, a tallish man whom I have not noticed, slightly bald at the temples, of ascetic appearance, rises from a chair to take the tray. I remark Francine's voluptuous smile as she regards him. Jealousy quickens. As I glare I recognize – myself! …

* * *

A queer numbness percolated; a dread that I was dead. Then luminously came the vision – for I must have turned my head away from the porthole in despair, of my tiny god soundlessly chuckling, as the middle eye closed in a month-long wink.

Again I peered hungrily at alter ego – and so very critically. To realize Burns's wish to see ourselves as other people see us,[15] approaches a unique experience. At times I had considered my face in a shaving mirror as insupportable, although not altogether as unprepossessing as many a man's: at others I had frankly loathed my features: frequently wondered how any girl could kiss me with enthusiasm. However, I was consoled by the reflection that most women have little aesthetic taste; would as lief adore any male as none. Now I had quite a thrill scrutinizing my exterior self as if I were a stranger. Well – the

---

Pelèrin – Charles Douglas," the latter being the pseudonym of Beadle and Goldring, the coauthors of *Artist Quarter*. But none of the auction houses connected with the drawing makes the connection to Beadle. (On page 209 on *The Esquimau of Montparnasse*, the Esquimau remarks: "I'm merely a pilgrim, I seek and never find.")

[15] A reference to the national poet of Scotland, Robert Burns (1759 – 1796) and his poem "The Louse," a line of which reads: "O wad some Power the giftie gie us / To see oursels as ithers see us!"

fellow wasn't so bad! He was slender; didn't move in jerks – as I had always slinkingly felt that I had, because in childhood I had been nagged for upsetting glasses and things; and the premature baldness on which I had spent so much money for quack remedies rather lent an air of intellectual distinction.

The eyes were dark brown, recalling that in romantic moments I had judged them to be of the color of cast iron, merely because some girl of my youth had told me so. In moments of depression, to me, they were just mud-colored. Now I perceive that neither estimation was correct;[16] that moreover they have the expression of a cudding cow. However, the chin was not as weak as secretly I had feared. The mouth – well, I had never until now seen myself talking amorously to a girl – looked quite kissable. I glowed with satisfaction. I had been so occupied with myself-that-was that I had forgotten those-that-had-been also.[17]

* * *

Suddenly I am aware of a newcomer – a smallish chap with large lizard eyes, the nose of a white owl, and the mouth of a whimsical fish set in a head which appeared to be as bald of eyelids and brows as a cranium. After he had pawed those

[16] On 12 September 1918, the thirty-six-year-old Beadle filled out a draft-registration card. It indicates that he was then living at the King George Hotel on 334 Mason Street, in San Francisco, and that he would be moving to 119 Central Avenue, in nearby Sausalito. Under the heading "Description of Registrant" it notes that he is of medium height with a slender build, blue eyes, and gray hair. His occupation is listed as "Novelist."

[17] The reflections of an older, more mature man looking back on life with a certain measure of newfound empathy, mixed with a tincture of regret, represents the third major theme of *Dark Refuge*, which was published during Beadle's fifty-sixth year, in June 1938.

whom he knows, myself, with a satirical smile, introduces him to Vee. As the gnomelike person kisses her hand, Vee titters, instead of purrs, her pleasure.

"Je vous connay biang par nom, mossieu!" she states. "Vos vers sont daylicieux!"[18]

"Prose poem, Madame, if you please,"[19] corrects the man of letters. "But you are too charming. I am ashamed to say that I have not yet had the honor to read Madame!"

"Oh, I am not well-known, mossieu, te! he! he! protests Vee, settling her skirt girlishly over plump calves. "I have not yet had the honor to be translated either."

"That is already done, Madame!" he assures her, "if I may have the honor. "

"Te! he! he! that is too good of mossieu!" replies Vee coquettishly.

Izzy regards her shrewdly, continues to stroke the glossy head of the Roman senator remarking mechanically, "Ça va Cecci?" and turns to myself like a hungry chameleon seeking a fly. "Y en a?"

Myself glances at the gentleman in white spats.

"Have you got any more, Tony?" myself inquires.

The young man grins. The three of them go into the studio. Tony returns slipping a fifty franc note into his pocket. Vee pours out a stiff brandy and seltzer; sips it slowly, listening to hearty sniffing disdainfully. Izzy comes back first, rubbing a nostril appreciatively. Ceccilini appears brighter-eyed, puts an arm around Izzy's waist and draws him onto the stone bench.

[18] A phonetic rendering of the Englishwoman's terribly accented French. Beadle also uses this device to poke fun at his fellow expats in his satirical novel, *The Esquimau of Montparnasse*.

[19] Along with his physical description, the "prose poem" detail helps us to identify the character as Max Jacob. The scene portrays Jacob's (imaginary) first encounter with the Englishwoman Beatrice Hastings.

Vee veils an angry glance by a te! he! he!, finishes her drink at a gulp. Myself sits beside her on the parapet. Rushes out Francine, eyes glittering, dances around the table, kisses myself on the mouth …

* * *

The ghost of that kiss still glowed; even the feel of her supple body and the peculiar odor of lubricity.

* * *

… Almost gasping myself breaks loose, vaults over the table, upsetting glasses and bottles, shouting:

"Tout le monde à poil!"

As myself begins stripping Eddie and Belle do likewise amid joyous squeals of laughter. Cecci, large eyes gleaming and teeth flashing as he hoots some Tuscan ditty, stands up, lets fall his corduroy trousers, and wrenches off his coat, revealing not a shred beneath.[20]

[20] "Tout le monde à poil!": Everyone naked! (or, "Let's get naked!"). According to the Welsh artist Nina Hamnett (1890 – 1956), who was a friend of Modigliani and whose memoir, *Laughing Torso*, chronicles this period, Modi rarely required any encouragement to get naked. An inveterate exhibitionist with a beautifully sculpted body, he would strip bare even while on the street. Describing one such incident that occurred while Modi, Hamnett, and Apollinaire were walking to a costume dance, she writes: "After a time Modigliani decided to undress. He wore a long red scarf round his waist like a French workman. Everyone knew exactly when he was going to undress, as he usually attempted to after a certain hour. We seized him and tied up the red scarf and sat him down." Hamnett first arrived in Montparnasse in spring 1914. See *Laughing Torso*, New York: Ray Long and Richard R. Smith, 1932, p. 54. Beadle explores this theme on

The pagan spirits of the party undress with the nonchalance of peeling off gloves. Vee watches them as if to be quite sure that everybody is going the limit, titters, hastily takes another drink, and titters again.

"Come on, Vee!" calls myself derisively, grabbing her by an arm. "I'll help!"

She struggles and squawks with a nymph-being-caught-by-a-faun note of delight; breaks away; scuttles into the studio to disrobe in modest seclusion. Then myself capers out into the garden followed by the others, except white spats and his girlfriend. We gambol like moondrunk apes, Eddie, slender as an immature youth, girlish of hands and feet, and the wistful lecherous mouth of a child; Belle, a Rubens model in miniature; Cecci, who gains muchly nude, a swart figure swiped from an Etruscan vase, dilated eyes rivaling the teeth as he twirls and twists, snatching flowers to thrust into the dense thatch of blue-black hair; Izzy, small and skinny, suggesting a crazy pale gnome; Francine, alabaster of flesh, broadish of shoulders and narrow of pelvis, a Greek youth dancing.

Then, just as myself pauses for a glance towards the trellis, Volodia emerges, hair like a bunch of blond aigrettes, playing a blood whipping Tzigane[21] air, a fiddling Hermes, but I note, so undeveloped that he resembles a eunuch. After a long look at

---

page 98 of *Artist Quarter*: "One of the effects of hashish on Modigliani was to reveal his exhibitionist tendency. At certain stages of intoxication he used to start to take off all his clothes, a procedure which greatly embarrassed his hosts, particularly if they were unaccustomed to his eccentricities."

[21] "Tzigane": The term "Tzigane music" refers to Romani music (once referred to as "gypsy" music). It was also the title of a composition by the French composer Maurice Ravel, originally created for violin and piano (with optional luthéal attachment) and regarded as a Hungarian rhapsody in the style of Liszt. The first performance occurred in London on April 26, 1924.

the prancing crowd, Silenus grins like an antediluvian satyr recently dug up, exhibiting black gums, and turns the hose on us …

* * *

Detachedly interested in myself again I was pleased to note that the belly was flat; that the build was rangier than the other males.

* * *

... Georgette, Volodia's girl, a Renoir built in circles of breasts, belly, thighs and backside, regards myself speculatively from the toes with pauses to the head. Behind her comes Vee with her comic veil and wearing hat and shoes: fingers in classic pose upon the bosom to hide the quickening droop. Laughing springs myself, wild-eyed, singing like a man in a frenzy of joy.

* * *

I glimpsed Francine who had stopped abruptly behind an arch of roses, and was malevolently watching myself and Vee. That look explained much of her character that I had never guessed. Then I was distracted by a sudden rush of myself to the trellis door.

* * *

"Come on!" I am shouting, "tout le monde à poil!"

Tony and his barroom girl are still seated on the stone bench spooning like a tweeny maid[22] and butcher's boy. A ray of the

[22] "Tweeny maid" (British informal): An auxiliary maid.

setting sun on the face of myself illuminates a malicious expression, almost the homicidal anger of an outraged Jahveh.[23] Then says the voice of myself with a growling purr:

"All right. But clothed Adams and Eves are not permitted in my garden. D'you mind going?"

Male and female sounds of expostulation; she tweety tweety, he a wheedling decayed baritone ...

That was funny! That is to me, inside my own skull; myself stark naked in the posture of an angel, with neither wings nor a flaming sword, sternly indicating the path to the gate of the garden. Yet the clitoris of my vanity was pleasantly tickled as I remarked critically that the lines of the torso and leg, the curves of the shoulder and neck, were quite sculptural.

* * *

... So they go, looking rather foolish, the wild notes of the violin and the whooping nude group mocking them out into the street, a too tight waisted young man and an overcolored lady weltering in Christian purity.

"But why wouldn't they stop?" demands Eddie, panting as he pauses to take a cigarette proffered by Izzy.

"Professional reasons, my dear!" retorts myself.

"Were they shocked? te! he! he! tittered Vee, who has covered her breasts with garlands of nasturtium.

"Of course they were! She's a whore and he's a pimp!" says myself.

Then myself, seizing Francine's hand, and the troop, proceed to caper, heedless of the flowers, beneath the hose of the resurrected gargoyle who, over his shoulder, is saying to the concierge:

[23] "Jahveh": The original text reads: "Iaveh."

"But for me, thou knowest, this is nothing! When I was gardener to Madame la Marquise de Mesdeux, every summer I watered the nobility of France! Name of God, Dame, oui! But that big one, she reminds me of a white brood mare down in Touraine. Tiens! if I were but twenty years younger and she in bed!"

"But she is disgusting!" protests the concierge. "She must have syphilis or something. Look, her buttocks and thighs are covered in sores!"

"Bah! thou art ignorant!" grins Silenus. "It is but the rash of the morphine needle. To a filly in bed they say it is like a bit of ginger to a stallion."

Prances Cecci who, grabbing my shoulder affectionately, demands so softly:

"Hast thou a little more of artificial paradise?"

"Chocolate or sugar?"[24] myself inquires smiling.

"Both!" says he, greedily.

"Sugar now then – and a little chocolate to take home," myself allows him.

Cecci emerges from the studio eyes glittering the more, shouting as he embraces Izzy. At them dashes Vee, te-he-ing; seizes Cecci around the waist. The three reel and caper among the flowers resembling maniacs while the violin flings notes like mad midgets in the sun.

[24] "Artificial paradise": A reference to Baudelaire's *Les Paradis Artificiels* (1860), which features poems about the hashish and opium experience. "Chocolate or sugar?" is perhaps a coded term referring, respectively, to hashish vs. cocaine. A character referred to as "the Chauffeur," who later appears in the narrative, explicitly refers to one of these "dope fiends" (Izzy / Max Jacob) as "an amateur of coke." During this period in Paris, both hashish and heroin were widely available in pill form.

Myself goes into the kitchen in the garden beside the studio to put on a kettle of water for coffee; follows Francine. She holds up her mouth …

* * *

The sculptural blending of the two nude bodies was admirable; suggested the Laocoön. Amusedly I noticed her hand – finely formed with delicate blue vein patterns – slide down the barren incurve of the flank into the fertile valley of the groin. Speculatively I regarded the expressions of insatiable hunger in the puckers of the pressed mouths; the growing rigidity of the male spine. As before I was conscious of the ghost of this passion; became curious to know what my own image was actually feeling.

Simultaneously an impulse made me turn away from the cornea porthole. In the reddish haze of my skull chamber I was aware of a faintly luminous streak. I stared, fearing that my strange Virgil had gone. Then I perceived that the streak was broadening and brightening. Gradually appeared the features, but out of perspective; the three eyes and the mouth came into focus, a phenomenon that puzzled me until I had realized that the god was two-dimensional, so that from a side view invisible, except as a spider thread of light.

The telescopic arm glided out in jerks; touched with an opalescent nail one of the filmy tapes which obediently I picked up. Then:

* * *

Myself-that-was: Concupiscence floods me. Inebriating is the taste of her spittle, the odor of her breath, the contact of her flesh; caresses. I draw her to me with such violence that she

whinnies through her nostrils. A recollection of her admiring Cecci's nude body stirs a sadistic jealousy that fans desire. Catching her hair savagely I bend back her head the better to suck the honey of her tongue. I release her panting; sink upon a kitchen chair; pull her astraddle. My guts bourgeon with ecstasy…

* * *

Once more I am back in my pate observing with a sense of astonishment; marveling that that girl had been able to afford me such ineffable pleasure of which even the memory had been effaced from the conscious. Much of the passion I had had for her remained, but of that particular occasion was no trace whatever. Hovered a hope that this strange spatial monster might likely have the power to transform me into the beings of others as well as of myself-that-had-been.

Instantly I was catapulted in the form of a gnat towards Francine who was now standing clothed, as was everybody else, about the table behind the trellis. As I darted up her nose she sneezed, and – I was in the sanguine chamber of her skull. I read the "instrument" board with the aplomb of an aviator. The heart gauge, the big, sullen scarlet one, was rising and falling normally; the needle of the nerve barometer wig-wagged steadily; the emotional dial shuddered around adoration-jealousy – these two states were marked at midday on the clock face as between fine-wet. The sex gland, although very low, was refilling rapidly. The fo'c'sle lantern, as I had dubbed it, was dullish; not nearly as bright as my own; and the imagination bulb as dim as a rushlight.[25]

[25] "Rushlight": A candle that consists of the pith of a rush dipped in grease.

While hesitating before the bladderish contrivance which tape to select, I remarked another gadget sticking out of the ecto-plasmic substance of the wall resembling handles. An impulse urged me to take hold of them … The first sensation was that of the solace of satisfied lust. Danced like gnats on a hot day hosts of impressions as on entering a foreign country, yet familiar, which I recognized, with the faint dismay that one has regarding a photograph of one's self in a crowd, as being undeniably "human, all too human." But swiftly that vague trace of my own personality faded into that of:

* * *

Francine: I can't stand that dirty Englishwoman when Beel[26] is talking to her. What he sees in her I can't get. Look at the crow's feet around her eyes! She's forty if a day! And that silly hat with a veil! All her clothes are old-fashioned. And her feet are large and she's knock-kneed. Look at the washed-out, never-was of a Volodia who sponges on him all the time for food and drinks and dope, just for making ugly sounds on his fiddle like an unoiled mangling machine! And that awful cow of his, Georgette! A flabby low-down woman of the Fortif[27] who should never have been allowed here. But Beel's a fool, although I adore him.

Belle is different, she's a grande dame, and so lovely, a body like a beautiful doll, and Eddie too. But he's a marquis. That's why I don't mind when we're all four together and Beel amuses himself with Belle and Eddie kisses me, and besides it's different when you're full of that stuff. You feel as if you

[26] "Beel": Phonetic rendering of the Frenchwoman's pronunciation of "Bill."

[27] "Fortif": Possibly a reference to the fortification zone in Saint-Ouen, which hosts the Thiers wall, constructed from 1841 to 1846.

weren't human somehow, and the sensations go on and on and on until you don't know where you are or who's there. And the bodies all united look so wonderful in the mirror and sometimes Beel will get up and sketch[28] Eddie and Belle and me tangled together. What I can't understand is why it doesn't seem to matter. It's just Belle and Eddie, but they're married anyhow, and I love them both in a way. I've often wondered why he never invites Cecci to these parties and I wouldn't mind if he did. But he's funny, Beel, he once remarked that Cecci had such a beautiful body that it was a pity he never washed, but there's a bath in the studio, so that was just silly.

I want to laugh right in the face of Vee as I hand her a cup of coffee and recall that her breasts are falling. There! Beel will go on talking, which I can't understand, and that makes me so angry I could smack her – and Beel too, because she is of the same race and ouf! that's like burning your fingers with an iron! But I will never let her have him if I have to slash her face with my scissors! and I won't let another woman kiss Beel except Belle for you can never tell what will happen when a man tastes strange meat, and Beel is too virile to trust far which is more than most men, except boys who don't know how to make love and only think of themselves like Anglo-Saxons.

[28] Perhaps Beadle dabbled in fine art. In April 1919, he published a fiction story in *Ainslee's* magazine titled "Uncle," which revolves around the theme of a young man setting out in life and hoping to become an artist in Manhattan's Greenwich Village. But his rich uncle, upon whom he is financially dependent, demands that he abandon his idealistic dreams and instead enter the business world. Beadle arrived in New York in November 1916, when the bohemian Greenwich Village art scene would have been flourishing. *Ainslee's* also featured work by Stephen Crane, Arthur Conan Doyle, Edna St. Vincent Millay, Theodore Dreiser, Jack London, and Dorothy Parker.

Funny, too, I like to kiss Belle. I like her taste. I smile at her as I think so and she smiles back and I wonder if she guesses. Beel likes her too, but not as he does me. I was jealous of her at first and made an awful scene when Beel wanted to have a party, but I had to give in for when he's like that he has the head of a mule and you've got to, but when Beel had Belle I didn't mind a bit because I'd had him several times and Eddie was kissing me so deliciously that I hardly noticed at all. Beel afterwards told me that Eddie was the politest man on earth for when Beel opened his wife's thighs, saying "D'you mind old man?" Eddie said, "Certainly, but not too strong, for she's not very profound," and then Beel would laugh as he added that neither was very profound, in the head or elsewhere, and he loved to tell that story, although I never could quite see why he thought it so very funny.[29]

But I'm sure that if I can keep Beel for a few years he'll get the habit of me and how I look after him and save him from being robbed by the concierge and other robbers, and then he'll marry me. Plenty of artists marry their models. If only he can get a divorce from his wife! How I wish she were dead! She's never been of any use to him and like all the Anglo-Saxon women she's as cold as a fish, Beel told me as much. If only she'd die I'd be all right for life as the wife of a writer even if he isn't well known. I've always heard that books sell more after they're dead. Then I'll teach my little bitch of a sister who puts on airs because she says she's a virgin at fifteen and engaged to a housepainter, that then I can't afford to know them, and as for mother she's always been a darling, and makes me cry when I think of her, for she's had a filthy time with father who always drinks and seldom has a job, and I know she's jealous of me in a way, thinking how silly she's been to marry father instead of living, when she was young, as I do, with a gentleman who has

[29] The French equivalent of the English word "deep" is *profonde*.

money, and will make a respectable woman of me some day, and I'll look after her too, and make her leave papa.

But oh! if only I could have a child by Beel that would make everything certain. Oh, if that horrible old woman and her brat would die![30] Yet if he wanted me to I'd adopt it just because it is his, and if what the doctor says is right that I can't have a child of my own. And how lovely it would be if I could and marry Beel, for then I could again go to Mass and confess and have my sins forgiven just as I did when I was a girl. Beel would laugh if he knew what I really believe but then he's a Protestant and nobody could swallow what they say …[31]

[30] If the foregoing account is based upon real events, Francine's remark would indicate that this scene occurred between 8 July 1915 (when Beadle's daughter Jane was born) and 13 September 1915 (when Beadle's wife, Sylvia Grace Ellen Hornsby, died in Cannes). But regardless of how much *Dark Refuge* is based upon actual persons or events, the intentional "time bends" that comprise so much of the narrative make it difficult to draw a logical or linear chronology. As the narrator says later on: "I was dwelling in a state where time is a curve. Delusion and reality had become so interwoven that there was difficulty to distinguish one from the other. No doubt, I reflected gravely, I had hit one of those famous kinks in time."

[31] From this point on we witness the author's use of an exceedingly rare (and challenging) form of fictional narration: the first-person omniscient, which allows for the narrator-protagonist to enter into the thoughts and feelings of the various characters in the story, who then speak directly to the reader. What makes *Dark Refuge* especially unique is that the narrator also makes various attempts to understand the mechanism that allows for this omniscient viewpoint.

Sixteen years before the publication of *Dark Refuge*, in Beadle's most commercially successful book, the pulp novel *Witch-Doctors*, the protagonist is "Moved by the ever-present curiosity to know what was going on in other people's minds." Another remark in *Witch-Doctors* foreshadows a major theme in *Dark Refuge*: "Natural

* * *

I paused to cogitate. The incident, unimportant in itself, I had wholly forgotten. However I had never had an inkling of Francine's matrimonial intentions and death wishes to serve her interests. To me she had been a charming companion on the sexual plane. Intellectually she had been nil – as are most lovely women! far indeed from the ideal such as I had imagined I had divined in the regal Theodosia. Still the experience of learning what other folks thought and never said, was extremely interesting.

I glanced curiously at her instrument board. The emotional dial was trembling on the jealousy side. The heart gauge was rapid; the nerve needle quivered; and the sex tube was full. Ah! I reflected, I never had had a notion that she had had a lech for Cecci. In retrospect I could quite understand; he had certainly been a handsome lad for whom women fell easily, and men, of that persuasion, too. Francine's observation about the bath was correct except that, as usual, she had missed the point. I had meant that he had one of those unfortunate greasy skins that always look dirty even after a Turkish bath, otherwise I should, probably, have invited him to our parties, for aesthetically, save for that blemish, he was as beautiful as a young god. Very naturally, curiosity pricked me to know what was passing in his

---

emotions suppressed find an outlet in some form." See Charles Beadle, *Witch-Doctors*, London: Jonathan Cape, 1922, pp. 148, 183.

As mentioned earlier, Ganesha's "elephant god" trunk is tentacular; it reaches out and extends into things, just as the narrator does via this colorful plot contrivance. In order to accomplish this in a manner that doesn't suspend belief, the author relies on the device of hashish intoxication; thus, the reader assumes that the narrator is describing a drug-induced vision.

mind at that relative moment. To dart, in the guise of a gnat down her nostril and up into Cecci's brain box was as swift as his sneeze. The fo'c'sle lantern was also duller than mine and of a slightly different hue. The heart gauge seemed bubbling; the sex tube was low; but the imagination bulb was burning vividly. Hastily I grabbed the present controls:

* * *

Cecci: O-oh! how happy I am! A wild desire to laugh and laugh and sing! Francine's face is very beautiful. I am delightfully surprised! The perky nose I had always considered ugly is elongated, her Botticellian mouth twisted marvelously, her long neck – the only point I liked about her – is so like a swan's that I feel the rapturous joy that Leda must have felt when the feathered body possessed her. The funnel-like structure grows even longer as I observe her. My fingers itch for a pencil, a chisel, to endow her with life. Yet I want to carouse I am so happy. But my throat is parched. I gulp the coffee in which I know dear Beel has put some of the elixir of heaven.[32] I am still thirsty. Singing I dance to the table and pour out some real absinthe which my rich English friend has bought especially for me. Everybody does things especially for me. Who can resist me, woman or man? I, godlike in art and love! A-ah, the divine color, the perfume, the taste racing down my throat! Francine smiles at me, her mouth twists adorably, almost to an ear. Hah! what a pair we should make for coupling, giving birth to litters of masterpieces. Then just as I am admiring her that absurd English woman shouts my praises in excruciating French.

[32] Possibly hashish, which was widely available in pill form and which could be swallowed or dissolved in coffee or tea.

"No, no, mossieu, please do not! You have already had too much.[33] I wish to talk to you, please!"

Saints of God, how I laugh!

"But I am so thirsty still!" I say.

"Then take some water with it!" says the idiot. "Pure absinthe will make you mad!"

Madonna! have I not been always mad? How can a madman be made madder? Then I recall that my friend Beel has told me that she is a poetess, and is crazy about me. But they all are! Yes, and she has money. She shall buy me paints and canvases and marble and stone, for I could feel her looking at my beautiful naked body. So, contemptuously I allow her to pour water, and I kiss her hand. I say:

"Madame, I drink to your beautiful eyes!"

Eyes: she has the small eyes of a calf on my uncle's farm, and when she laughs she makes noises like a hen with a toothache. I, too, laugh. How I laugh! for she does not understand – nor do they, the fools! As the divine liquid cascades down my gullet I hear her chicken noises darting upwards like scared flies. Then as I put down the glass she catches me in her arms and kisses me on the lips! Ouf! a kiss like cold macaroni! Oie! Oie! I shout, and grabbing her waist I pull her into the garden, and we dance – but she is as stiff as a wooden Madonna, and I thrust her from me and sing songs of my country …

* * *

[33] Upon his arrival in Paris, Modigliani presented a letter of introduction to the Russian Jewish artist Samuel Granowski (1882 – 1942). According to Granowski, during his decline Modi would consume "four of five absinthes at a single setting," a potent and dangerous quantity. See *Artist Quarter*, pp. 74-75. Granowski was arrested by the French police and deported to Auschwitz, where he died in 1942.

Suffocated by a sense of reeling through space in which people and houses were whirling like scraps of paper in a gust of wind, I fled. Then from an eye in my own dear skull I saw him who was so lately 'me,' rather I 'he,' squatting cross-legged in the middle of the garden smothered in, and tearing up by the roots, nasturtium and wallflowers, howling as unintelligibly as a dervish, oblivious of everybody.

Excitedly Vee runs to lift Cecci to his feet. Angrily he shakes her off; yowls the louder. She lets him go reluctantly, and, raising her skirts above her knees, capers about like a sucking pig with its throat cut, uttering pink squeals of laughter.

Cecci, with his gleaming eyes and teeth seen through a carnival mask of flowers, resembles indeed a drunken satyr. During his paroxysms he has torn open his velvet coat revealing the twilight tint of the torso.

As I watched the crowd, and among them myself, fluffed of hair, pelting the others with flowers, I gravely remarked that we were all drunk. Then streaked a falchion-edged desire to know again the being of that singing Bacchus. Instantly I had sped back into Cecci's skull:

* * *

Cecci: On the peak of a mountain am I seated, garlanded with flowers. Eagle talons are my feet. Wondrous music wisps from pipes that are made of the tibias of virgins played by mine own nine-clawed hands. Beneath a square black sun low in a gray sky dance in and out cactus of ebony, youths and maidens. Goose white are they, and all are somber and slitted of eyes, swan-necked and fluted of nose, clothed in down instead of hair.

Each and every one have I made with mine own marble hands, chiseled and stroked, smoothed and polished, into the immortal perfection that is theirs. And satisfaction fumes like the incense of pagan priests.

From behind a wrought iron yucca peeps a wine-lovely youth. His smile is perfumed with the eclectic sins of Greece. His lips and sex are more fragile than orchids. Sweet Yt-sar-edep![34] I call, for thus have I named him.

Before me he dances, and having done, trips to kiss me on the mouth so that the square black sun pauses, gray birds stop in midair, dark insects stop from shrilling; and all the company stands agaze at the sweetness of our joy.

I laugh and putting pipes to lips render pleasure, to these my children. When the bacchanal has set dear In-oy,[35] she whose breasts have cost me years of work to find their pure symmetry, breathes my breath and makes the world to sigh in awe at the ecstasy of child and maker.

Then as if worms were swarming in my guts an anger swirls. I perceive that these my creatures are two dimensional and have no color. Rage smokes like a midden. I arise and poison them with flowers so that not one is left, and strike the silly sun from the line-scratched sky with my bony pipes, swearing that I shall

[34] The word "pederasty" spelled backwards.

[35] "Yoni" spelled backwards. In ancient Sanskrit, the terms *lingam* and *yoni* are not actually used to denote a man's penis or a woman's vagina. Instead they're larger, more generic terms for a cosmic male and female principle: the manifest cosmogonic energies that are perceived as a duality but that are, in fact, one. Only in the West, and only after Sir Richard Burton's intentionally inaccurate translation of the human sex organs in the Kama Sutra, were *lingam* and *yoni* used to denote the human reproductive organs. By appropriating these exotic Sanskrit terms, Burton hoped that he might narrowly avoid censorship of the text.

create them all again in colors, and in three dimensions such as never yet have been.

Drunk with wrath and chagrin I chaw up roots and stones, spit colors on the ground, and, plucking up an oak tree, I paint upon the heavens In-oy and Yt-sar-edep, swan necked, somber of eyes and slitted. For ages I labor. Yet they mock my efforts.

I tear a continent from the rocky earth and dip it in an ocean to wipe clean the muddy sky. For aeons I toil. But yet they are not as before; no life is in their members; no passion in their souls. To my breath sluggishly they stir, and are as drab as El Greco's dreary Christs. In mad despair I seek my pipes, but I do not know what I have done with them.

Raging, I glare at my pallid world that has no color. I scream with bitter scorn that I am a sculptor and no painter.[36] Aloes regurgitate. I vomit a hydra-headed dragon with eight limbs and two tails which winks obscene eyes, cocks two legs, and washes out my slubbish[37] paintings.

* * *

I released the controls as, like a theater curtain, unconsciousness hid the scene. Curiously I glanced at the instrument board. The heart gauge is low, dark, and scarcely heaving; the nerve needle is near zero; the imagination bulb is extinct. The light from the fo'c'sle lantern is so dim that I can barely penetrate the reddish gloom.

[36] For many years Modigliani's principal desire was to sculpt, but the difficulty of obtaining costly materials led him to eventually focus upon oil painting.

[37] Beadle is creating this adjective from the verb *slub*: "to extend (slivers of fiber) and twist slightly." A reference to Modigliani's quasi-mannerist style of portraiture (especially when the subject was clothed).

I reflected, wondering whether the subconscious, as I imagined to be represented by that other bladderish contraption of memory, functioned when the actual body was at a minimum state of vitality. I selected a tape at random:

* * *

Cecci: I am extremely depressed and irritated. Even tobacco and alcohol seem to have lost their effects. Sunk in a café chair on a terrace I am staring across the boulevard at an imbecile advertisement, a horrible thing with neither drawing nor talent. The artist, I think savagely, should have been strangled, but that's what the public wants. I'm no good anyhow. Yet I was so cocksure that I could paint just because I won a local purse. Imbecile! But I *can* draw in stone. That's *my* material! Broodily I take up a portfolio of sketches and turn them over despondently. Yes; that fellow was right when he said that they were merely imitations of the classics. They want something new – original. Degas knew that. He could draw as academically as Ingres. "Nobody," he must have said to himself, "can draw better than a Leonardo, a Michael Angelo, so why try? Invent something new from a different angle!" Ah! but he was inspired! Again he's right, that chap. I have no sense of color. No. Form, yes. I'm a sculptor, not a painter. I shall throw away my paints, and stick to stone. I snatch the sketches and begin to tear them up.

"Oh, my darling!" exclaims a voice, "what are you doing with your pretty sketches?"

I had forgotten Magda. She looks across the table with her silly face puckered with anxiety. Pretty sketches, the idiot! But she's right, too. "That's all they are, pretty!" I mutter irritably, throwing them in the gutter. She utters a scream as she rises to

stop me, and knocks over my glass. My trousers are drenched. Angrily I pluck a silk handkerchief from a pocket.

"Clumsy little fool!" I tell her as she drags out a tiny bit of lace, "you've ruined a new suit which cost a lot of money!"

"Oh, dearest, I am so sorry!" she wails. "But that won't stain. I can take it out for you with –"

"Oh, shut your jaw!" I say furiously. "A delicate pearl gray like this is spoiled by the slightest thing! You don't understand anything!"

I stare at her stupid face, reproduced by dozens in my sketches, as if I had never seen it before. No wonder my stuff is rotten with a model like that! I must have been cuntstruck, that's all, because her body pleased me in bed, and she looks like a Tintoretto angel. Disgustedly I sigh and swear, and throw the portfolio into the roadway. Squawking, Magda rushes to pick them all up, the idiot! My god, what a fool I've been to have wasted my time on a fluffy little skirt when there are hundreds of women I could get by holding up a finger.

"Garçon!" I beckon to a waiter. "Bring me a bottle of absinthe!"

"A bottle, m'sieu?" the man stutters.

"Yes, a bottle! Here!" I pluck a note at random from a pocket. "There's fifty francs. Quick, can't you?"

Magda comes back with the portfolio and some soiled sketches. I light a cigar and take no notice. I decide that I've got to get rid of her – immediately. The very sight of her makes me ill. For a few hundred francs she'll be glad to go without making a fuss.[38] She'll soon find another fool, maybe richer than I! I laugh disgustedly.

[38] The "Magda" character closely corresponds to an actual figure in Modi's life: a young professional courtesan of the demimonde named Elvira, also known as "La Quique," whom Modigliani met one evening in one of the more disreputable cafés of Montmartre. (Not to be

"Oh, dearest!" squawks the idiot again, as the garçon puts the bottle of absinthe, glasses, sugar, and water on the table.

"[Will] you shut up and let me alone? That's all I ask!" I say as I pour out half a glass of absinthe.

She looks at me queerly, puts sugar on the perforated spoon, and begins to drip absinthe for me.

"Oh, don't bother, please!" I tell her impatiently, and drink the liquor right off. "Now I'll wait if you like, and you can make another for me."

I lounge back and watch her as she tends the second glass. She is pretty but so stupid. No soul. What I need is a woman who can inspire me. As Beatrice did Dante, Mona Lisa, Leonardo. Ah! but where? where? Such women no longer exist! I know lots of women. It is so easy for me. But not one is *that* woman. No, not one! I feel very sorry for myself, but at the same time more cheerful.

"Evening!" says a voice and a hand touches my shoulder. I glance around. He is a little Frenchman with a bald head, a poet of some sort,[39] although I scarcely know him. Anyhow, he is not a painter, for I loathe painters.

---

confused with a model also named Elvira, whom he painted six years later.) Modi briefly provided shelter for her in his rundown flat but eventually grew bored and finally offered her money to leave him alone. See *Artist Quarter*, pp. 103-108. Biographer Pierre Sichel gives Beadle full credit for uncovering this tidbit: "Modi's friends do not seem to have met her. Only her name is mentioned in their reminiscences. The idyll seems to have been brief but passionate and – for the most part – a private affair. Elvira's background would have remained a complete mystery except for the excellent detective work of Charles Beadle." Pierre Sichel, *Modigliani*: *A Biography of Amedeo Modigliani*, New York: E. P. Dutton, 1967, p. 242.

[39] As mentioned in a previous note, this figure is clearly based on Max Jacob. Cecci later describes him as shaking his head "like an old penguin," while the character Bill is quoted as saying that he's a

"Sit down!" I invite him, joyously, "and have something. Plenty of it, eh?"

As he accepts I notice that his eyes are very bright. The garçon brings another glass, and Magda prepares the new drinks. The stranger looks at me queerly as he lights a cigar I have offered him.

"I'm enchanted to see you again," he tells me. "I've often inquired where you were, but they tell me that you are a funny person. Don't like society. Won't give your address because you don't like callers when you're working. Is that so?"

"Oh, yes." I admit, "that was so when I was working, but not – Well, I'm only too glad to meet such fellows as you!"

"Thank you!" he says, looking at me again intently. "You're very handsome." He glances at Magda. "Madame is to be congratulated!"

Magda doesn't look pleased. I recollect that I have forgotten to introduce them. But then I don't know his name, nor hers – not her proper one. So I say simply:

"Ma'mzelle Magda!"

He half rises; bows with a queer smile. Magda scowls as he turns to me. She is never content, that one. He takes up the portfolio.

"Is this your work?" he inquires. "May I see?"

I am ashamed of the sketches. He turns them over courteously. But I can see that he is not interested. I am very angry. To be polite I drink my absinthe. Magda pushes his glass towards him. He bows again. I feel that I am going to dislike him, and wish he hadn't come. I know very well what he thinks, and curse because I allowed him to open the portfolio. But he continues to look over the hateful sketches. He is very polite

---

"brilliant poet." And Vee identifies him as a Frenchman who writes prose poems. Jacob was one of Modigliani's first acquaintances in Paris.

and well brought up, I see. I scowl, wanting to snatch them away, but I, too, am well brought up.

"Yes," he says at length, "evidently you draw exquisitely, but you have no inspiration."

I am startled. The man seems to read my own thoughts!

"You must forgive me, dear friend," he says gently, that I speak so frankly, but ... do you not feel it, yourself?"

"Yes," I admit reluctantly, conscious that Magda is furious, and very coolly sip my drink. He glances at her and then at me, and shakes his head like an old penguin.

"Alcohol's no good for you," he continues, drawing a tiny phial from a vest pocket. "If you will permit me?" Then he pours out a few drops of sticky dark liquid into my glass, and after some into his own.

"Ma'mzelle?" he inquires politely.

"No, thank you, m'sieu!" snaps Magda, glaring at him.

But he takes no notice, and stirs both glasses with an absinthe spoon.

"Now, drink that, my friend," he commands me.

"What is it?" I inquire.

"Artificial paradise,"[40] says he, with a strange smile, and again I wonder at the brightness of his eyes.

[40] The ingredients of this particular form of "paradise" are anyone's guess, although we can perhaps narrow it down. Since Izzy / Max Jacob pours just a few drops of this "sticky dark liquid," we know that it's a highly potent elixir with perhaps a brownish color. The darkness and the stickiness would argue in favor of hashish; but, as mentioned earlier, when hash wasn't smoked it was usually imbibed in pill form, especially during this period; or the pill was dissolved in hot coffee. (Modi was said to have first experimented with hashish when he was a teenager in Venice. He was also known to occasionally use cocaine in Paris.) The impoverished poet's standby intoxicant was ether, then readily available in French pharmacies for only 30 centimes a dram. In *Artist Quarter*, Beadle says that some of Max's neighbors "frequently

"Drink it all," he urges, and I do so, a nasty bitter taste which spoils the perfume of the absinthe.

"Is Madame a painter, too?" he queries of Magda.

"No, I'm a model, and before I was a whore,"[41] she replies brusquely, and I am very annoyed at her lack of manners. For some moments I seem to forget what they are saying, and then suddenly both of them appear to be funny – so funny that I cannot help laughing. He looks at me sharply, and rises.

"Excuse us, Madame," he says to Magda, "but I wish to talk to your friend." And to me[,] "Come, dear friend!"

I follow him into the lavatory. The people in the café seem to be very funny. There's a man with a beard staring at a chessboard, and he keeps on pushing up the beard as it falls off, and nobody appears to notice it except the chessmen, and they're all laughing at him. I stop fascinated, and begin to laugh, too. Oh, [how] I laugh! And the more I laugh the more they laugh!

"Look!" I say to my dear friend as he takes me by the arm, "don't you see? Look! it's dropping again."

"Of course" he says, "it always does that. Now come along." And I obey, feeling that he really does understand me, this extraordinary man. Still I can't help laughing, for ,that fellow

---

complained of the smell of ether" effusing from his tiny flat, adding that "ether had been one of Max's favorite drugs." (*Artist Quarter*, pp. 53-55.) But ether in its liquid form resembles a clear, colorless liquid. That would leave laudanum as a likely culprit: a dark, reddish-brown tincture created by dissolving opium into alcohol. At that time laudanum contained all the alkaloids found in the opium poppy, including morphine and codeine. Highly potent and toxic in larger doses, it was carefully dispensed by dropper bottles.

[41] In the Paris of this period, even prostitutes looked down upon artists' models.

was a scream, and he didn't seem to notice that his beard was falling. *That* was what was so damned funny!

In the lavatory my friend begins to do something with a knife. It's going to be very comic I'm sure, and I begin to laugh again. Then I notice his bald crown in the mirror, and it has bumps on [it], and I think how lovely it would be to slide down one and run up the other.

"Listen!" he says sternly, and then I want to cry because I see he's read my thoughts and is offended. As I try to weep on his shoulder he pushes me away brutally. I wonder why. I see that he has a snuffbox in his hand, and is taking out some white powder on the penknife point. He holds it up to my right nostril.

"Sniff, you idiot!" he orders. I obey, not knowing why I do. Then he does likewise with two others. I feel another queer sensation, and wonder what is going to happen. But I can't help watching the bumps on his crown, although they don't seem so fascinating as they did.

"Now," he tells me sharply, "that will counteract the other, and make paradise heaven – even better than women!"

I don't understand what he means, but docilely I follow him out. Then the sensation, the new one that I had begun to feel, leaps. I straighten up. A sense of marvelous well-being shoots through me. The people in the café don't look funny anymore – but just miserable souls. The man with the dropping beard seems to have got it to stop on now, and he is very sad. I smile contemptuously as I pass. I know my own superiority. I recollect that, but I cannot possibly understand why I felt glum and discouraged a while ago. Why, I am boiling with genius!

We sit down. That sense of power remains. There is a queer hush which isn't a hush. I seem to have lost my way in a world which is foreign, yet the people are familiar. That is extraordinarily strange, and I ponder deeply where I can be.

Perhaps my friend mistook the way out of the café and we are in England – or America? But I've been very well brought up so I know that you have to cross the Atlantic Ocean, and I couldn't possibly have failed to notice such a lot of water – particularly when I hate water so much. I want to ask my friend, but I fear he would laugh at me for not knowing, and besides I don't know quite where he is. The chatter of men and women on the terrace sounds a long way off, and I can't make out why they grimace so. Are they laughing at me? I stare angrily. No, they all are bowing to me! They have recognized me, that's it! I'm a great genius! Yet it's incredible I should have forgotten that for the moment. There's a banging and clashing and hooting going on. I suppose that it must be a jazz band somewhere. Very annoying as I want to ask my friend with the lovely humps on his head about it, but I can't recollect where he is. I feel that I should like to kiss one of those shiny bumps. But I can't decide which one. The left one, or the right one? That is of great importance. I shake my head sadly, for I know that is a problem that I shall never solve. I have no words, but great despondency. Then I am aware of a ray of Naples yellow illuminating a marvelous face of a woman – eyes that are somber and slitted, a long nose, exquisitely beautiful, upon a neck like a swan's. I am speechless with the glory of her. *She* is my inspiration, the woman I have sought these centuries! I start up to embrace her.

The vision vanished. Something crashes like a falling building. The ordinary stupid face of Magda is there, crying shrilly to break the eardrums.

"Oh, you've broken the bottle!"

My being seems frozen. Something goes "click." I realize that I have been looking at Magda herself through the neck of the

absinthe bottle.[42] "No, no," I shout fiercely. Life surges back into me. I laugh to think how silly I was. I am happy. I have found "her" at last. Thousands of people annoy me by rushing about idiotically hunting for something. Then one face keeps still for a moment. Ah! my friend, my benefactor. I clasp him to me, kiss him. Then I call proudly:

"Taxi! Taxi! We shall dine royally in Her honor." From afar the hideous voice of Magda screeches:

"No, no, m'sieu, we must take him home."

I glare at her open mouth which seems as if it were never going to shut. I never knew her face was so ugly, yet distorted beautifully. The gold stopping of a tooth looks like a black hole containing slaughtered sailors. I wonder who they could have been, those sailors, and why they were buried there. I've always known she was cunning, Magda. They must be murdered lovers, for no one would think of looking for their corpses in a rotten tooth. But I am still watching the open mouth, fearful to see the rotting bodies, and I sigh with relief when the lips come together. Then a terrible fear seizes me that they may open again, and I shall be forced to gaze on the skeletons, and I hate

[42] Beadle also toys with this notion in *Artist Quarter*: that Modigliani, intoxicated, peered through an absinthe bottle at a woman, whose form was now distorted by the bottle's shape – giving him a flash of inspiration that led to the elongated, quasi-mannerist style of a typical Modigliani portrait. But in fact Modi was already developing this style well before drinking absinthe. On page 97 of *Artist Quarter* Beadle writes: "When I once flippantly observed to Modi, and meant it flippantly, that he got his swan-neck inspiration from glimpsing a mistress through the neck of an absinthe bottle – empty, of course, as the absinthe would be inside him! – the reasoning was logical. It was the distortion resulting from his alcoholic vision that fired his imagination. But the absinthe inside him could never by itself have produced the talent to enable him to make such marvelous use of the distortion."

to see skeletons because they remind you of death. I never did like death. I shudder to think what I have escaped. Evidently she intended to murder me, too, and bury my body in her tooth. How wise I was to decide to get rid of her in time. And the diabolical cunning! She must have got a poor innocent dentist to put a gold tombstone on their grave.

Brutally someone shakes my arm. A long way off a crowd is hooting and grimacing. A strange face with hair sticking out of its nostrils grins at me. He has a black tie and a white coat. Silly, I think, I should never dress like that. An enormous pressure under an arm threatens to throw me into the air. Desperately I cling to my new friend. I crash beside him as if I had fallen out of a balloon. Then I realize that I am in a taxi which jumps away like a frightened frog. I am terrified that it will dash into the millions of people and cars, but it seems to know what I want, and stops as if it had hit a monument.

I gaze up at a building and wonder why I have never noticed that it was so high. My neck is nearly dislocated in the effort to see the top which appears to pierce the gray skies. As I stare, it bends towards me as if about to fall on us. I clutch at the shoulder of my friend in alarm as I cry out. But he shouts in my ear to be still. I obey, but now it is strange that he is there for just now he wasn't.

"Where is Magda?" I whisper, stupidly.

"Here, dearest!" she screams like a siren, and I notice that I had forgotten that I had hated the sound of her voice.

"Go away," I say with great dignity.

"Slip away, ma'mzelle," I hear my friend say, but why?

"No! No!" she screeches horribly.

I discover that the taxi is moving, but slowly, like a snail. Why, at that rate we shall never get – where I wanted to go.

"Where're we going?" I inquire politely, as I shrink to avoid a house which is falling on us.

"To your studio, dear pal," says my friend, who still seems a long way off although he is beside me, which is strange. "But a few moments and we shall be there."

A few moments! Why, we've been in the taxi for hours and hours. Then I wonder why he whispers, and so do I, yet Magda screams. That, I decide, must be because of some psychic affinity, and the idea pleases me. That explains why he understood me from the beginning. A large vehicle passes at a terrific speed with people hanging on the end and making faces at me. Why? Then the taxi swerves round giddily, starts to fly, and then stops with such a jerk that I should have fallen out if my friend had not held me tightly in his arms.

But I am very angry because distinctly I felt Magda pull on the other side trying to make me tumble out. Just the sort of thing she would do, for I know very well she wants to kill me. I try to strike her, but my arm won't work. I mean too slowly. It just rises and descends like a falling leaf without enough force to crush a fly. Yet she screams:

"Oh, dearest, you hurt!"

Again her mouth yawns, and as I can't bear to look at that golden tombstone I turn my head away. There is an alley before my studio, I can't make out what is the matter with it – it's at least half a mile long. I try to hurry, but my friend hangs onto my arm so that we walk as if at a funeral. Of course he's drunk, I know, but that's very annoying. I do my best to hold him up.

"Hurry! hurry," I implore him, "or we shall die of thirst. You'll be all right when you get there."

Then suddenly we rush forward at a terrific pace and reach the door panting. Vaguely I am astonished that we crawled at one moment and ran afterwards. Then just as Magda opens the door I recall that I had intended to go to a swell restaurant. Good God! I had utterly forgotten! I cry out in horror, and turn towards the alley, calling to my friend to come. But suddenly he

is brutal; he attacks me like a drunken apache[43] and throws me on the divan with incredible ferocity. As I gasp in indignation he says:

"No, no, my dear, we'll feast here – in Her honor!" and holds out a glass of brandy. I forgive him for that as I drink gratefully. "Look!" he continues, and taking out my pocketbook he gives money to someone behind me who, I suppose, is Magda. "She will go and buy things for us!"

An exquisite voluptuous sense comes over me as I lie back. I can see the brandy coiling and wriggling like a worm of sunlight down my throat and into my guts, and laugh with joy. I hear them talking some way off, but I am not interested.

From the ceiling is suspended a Moorish lamp with one glass tube which glows with golden light like the nipple of an udder of the Hindu sacred cow. An impulse urges me to rise and suck it, for thus shall I get inspiration. As I sit up the teat changes into a penis, and I bury my head in the cushions ashamed of that strange desire.

I hear my friend moving about, but I can't think what he is doing. I am angry with him but, again, I can't think why. Oh, yes, I wanted to go to a smart restaurant, and he plotted with Magda to stop me. Now why did I wish to go to a restaurant? For some special reason, and again I can't think what. Something very important. I can feel the memory of it fluttering about in my brain like a bird in a dark room, but I can't catch it. I wonder if he could help me, my friend? He is so clever. Now that's funny, I don't know what his name is. But is he a friend? Perhaps he's an enemy in disguise? Perhaps a painter come to steal my ideas? That makes me laugh. For I haven't got any. Yet I have one, that idea that's dashing about in my brain. If only I could catch it. If I keep very still maybe it will settle, and I shall

[43] In the Parisian argot of the time, violent street urchins were often referred to as "apaches."

be able to nab it. I lie like one dead. But no, it still flutters. They're making such a row in the studio. That's it, the idea is frightened.

"Shut up!" I yell loudly.

"One little moment," I hear him say.

There is a bit of silence. I listen intently to the fluttering wings. There! There! Oh, Madonna! a clang of glass has scared off the idea again.

"Here, dear friend," says the voice once more.

Furious at being disturbed I raise my hand from the cushions. He is placing another glass of brandy on a stool near me. True, I am thirsty. I had forgotten while chasing that idea. As I drink I see some bottles on a table. I start violently, upsetting my drink. Sacred name! I shout, jumping up. I've caught the idea! The face of the Divine One, my inspiration, which I saw through the neck of a bottle on the café table!

As I rush to my palette table before the easel my friend follows, crying:

"Wait! Wait!"

Swiftly he proffers me a pinch of that magic white powder on the tip of his penknife blade. I sniff obediently. A marvelous strength surges. With terrible strokes I brush in the outline of the portrait of my Divine One. Feverishly I rub in the background over another silly sketch of Magda. I mix colors with the rapidity and sureness of genius. Vaguely I am aware of my dear friend watching me with the eyes of a man regarding his beloved. I laugh, pleased. I feel that my hands are guided miraculously as the Divine Face grows, somber of eyes, swan necked.

"Brandy!" I say once.

Instantly a glass is thrust beneath my mouth. Furiously I continue. At length I stand back to observe. It is good. I have done. Strength fails. I totter back to the divan, but I laugh

exultantly, triumphantly. Suddenly the horrible face or Magda swims.

"Putana della Madonna!"[44] I shout in my own tongue. "Drive away that daughter of a thousand whores!"

"But, dearest!" squeaks the animal, "the dinner is ready, and I have brought Lacrima Christi[45] which you so love, and –"

"Tears of Christ!" I scream furiously, "Blasphemer! what do you know of Christ?"

She jumps away. She is frightened of me.

"Go away, ma'mzelle!" I hear my friend say. "Go quickly, and don't come back tonight, or he'll kill you!"

How does he know that? I wonder. He is marvelous, that man! He brings me genius!

"Here," he goes on[,] "here's a hundred francs. Go and amuse yourself."

She holds the note, staring at me. Tears are in her eyes, the little fool.

"Go! Go, I tell you," I yell.

"You'd better go, ma'mzelle," urges my dear friend." I'll look after him. You don't understand him!"

Weeping, the silly idiot turns away. I laugh and kiss my dear friend …

* * *

The experience ceased as suddenly as a light switched off. Cecci had collapsed under the effects of alcohol, the drugs and the artistic effort, I mused. I had often wondered what had inspired that peculiar form of distortion which marked all his work. Before he had started to get drunk he had reasoned

[44] Literally: "Whore of the Madonna."

[45] "Lacrima Christi": "Tears of Christ," a Neapolitan wine from Mount Vesuvius.

rationally enough, I reflected, regarding Degas. There seemed to be much probability in his contention, evinced by his own thought process. Many other painters too, possibly, lacking originality and being intelligent enough to be aware of it, had invented a pseudo which the dealers successfully persuaded the fool public was genuine! How much, too, of Cecci's work was due to alcohol and drugs? I had never known him really sober; the nearest was a subnormal state of jitters for the need of the poison: to be full of both appeared to have become for him normal, the only condition in which he could work.[46] I smiled at the cool cheek of Izzy appropriating his cash, and at the same time seducing him! Evidently Cecci had had money in those days. How much had Izzy been responsible for? Still, once started on a head dive, as he had, drugs would soon gnaw into a bankroll. I darted back to my observation post of the left cornea …

* * *

A disheveled group in the ragged garden bends, as if in reverence, over a fallen god. Myself stands silhouetted against a burning ochre sunset which caresses with bold fingers the violet field of the roofs of Paris. Rather amused I notice that myself has an expression of indignation diluted by fear.

"Damnation!" says myself peevishly, "did you give him more coke, Izzy? I told you not to. He can't stand more than two shots on top of the others, and I've no fancy to have the studio cluttered up with corpses!"

[46] In *Artist Quarter* Beadle's contention is that Modi required intoxicants to function as an artist. See my Afterword for more on this subject.

The backside of the brood mare of Touraine clad in pink silk, develops shoulders and a head; follows a hungry mouth and inviting eyes.

"Oh! Oh!" she squeals, "Who's got some? Do give me a sniff, Beel, just one!"

"Ow! Ow!" squawks Vee, who is stooping over the vomit-soiled flowers, wiping the lips of Cecci. "Ow! He's dying! He's dying!"

"Don't be a fool!" says myself sharply. "Come, you help carry him into the studio. And Francine, please make some tea, strong. That will pull him together. "

The males lift Cecci by shoulders and feet. Vee, half teetering, half crying, staggers along, clinging to his buttocks under the impression that she is aiding. They place him on a divan. Myself irritably tears open his velvet coat, wrenching off the bottom button. Myself listens to his heart, and holds his pulse.

"Oh, he's not dead!" says myself as if disgustedly, dropping the wrist and going to a Moorish table to get a cigarette. Vee flops on the divan above Cecci's head, eyes wet, and hysterically making tiny noises like a hen with the croup as she futilely pats Cecci's temples with a scent- and tear-soaked handkerchief; while, at his feet, Izzy, his bald head suggesting an old ivory world globe marked with strange continents, chafes his ankles, suspiciously watching her with dilated eyes. Eddie and Belle have collapsed on another divan, she fondling him as he stares as if speculatively at the orange glow of sunset on the frosted window of the studio. Then I notice that Vee is glaring furiously. As I enter her skull she sneezes all over Cecci's face.

The chamber seemed smaller, or perhaps, lower in the vaulted ceiling. The fo'c'sle lantern was of a smoky bluish tint. The heart gauge of a lighter scarlet than any I had yet seen; the rhythm quicker and irregular. Imagination bulb dim; credulity fairly bright. I took the controls:

* * *

Vee: Why is that fool Bill staring at me? He's a perfect beast! Doesn't understand anything. I suppose he thinks I'm crying. I'm not. Yes, I am; crying because *he's* so beautiful. Bill is utterly incapable of understanding that beauty can make one cry. And he's brutal. Just tore open Cecci's beautiful coat and tore off the button, too. Just like a man. All he cared about was whether Cecci was dead, and he'd get into trouble for giving him that beastly drug. Of course he's really in love with him. Oh, I know, the swine. I recollect that he talked about him in London just the way a man talks about a girl he's in love with. They all do that to pretend that they aren't *that* way. And that beastly fellow Iz – Iz – whatever his name is, is just the same.[47] Band of rotten,

[47] The antagonism between Vee (the character modeled upon Beatrice Hastings) and Izzy (modeled upon Max Jacob) is curious, since Hastings and Jacob became close friends. Perhaps they rubbed each other the wrong way during their initial encounter.

The scene described here would have had to occur shortly after Hastings arrived in Paris in April 1915. According to biographer Rosanna Warren, Jacob's poem "'La Rue Ravignan de Montmartre' would become famous," and Hastings "contributed to the poem's renown by printing a translation in the London journal *The New Age* in 1915." And she continued to translate and publish many of Jacob's prose poems for *The New Age* magazine. Shortly after Hastings moved to Paris as an expat from South Africa, Jacob wrote to his cousin Jean-Richard Bloch: "I've met a truly great English poet, Miss Hastings, a drunk, a pianist, elegant, bohemian, dressed in the fashion of the Transvaal and surrounded by bandits who dabble in art and dancing." (Jacob's limited English language skills may have led him to overvalue her poetry, which was far from remarkable.) Warren adds: "Around the same time, he wrote Apollinaire that Hastings would get drunk all by herself on whiskey, a habit that appeared to him exotic. If

stinking pederasts, that's what they are. Oh, how exquisitely funny he is glaring at me as he strokes my darling's feet. The fool's madly in love with Cecci. Anybody can see that. But who wouldn't be? Look at the lines of his nose and the curves of his lips. And oh! just within an inch of the left ear is a tiny mole with the weeniest hair resembling a flower. Oh, how I want to kiss him! and that lovely body of his – the feel, just like the inside of a lily!

A thrill, resembling the bubbling of a warm spring, arises near my navel and disperses deliciously through my belly, I laugh at the fellow Izzy with his bald head as he stoops, and laugh once more to cover the aching desire to kiss and kiss my newfound darling. Tears well in my eyes, and I want to hide them in his tumbled dark hair. And those idiots won't go away. Why *won't* they leave me alone with *him?* Torturers! Fiends! I'm quivering at the prospect of holding that wonderful body in my arms. I gaze entranced at the shells of his nostrils, and – how strange! – they remind me of my lost child. And I'm doing the same thing as I did then, sponging his darling little forehead with vinegar cloths as he was dying of brain fever, all the fault of that brute, my husband. Oh, God curse him! Oh, how I want to snatch Cecci to my breast as I did my little one, and kiss and kiss him! Why won't these idiots go away?

There's Bill still there smoking just as if nothing – *nothing* were happening. Oh, he's jealous too, and he's in love with me, the clown! Oh, I could feel how he watched me when I was naked. That's why he suggested that party – just to see me. The beast! Francine knew it too. Why can't he be reasonable? I've always

---

Max Jacob berated himself for his vices, he looked downright sober compared to Hastings and Modigliani, whose intoxicated fights could be heard out on the street to the tune of shouts, blows, and broken windows." See Rosanna Warren, *Max Jacob. A Life in Art and Letters*, New York: W.W. Norton Company, 2020, pp. 208, 228.

liked Bill, but not that way. He's fairly intelligent and that's why I can't understand how he can get along with Francine. Why, she can't understand a word he writes. Oh, he did say that that was her greatest charm, but that was just to be smart. She's pretty and has a nice body, but she's just sex and she can't satisfy him – I mean intellectually – just as I teased him. Poor Bill in search of a mistress. Funny he can't get a better one for he has rather a nice body – much more pleasing than I thought, and if Cecci hadn't have been here – Oh, but those lovely pouting nipples, and the hair which curves on each side of his groin. I'd love to wet them with my tongue, and make them like a girl's beauty curls. And his sex curving like the stalk of a dark mauve flower! There! Those two fools both staring again. Just as if they knew what I was thinking about. I blush and defiantly kiss Cecci's forehead.

Oh, but I wish he didn't remind me of my lost Bernard, because that always make me think of my beastly husband, the murderer! That's what he was! Oh, I'll admit that he loved the child, but just because it was his. Thank God, it didn't resemble him. And then he had the cheek to tell people that he drank because I left him. Would any woman stay with a man who'd killed her child? And anyhow Gerald – Oh, I don't know. Perhaps I should have run away in the end. I never knew what love was until Gerald taught me. And he was a cad, too. Just funked because his people were shocked, and then left me in the lurch. Still he was only a boy, it's true. But I can't forget him. I never have and never shall. Even since I've known the same sensations that he gave me. Ah! Gerald, I wonder where you are now?

Thank heaven that violinist fellow has called Bill away. But this Izzy creature won't go, oh no, he just stops there to spite me. I shuffle back on the cushions and take poor Cecci's head on my lap, and kiss his eyes, and I don't care whether that vulture-

headed old beast likes it or not. I know why Bill really went away. He's jealous and can't bear to see us together. He's furious because he told me about Cecci in London, and how beautiful he was, and that he was just the ideal man to console me for Jerry. Little Bill knew that I had been sick of Jerry for a long time – Pouf, how many times I cheated Jerry with his own pals he was too conceited to guess – and if it hadn't have been for the money I'd sunk in his beastly paper I'd have chucked him over years ago.[48] And who made the paper what it was

[48] "Jerry": A character who closely resembles Alfred Richard Orage, British socialist, theosophist, and lover of Beatrice Hastings, who edited *The New Age* prior to World War I. In the mid-1920s Orage went to France to work with Gurdjieff and later translated several of his books. (Gurdjieff was known to be abusive to Orage and constantly demanded money from him.) Orage and Hastings first crossed paths at a theosophical meeting in England in 1906. In his critical history of spiritual movements, *Madame Blavatsky's Baboon*, Peter Washington writes:

> Beatrice suffered from delusions of literary grandeur which were strong enough to dominate Orage and the *New Age*, the influential magazine he founded with Holbrook Jackson in 1907, partly on money borrowed from George Bernard Shaw.
>
> Over the next decade literary journalism displaced spiritual questions in the lives of Orage and Hastings. The *New Age* became the most prestigious literary magazine of its time and Orage was the center of a circle which included T. S. Eliot and Ezra Pound.

Hastings also published Katherine Mansfield in the *New Age*, with whom she developed an intense, intimate relationship. See Peter Washington, *Madame Blavatsky's Baboon: A History of the Mystics, Mediums, and Misfits Who Brought Spiritualism to America*, New York: Schocken Books, 1995, p. 203.

when I left it – or he turned me out, the scab! – if I hadn't myself? Why, when I couldn't appear anymore the circulation fell to nothing. How I recall that evening in the Café Royal when Bill was nearly blubbering over me because he thought that I was really upset over Jerry, and he stroked my head. "Come to Paris" said he. "I've got a genius for you and an Apollo to boot!" Well, that was true, but Bill didn't mean it: He was scheming to get me to Paris to make love to me, and now he's sulky about it.

Francine knows that. That's why she hates me. There's Bill back again. But he glares and stamps away. I laugh. Old bald head gets up with an irritated air, pulls out a gold Napoleonic snuffbox, and ladles out some of that beastly cocaine[49] with a penknife blade and sniffs it. I'm perfectly certain he taught poor Cecci to take it. But *I*'ll stop that! Now he grins at me like a skull and crossbones, a kind of triumphant sneer. Oh, God, I never thought of that! Perhaps they *are* lovers already! Have been for a long time, for all I know! Perhaps Cecci's been perverted by him, and is no longer any good to a woman? Oh, the beast! I shiver with rage and disgust. All Frenchies, they say, are perverted – even with women.[50] And fancy giving him that stuff that destroys the mind. That's why it kills all sense of decency, morals. Lots that pig cares about art. Bill said he was a brilliant

[49] "Montparnasse, a foreign quarter, is entirely mad. I find this word recurring in my impressions. The illicit sale of cocaine and hashisch (sic) must be something enormous [...] I know a charming girl who is going to pieces with hashisch, which is sold for twopence the pill! [...] every spot is more or less of a hashisch den now." Beatrice Hastings, from her weekly column, "Impressions of Paris," published in *The New Age* on 21 January 1915 under the pseudonym "Alice Morning." See Benjamin Johnson, Erika Jo Brown, *Beatrice Hastings*, Warrensburg, MO: Pleiades Press, 2016, p. 124.

[50] The original reads: "even with woman."

poet. Bah, I'd tear him to bits! I haven't been a critic for years for nothing. I'd make mincemeat of him!

Now what's he after? He gets up, goes across to the table where are bottles and things, and pours out a glass of brandy and seltzer. But instead of drinking it himself, as I feared he was going to do, he comes across to me. That was just what I had been longing for. A torture! But I couldn't move poor Cecci's head out of my lap. I thank the bald-headed toad, and drink, but still I can forgive him lots for that. Then he grins and lifts Cecci up by the shoulders, saying in French: "Come on, old man; you'd better go home and have a good sleep."

Oh! what a mean trick! I leap up furiously, slopping my drink all over my frock, but I don't care.

"No, no, you won't!" I tell him sharply. "He doesn't need any more of that beastly stuff! I'll get a taxi and take him home myself."

"Madame does not yet know where he lives, I believe," he sneers, grinning evilly. "And he will be of no use to Madame tonight."

Oh, the dirty, beastly Frenchman! As if *I* were thinking of *that!* I could slap him, beat him.

"You are disgusting!" I tell him, angrily. "Only a Frenchman could think of such a thing. Oh, you're too disgusting! But you're *not* going to have him."

Then he leers and shrugs his shoulders just as poor Cecci opens his eyes and peers, looking for me, I know. But with astonishing strength for such a little white rat, the man brutally wrenches Cecci onto his feet.

"You shan't! You shan't!" I shout at him wildly, taking Cecci gently by the arm. "Leave him alone, please! He can walk. I'll get a taxi."

He tries to push me away, the brute, and then the three of us fall on the divan and roll onto the floor. I am so angry, and the fool – Oh, there's Bill standing there laughing and …

* * *

I rushed back to my own cranium, curious to watch this comic scene which I had forgotten, much diverted by Vee's ridiculous feminine conviction that I had been in love with her and Cecci to boot. This pastime has become so absorbing that I am oblivious of my patient tiny god, indulgently, if cynically, regarding me.

* * *

Vee, with her hat on one ear and a fringe of hair mixed with the veil over one eye, is seated on the floor, erratically pulling at one arm of Cecci who, back to the divan, gazes sublimely indifferent, his head wagging like a mandarin, while Izzy, on his knees, tugs the other way at a shoulder. Myself, grinning, goes across to the ridiculous triplet and yanks Cecci to his feet, saying:

"Now, don't be an idiot, Vee. Izzy will take him –"

"He shan't! He shan't!" she squawks, tries to rise, collapses on the divan, and weeps copiously. Cecci's precarious equilibrium is upset by Izzy letting go a shoulder. He sits down suddenly on the divan; smiling idiotically commences to sing. Izzy clambers up; stands back.

"Apollo," he announces sardonically, "chanting the virtues of the new Aphrodite."

"I've got a taxi," shouts Francine, rushing into the studio."

I remark the reluctant look of gratitude as Vee lifts her smudged face to Francine. Follows a glare as myself says:

"All right, Vee, you can take him home and Izzy will show you where he lives. Come on!"

"No, no," screams Vee, jumping up and making a grab at Cecci. "Not that horror. I'll – I'll –"

She misses Cecci; sprawls over the divan. Francine, spluttering with laughter, clutches Cecci's arm; leads him towards the door with Izzy supporting the other shoulder. Myself half carries Vee bawling that she'll kill Izzy, out to the waiting taxi in the Place.

When we return to the studio both Eddie and Belle are on the divan still oblivious. His fair head against a black cushion looks as innocent as a handsome choirboy, and Belle, with her flaxen curls, suggests a Raphael cherub. Between gusts of laughter Francine exclaims:

"Oh, la! la! she's as drunk as a piano shifter. Izzy will choke her if she tries to get him to her place, and she'll murder him if he gives him any more coke. Oh, la! la! it 's killing!"

"Where's Volodia and Georgette?" myself asks as she turns on the lights.

"In the bathroom taking a shot with the needle," she replies. "Ouf, I wouldn't stick that thing into myself for the contents of the alms box of the Sacré-Coeur. Not me. Fancy making your body full of hideous sores. Ouf, you wouldn't want me anymore, would you, my cabbage?"

"I certainly shouldn't," says myself. "It's unaesthetic to destroy the beauty of a body."

"Has it the same effect as by the mouth?"

"A little quicker and more violent."

"Grrgh! I should never again be able to kiss you, my love!" declares Francine. Tossing her chin in the air, a favorite trick the better to show her profile, she dances across to the divan and kisses Belle on the lips, saying:

"Come wake up, my dear, and have some tea, strong tea! Volodia's just had a shot and he's going to play, and when he's

full of that stuff he's wonderful, a genius for ten minutes, Beel says!"

* * *

A suspicion of lesbianism in Francine which I had never had in those days, sent me darting into her skull. The heart gauge was beating strongly and steadily; the nerve needle swinging widely, not quivering; the sex tube high. The imagination bulb as before rather dim; the credulity high. The "present" controls I took in hand:

Francine: Beel is lying between Eddie and Belle. One of Eddie's arms is behind Beel's neck caressing Belle's ear, and the other is fondling Beel's head. Suddenly I am so angry that I could scream. I don't quite know why, but I hate Eddie or Belle touching Beel when I'm not there, and I can't understand because he doesn't talk to Belle, but to Eddie. Yet once he told me that I was passionate but not voluptuous, and Belle was voluptuous and not passionate, and that he wants both, and added that Belle had nothing in her head, and neither had Eddie. I hated Belle for a long time after that. Of course everybody knows English girls haven't got temperament, but Beel doesn't want me to lie and sigh, does he? Oh, I was so mad! When I asked him he laughed, and said that it was an aphrodisiac that he hadn't thought of, and he'd tell me that every night. Then I laughed, and wasn't jealous anymore. And once when he was very drunk he told me about his wife. She was neither passionate nor voluptuous. That's why he couldn't live with her. I saw her once. Oh, an awful fright! Ugly and all dressed up like those old English virgins you see in hotels. Peugh! I was never jealous of her. And when I asked him if she had lots of money and that's why he married her, he said she

hadn't; and when I said "why did you marry her then?" he got cross and said "God only knows, I don't," and muttered something about "logique française" but I never understood what he meant.

Suddenly Belle sits up smiling. Lovely, just like a baby – Ah, the baby I should like to have by Beel. That thought makes me angry because, although he insists that I take precautions, I've cheated him many times and nothing happens, and yet with another man whom I didn't love I got caught the first time, so am I barren? Beel has had a child – several, by other women. It's true the doctor said after the operation for that abortion that I might never be able to have a child. And I thought that was wonderful then! Oh, great God, what a fool I was! Oh, name of God, how that hurts, hurts continually like a sore on the foot when you're treadling a sewing machine all day,[51] good Jesus!

Ah! now I am certain that Eddie is in love with Beel, for he is stroking one thigh which is sticking out of his kimono, and Beel is kissing Belle's breasts. Oh, I tremble so that I nearly upset the tray. Then Beel looks up and says,

"Francine, isn't she a lovely thing? Come and kiss her!"

Kiss her! I'd bite her! Then my heart jumps as I wonder whether Beel has seen me kiss Belle and is jealous? Oh, I'd kiss her – I'd do anything to her, if that would make him jealous! Oh, a rage like the flame of a gas stove burns me as I recall that I have never been able to make him jealous!

As I stand pouring out the tea and watching him lying between Belle and Eddie, I sense that he wants to have Belle again and that Eddie won't object as usual as he's in love with Beel, too. But when I'm not being loved I can't stand it. Besides I want Beel myself now.

[51] This remark foreshadows a subsequent scene in which Francine is working in a factory with several other young women, treading sewing machines.

"Stop it!" I scream. "I won't have it!"

Eddie stops fondling Beel's thighs and says:

"Don't shriek, please, Francie."

"Oh, Francine darling, don't!" whispers Belle, but I can't help it. I rush upstairs into the bathroom.

Then, sticking my head through a window of the bathroom which looks down into the studio, I yell:

"I've had enough: I'm going to throw myself off the balcony."

I hear Beel say in English: "Oh, hell!" and Georgette staring up with her great moon eyes, says: "Don't, dearest, you['ll] make such a noise!"

I slam the little window angrily and run to the other door. I listen. I can hear Volodia still fiddling in the garden, and the creak of the stairs. I wait until Beel has reached the top. As he enters the room I slip out on the balcony and bang the door and hang onto the outside handle. He pulls. I shriek. He shouts to me to shut up or I'll rouse the quarter, but I don't care. Then I let go the doorknob and jump to the rail and put one leg over. There's the top of an acacia tree just on the level of the verandah. I know Beel can see my body outlined against the summer sky. He leaps and seizes me. I struggle and nearly faint with joy as he clasps my thigh. I continue to screech, but not too loudly as he carries me back into [the] bathroom.

But I still fear that he won't, so I fight as hard as I can – really. I bite him on the arm. I love to see all the blue marks I've made, for that always excites me. He swears angrily and then I know I've got him. His muscles tighten and he grips me until it hurts gloriously and he forces me – Oh, how deliciously I struggle and worry his arm! – onto a divan and I bite and kiss him until I swoon.

He goes down the stairs still panting. I smile at the rising moon through the glass door of the balcony window as I wash. In another kimono I dance down into the studio and kiss Belle

who is in Eddie's arms and she looks up at me with a lovely childlike surprise. And then I kiss Eddie, too. As Beel measures out hashish into the tea cups he says coldly – Oh, I hate that icy voice when he's like that, because I know that he has some of those horrible thoughts that he will never tell me:

"You're a fool, Francine. You thought you could make me jealous."

"Oh, la! la!" I tease him.

"Because I followed you upstairs? I've said already today that I don't want the studio cluttered up with corpses. Besides certain quantities of alcohol, cocaine and hashish[,] mixed with a little masochism and sadism, make an excellent aphrodisiac – the secret is mine."

I don't quite understand what he means – not the last part. But it's quite true that hashish does make things seem more wonderful; even a caress appears to last for hours deliciously, and the funny part is that the sensation seems alive all by itself somehow, and – Oh! when you really make love – oh! you go on and go on and go on and just when its insupportable it fades away and you begin all over again until you feel you're going utterly insane …

* * *

The memory of that sight of interlaced limbs when the taboos of each person were forgotten, and far travelling dreams had remained fairly distinct, unindividual, intangible and sublime, frolicking in timeless space gathering stars to make a garland for a Heloise, a Gito[52] whose flesh was of the company all compounded. I remained staring vaguely at the bloody walls in the dim light of Francine's skull, pondering on the revelation of her own self. Again I remarked that I had had no inkling of the

[52] "Gito": A character in the Satyricon.

preposterous jealousy she had had for men as well as women; and particularly of the jealousy caused by her inability to understand the conversation with others. On reflection I realized that such a case may be irritating to another, but then had she understood English, little would she have comprehended. I had never been, as usual, very interested in her past; but several of the expressions had quickened my curiosity. I glanced curiously at the instrument board to see what her state was at that given moment. The heart gauge was regular; the sex tube empty but slowly refilling; the needle of the emotional barometer was steady at "adoration." For the moment, I mused, an organism satisfied. Then at hazard I took up a filmy tape in the box of memory:

* * *

Francine: "And then?" I am saying as I turn the hem of a skirt.

"Oh, she looked at me queer like and told me to take another card," says Suzie, opening her big blue eyes as she stops treadling. "Funny-looking things they were too."

"Not a playing card?" inquires a dark girl, my neighbor.

"No, no!" exclaims Suzie, impatiently. "Nothing common like that. Something special. She did things proper like. Ta-ta – Oh, I've forgotten what she called them."

"Tarots," cries Lolotte, the brunette triumphantly. "They've got funny kind of pictures not like the others? I know. They can't go wrong. I had an aunt who –"

"Oh, shut your jaw!" exclaims another girl pettishly.

"Go on, Suzie."

"Well, she told me that the fair man was a scoundrel," continues Suzie, "but that I'd fall for him and he'd be my ruin."

"You did? You did?" ejaculate other girls, stopping work. "Tell us! What did he do? What happened?"

"I'm telling you, ain't I?" protests Suzie, blushing scarlet. "Because it's true what they say, those women. At the time I laughed, but I haven't since."

Tears rush into her eyes.

"Don't, Suzie darling!" I soothe her. "Don't if you don't want to tell us."

"Oh, but I do," insists Suzie, wiping her eyes with the back of her hand, "because you're – you're all so – so nice to me, and if one of those horrible women with them cards tells you anything, it's true. I didn't believe, but it was true, on the head of my mother!"

"Tell us, Suzie," implore several girls, and I feel a delicious sensation going up my spine as I recall what the woman who lives next door to my mother told me last night.

"Oh, do stop it," cries Suzy, irritably, to a girl at our back who is singing at her work instead of listening.

"Yes, shut up, do," chorus other girls.

"Shan't," defies the singer. "Can't a girl sing if she wants?"

"Go on, Suzie, never mind her," I urge. "Did you meet the fair man like she said?"

"Of course I did," says Suzie indignantly. "Everything they say is true. You just can't help it. Why, it wasn't two Sundays later when he came along, that fair man. He was a friend of the son of the concierge, a nice fella too with blue eyes and dressed swell. Worked regular in a shoe factory at St Ouen, he said, and asked me respectful-like to go along with him and Fred – that's the concierge's son – and his girl to a movie. It started like that and he was always correct and nice, bought me chocolates and – "

"They always do that," puts in an elder girl. "Me, I knows 'em!"

"Mother didn't see no harm in that, and one day about month later when we were getting on fine and he was tellin' me how

he hoped to get a rise and be foreman, he wanted me to go to a bal musette.[53] I've always been well brought up, I have, and I knew mother wouldn't hear of me going to such a place, but I couldn't help wondering what it was like, and lots of other girls I knew went with their fellas. So I told him, like a little fool, that I'd like to, but he'd have to tell mother something, so him and Fred told mother that they were going to a wedding party of a niece who was giving a dance. At first mother, she was so strict, didn't want me to go to the house of folks she didn't know, but I cried and cried and she let me go. You see, mother *did* know nothing good would come of it. And wasn't it funny? I'd clean forgotten all about what the cards had said, and him being fair too! So we went and had a jolly party and he was a lovely dancer and he teased me until I had a drink with him, and perhaps I had more much later when Fred and his girl had disappeared and I felt so excited and happy with him that I did let him kiss me, but just as we finished the last drink and he was going to take me home I came over funny – and I didn't remember nothing until I woke up in a strange bed in a strange room."

"Oh! Oie! OO!" exclaim several of the girls. "Whatever did you do?"

"Oh, I was nearly mad with fright," says Suzie. "And I couldn't understand why I was so sore – there! I didn't know – not then."

Suzie stops crimson with shame. Nearly all the girls, the singer as well, have ceased treadling to listen.

"Go on Suzie. And then? What happened?" they call in whispers. "Whatever did you do?"

"Oh, I didn't not know what to do," Suzie goes on. "I sneaked out of the hotel frightened that they would catch me and I hadn't got more than fifteen sous to pay for the room. But the

[53] "Bal musette": A dance hall with an accordion band.

concierge didn't take no more notice of me than a fly, and I simply ran down the street. He must have made me drunk, I thought, but I couldn't understand why, 'cos I liked him all right, but not like that – then, for I didn't know what that meant. So I went straight to Fred's home and he began to tease me about refusing to come home with them and going off with his pal in a taxi, which wasn't true –"

"But you said you didn't remember," says a girl.

"No, no I didn't but it couldn't have been true," insists Suzie. "I'd never do a thing like that. I've been too well brought up, I have."

"Go on! And then?" breathe the others.

"Oh, I cried," says Suzie, "but I didn't tell him things of course, and when I asked him what his friend's address was or where he worked he laughed and said he wasn't a friend of his at all, but had paid him to tell his mother he was."

"Oh! Oh!" gasp the listeners. "The cad! The swine! The bandit!"

"Oh, I told Fred so, and how!" assures Suzie. "You see I never would have anything to do with Fred when he tried to get fresh one time, as he was just a vulgar butcher's boy, and he'd always been mad because I wouldn't. Oh, I didn't know what to say to mother when she began at me and I sobbed and told a story that a girl called Mamie from the shop had been at the party, and that I'd been taken bad and as she lived near she'd taken me in and I'd slept with her, and mother wouldn't believe it. So I rushed off to the shop and promised Mamie a new frock which an aunt had given me for my fourteenth birthday if she'd come home with me and swear to mother that what I'd said was true. So mother believed her, and didn't find out about the missing frock – until it was too late. I mean that when mother found out about the frock it was the same time that she noticed that my monthlies had stopped and started asking questions. I didn't

know what to say and I told everything to a girlfriend who was married, and she laughed and laughed. "Why, you silly little fool," she says, "he must have put some dope in your drink – they often do that – and had you when you were drunk! But how could you have been so stupid I can't guess. Why, even *I* knew enough at your age not to get trapped like that although many of 'em tried, the Good God knows!" And again she laughed and laughed and I cried and cried with fright and cried with rage because I had never known whether it was nice!"

A lot of the girls laugh.

"Idiots! Imbeciles!" Suzie cries furiously. "If I'd got to suffer for it, why should I be robbed of the pleasure?"

"Oh!" says one girl, giggling, "she didn't even know whether he had a big one or not!"

Again the girls laugh and one called Madeleine with a long face and horse teeth, sneers:

"Oh, you innocent suckers, that's a yarn! As if a girl could go to bed with a man and remember nothing about it, nor what he'd done to her!"

"What do you know about it?" snaps Suzie. "I'll bet you never had a lover in your life, with a face like that!"

"I've had far more than you, you she-camel!" retorts Madeleine.

"Perhaps," says Suzie, tears of rage in her eyes, "walking on the streets – and I'll bet they didn't pay you more than a hundred sous!"

"You slut! You little whore!" screams Madeleine, and jumps up looking as if she'd spit her teeth out. "I'll show you! I'll tear your eyes out!"

"Oh, shut your jaw!" hiss several girls, beginning to treadle furiously. "Here's Flat Guts."

I, too, start to work hurriedly, as the forewoman, tan and flat breasted, with big spectacles, comes into the workshop.

"Huh!" she sneers, peering about, "always the same, eh? As soon as my back is turned, nothing but gossip. No wonder Beauchamp's across the street can turn out more stuff in a week than you lazy, gossiping sluts do in a fortnight. Think I can't hear from down below when the machines stop, huh? Imbeciles! Who was doing all the talking? You Francine?"

"No, ma'mzelle," I say, treadling the faster.

"You, Madeleine? I heard you screaming!" she inquires of Horse Face.

"It wasn't me," asserts Madeleine, glancing sulkily at Suzie.

"Huh," grumbles Flat Guts, "if I have to speak again I'll sack the lot of you and get a new gang. They couldn't be worse if I picked 'em up on the street."

We all go on working. A girl at the back giggles. Flat Guts turns sharply, glares, and begins to go from machine to machine examining our work. She's a good girl at heart. She jaws, but she never does what she says she will. She's been one of us and knows what's what. She's got a man who lives on her and does nothing but drink and all of us girls know that, and we love her. Later on she is called below to fit a model. As soon as she's gone I stop treadling. I must know the end of Suzie's story, because I can't help thinking about what that woman told last night.

"Suzie!" I whisper, "what did your mother do afterwards?"

"Oh, yes, yes, do tell!" comes a chorus.

"Oh, nothing," says Suzie, darting a look at Horse Face. "Oh, Suzie darling!" I implore.

"Well," she begins, "my married girlfriend had a lover who was a medical student and I went to her flat when he – the husband, of course – he was a commercial traveler – was away and the student did things to me and –"

"Oh, I know!" exclaims a girl. "A midwife did that to me. Did yours hurt much?"

"Oh, a little, but I felt awful afterwards," says Suzie, "and I had to tell mother that I'd fallen downstairs in the shop and the doctor had said that I had hurt my inside, and she didn't suspect nothing, so I didn't care, but she told me that if it had been what she had feared it was she wouldn't have known what to do, for father would have killed me if he had known that I was going to have a baby and disgrace them all, and he would too, I'm sure, for he's terrible, my father; he's president of something or other to do with clocks – he repairs 'em – and I remember how he carried on when someone of the society's daughter ran away with a man,[54] and he said that if he was her father he'd shoot them both for bringing dishonor on the family. He says that any girl who goes to bed with a man who isn't her husband is a whore. He's a very good man, my father."

"So's mine," snapped a girl who hadn't spoken before. "Mine has lots of money, and because I was a little fool like you he kicked me out and told me to earn my living on the street. That's what my father did after he'd tried to seduce me himself and he'd never have dared if mother had been alive, and he's a schoolteacher too, although he doesn't do anything because he can live comfortably on the money mother left him. That's why I'm here."

She began to cry, but nobody took any notice because she had always been stuck up and never talked to us girls.

"But what did you do afterwards?" queries a girl.

"Oh, well, you see," continues Suzie, "if it hadn't been for my nice medical student I'd have to go away and drown myself in the Seine."

"Yes, but didn't he go to bed with you, your medical student?" says another girl.

[54] The narrator seems to be saying that an employee in the company (or "société," in French) had a daughter who had eloped with a man.

"Why, he was my married friend's lover!" cries Suzie indignantly.

"And besides," defends another girl, "how could he when she was like that?"

"But he might have later?" insists the other girl.

"Not likely!" snorts Suzie. "I'd supped enough, thank you. I wouldn't go to bed with a man now if he was a millionaire unless he married me first. Oh no, thank you, I know men now!"

"Oh!" scoffs a little girl with a fuzzy head, "you are a little fool. You'll be an old maid and treadle a beastly machine until you drop. Not me! I've got a lover who's my regular fiancé and he's a grocer's assistant, and when he's earning enough money he'll marry me and we'll have a shop and –"

"Oh, listen to her," mocks another girl. Don't they all tell the same tale? When a man's got what he wants and trouble comes, he's off!"

"Still," remarks a very pretty girl with a cheeky nose, "once you've had a man you always need one. But if a girl's slick she don't get caught, and if he goes there's always another round the corner – perhaps better! I'm like that, I am, I take all the fun and money out of 'em I can before they drop you. I ain't, and you ain't either, like them as has a dot[55] to buy a man for keeps. So why not?"

"But what are you doing here, then?" snarls someone.

"Oh, I ain't a whore," retorts the pretty girl. I wouldn't let any man *think* that he keeps me, oh no. Not much! I know 'em too well. I'm independent, I tell 'em, an honest working girl. That keeps 'em going. Once they think you're on their hands they get fed up with you." She giggles. "But they don't with me. I put away what I can get out of [it] and don't say nothing. In a few

[55] "Dot": Dowry; the estate that a woman brings to her husband in marriage.

years I'll have enough to tell 'em all to go to hell and keep a man of my very own if I want to. Oh," she adds, "there's Madeleine at it again."

The horse-faced girl who had refused to listen and had been all of a sudden working furiously, had uttered a groan, and then with a wailing moan stops treadling and collapses over her machine making funny little noises.

"O-oh, what a relief!" she sighs, and lifting her head, begins to giggle.

"That's the third time today," exclaims the pretty girl. "There, that's what comes of not having a man."

A factory whistle blows six o'clock. We all cover the machines and hastily put our work in order. As I put on my hat and powder my nose I cannot help thinking of what that old woman friend of my mother told me last night from coffee dregs. I had had an affair, she had said, with a man I didn't love, and a miscarriage. That was absolutely true. Mother had pushed me into his arms because he had money, for she said it was better for a girl to a have a rich lover than to marry and slave her life out for a drunken brute like father, and the miscarriage had been caused by my father in a drunken fit striking me because I hadn't brought home enough money from my lover for him to booze! Oh, my God, that was true!

I was ill for a long time after that and my lover sent me money for a time, which I gave to mother, and then he took on some other girl and I never saw him again. Really I was glad for after that I hated him worse than ever and his silly moustache and potbelly and silly stuck-up ways, but I pretended to mother that I was brokenhearted, or she would have nagged me for losing him, so instead she tried to comfort me by saying that [there] were plenty more and richer ones. But not me! I loathed men and went back to the shop rather than listen to any of 'em. But that fortune-teller last night had said too that I would meet a

dark man from over the seas who was married and that his wife would die and he would marry me and I should be happy always. Mother cried with joy. But after all, if the first thing she had said was true, why shouldn't the second be too? And now that story of Suzie. Didn't that prove absolutely that what those old women say comes true? But where was my dark man from over the seas?

The very idea gives me a thrill all over. What that pretty girl had said was true too, that once you have a man you always need one, and that is why I understand the horse-faced Madeleine they all laugh at. Oh, but I've had enough of *that* beastly way.[56] Then I start, smudging rouge on one side of my mouth, as I recall that I had seen a dark man who pleased me the other day when taking a shortcut through an arcade, but he had scarcely looked at me and hadn't followed, and of course I couldn't know whether he came from over the seas and was married.

Somehow I feel queer as I leave the shop as if something is going to happen and I refuse to walk part of the way home with Suzie and some of the others as usual. Oh no, I think as I make my way through the crowded streets, I was born unlucky. Nothing like that will ever happen to me. Someday I shall marry a stupid workman for the sake of getting out of the shop and have kids and slave all my life just like mother does. But something strange urges me to go through the arcade again, an uncanny sensation of excitement.

Halfway through I pause before a shop where are some lovely dresses. The tailor-made my rich lover bought isn't bad and tailor-mades suit me. That small check model would go beautifully with a georgette blouse, and I wonder dismally what I am going to do when mine is worn out. As I turn away I stumble over a cane. As I stop to apologize I see a tall dark man

[56] "That beastly way": A euphemism for masturbation.

who is handsome with big eyes and a slender body and well dressed and something of a foreign air about him.

"No harm done, ma'mzelle," he says with a strong accent and a charming smile. He is the *same man* I saw the other day in this arcade. I am so confused that I cannot return the smile and hurry on. When I reach the end of the arcade I cannot resist looking back. Yes, he *is* following. I race forward and then stop before the window of the last shop, saying to myself, "don't be a silly fool! The old woman *is* right. Don't be a silly fool!" I dare not look round. Then I feel him alongside me. He catches the reflection of my eyes in the window and says softly:

"Pardon, but are you in a great hurry, ma'mzelle?"

"Yes, m'sieu," I say stupidly, "I'm going home."

"So early?" he insists and I love the sound of his voice. "I'm so lonely and bored in Paris. Won't you give me half an hour? Look, there's a nice café. Won't you have an aperitif?" And then he adds with a funny smile: "And maybe a little dinner afterwards?"

"I don't know, m'sieu," I say, acting coyly in spite of myself. Then something urges me to ask: "You're not French, are you, m'sieu?"

"No, I have not that honor," he replies. "I'm English. Does that matter much?"

"Oh, no, m'sieu," I murmur, as if I were choking from the strange thrills that are running all over my body, and not quite knowing what I'm doing I follow to a café table.

"Do you often pass through this arcade?" he goes on as we sit down. "I think I saw you the other day?"

"Ah, yes, m'sieu?" I mutter, feeling an idiot. I ought to say something, but I can't. I have to choke an impulse to ask if he is married. Dimly I hear him asking me what aperitif I'll take and he continues to talk but I don't hear him, for my soul is singing: "The tall, dark man from over the seas!" …

* * *

I smiled as I dropped the memory tape. Poor Francine! what absurd ideas govern many women's acts. I recollected how she frequently irritated me by her superstitious devotion to fortune-telling. That wretched old woman's prophecy had certainly been far from the reality. Vaguely I wondered what had become of Francine of whom I hadn't had news personally for years. Queer, at that time I had been looking for a mistress. She had attracted me strongly physically; intellectually I had asked nothing of her; in fact had found it an advantage, or as Vee reported me as having said, "a charm," that she knew nothing of my work nor my thoughts. I had been disabused of "intellectual" women, finding them mostly bores and usually ugly. Only one had for a while seemed a possibility, and Theodosia I had never even known to speak to. Francine, I had counted, would not vex me with social ambitions as a girl of my own class would inevitably have done.

Back in my own skull my phosphorescent friend was sitting cross-legged, two eyes as ever, indifferent apparently, gazing into eternity; but the middle one had still the friendly twinkle. Peering through the left cornea I saw Francine fondling Belle and Eddie, and myself smoking a cigarette as we drink hashish tea while Volodia plays the violin in the garden, lost in his own morphine world. Possibly the association of ideas suggested by Francine's curious speculations regarding my wife reawakened curiosity to know what had been my attitude in those days towards her. Attempts to fish up a memory of her in this queer pool had failed. Now I glanced imploringly at my occult tutor.[57]

[57] "Occult tutor": Thus the narrator signals that, rather than promoting mere escapism, the porcelain-bellied deity is here to teach him about things otherwise hidden.

Once more a telescopic hand shot out obligingly and a long nail indicated a certain fold.

Myself: I am seated on a horsehair sofa staring absently at the gilt lettering of a large family bible on a whatnot,[58] while a voice, as dry as the woolly strands of an antimacassar[59] under my head, maunders on and on; words bob up, like fish breaking water in a shady pool – "duty" – holy matrimony – husband –

I am wondering what strange attraction made me fall in love with Eve?[60] I had had many experiences and had formulated definite principles regarding the lunacy of marriage as conventionally conceived; particularly without trying out each other sexually and temperamentally. As if I had suffered from simultaneous strokes of amnesia and myopia, I forgot my lessons and couldn't see the most blatant sign, the tight prudish mouth with the warning droop at the corners. When I met the mother I did notice the stigma but, I argued, biologically a child is not bound to inherit every trait of the dam. True, the sire had been an ardent Calvinist and a professor – bad stock, I reflected, to breed from.

"William!" says a sharp voice.

I glance at my wife sitting bolt upright in a chair too high for her. That the chair is far too large for her seems of importance somehow; suggests that she is too small for the wife job she's undertaken. And the voice! Under the slightest emotion that voice tends to be shrill, the shrew note. I must have been deaf as well. What, I ask myself again, had worked this miracle? I had always flattered myself that I was too intelligent to be

[58] "Whatnot": A light open set of shelves for bric-a-brac.

[59] "Antimacassar:" A cover to protect the back or arms of furniture.

[60] "Eve": Possibly modeled upon Beadle's wife, Sylvia Grace Ellen Hornsby, daughter of Teresa Isabel Ashwell and Edmund William Hornsby.

sentimental, yet now I recall that the first time we had been alone and in a punt on the river, I had been content to hold her hand in mine like any lovesick clerk. Recollections of myself in those days were incredible. I must have been under a spell – not myself, by God! What were my physiological and psychological states when I met her? Yes, I had been deprived of sex for some time and was very discouraged about my work. Eve had been very sympathetic, flattered I suppose, in reality, because I was a real author, the first she had met. Print seems to have an hypnotic effect on feeble minds; impresses without any relation whatsoever to the content. I, as do all young and imbecile authors, had given her a book. She had raved about it – although, even then, I recall, I had a vague suspicion, swiftly stifled, that she hadn't understood what I had been driving at. I was the flattered fool, too. Starving, although I wouldn't admit it, for comprehension and encouragement, I had grabbed at a soap bubble. And now she neither understands nor approves of my work – although how one can disapprove of any given subject one doesn't comprehend I'm damned if I know. But such little problems never worried Eve.

"– the duty of a husband is to comfort his wife in sickness and in health, and when my respected husband –"

Yes, but what was the springboard, as it were, from which I had dived into the abysmal idiocy? Stupid vanity; weakness; that silly squalling for someone to pat you on the back and say what a fine fellow you are. On that jerry-built foundation of vanity-needs I had built a spectral structure – the ideal sexual and intellectual companion, a wife. All my natural desires had been smothered by that appreciation-hunger – until resuscitated by the connubial couch. During the brief courtship she had had a refrigerating effect upon me; but I had persuaded myself that she was virginal and merely needed awakening. The shock was considerable when I realized that I had married a marble statue;

although I could not say that she was dumb. Oh, my God no! Physical contact was, and remained, disagreeable to her. When in normal fervor I caressed her and wanted her to reciprocate, she repulsed me, saying that sex was disgusting. Still I was patient. I attempted to employ every art of love that experience and study had taught me, but she refused to be fondled or passionately kissed; said that sex was horrible and wicked, the original sin, and all the rest of it, half the night; said that she had only submitted to me because it was her "duty." My God, I could have struck her! Who, I wonder bitterly, was that son of a bitch that invented "duty," the last resort of the feeble? When I asked her why then had she married me she began discourse number one on Calvinistic morality. Oh, the agony of lying alongside this being whom I was persuaded I loved; who reacted like a cross between a jellyfish and a fanatical stump orator. Frequently in the morning I could scarcely keep my hands off the maid, and ugly she was. Why I didn't rape one of my wife's sex-starved friends God only knows! Under this superheating I became sex obsessed. I couldn't meet a good-looking girl, or a woman even, in the street without imagining how I'd like to have her.

"William! You're not listening to mother!"

"Oh, yes, I am, dear," I lie blinking, wondering why I should be supposed to be listening, considering that I've heard the same repetitive phrases before – oh, so many times! In bed and out of bed and in ma-in-law's chamber, runs an idiotic line in my head.

Then after Eve was enceinte she flatly refused even what she called her "duty," which had long become to me, not a pleasure, but a relief. When I couldn't hold out any longer without being unfaithful – and in the environment that was no virtue, for none was there who was aesthetically pleasing – I had her examined by a specialist. He stated that she was anemic, which accounted

for her anesthetic sexual state. I wondered bitterly what relation there was between anemia and souls of which she was always talking, and why red-blooded people, such as I, had apparently no souls, according to her doctrine.

"William! will you please answer mother?"

"Yes, yes, of course," I say. "Delighted – I mean, yes, Eve."

"Oh, you're impossible, William! You never listen to anybody except yourself," says my wife. Her eyes are angry and her lips pursed; the lines in the corners are drawn tightly.

"Yes, of course," I say, "that is –"

"Well, William, what have you to say?" demands my mother-in-law.

How I hate that name (why hadn't I been called Marmaduke, or Clarence, or Montmorency St Clair de Plushbottom?) on their lips! I look at her, the mother-in-law. Impossible to imagine that she had ever been human; had had a man. Her husband must have masturbated into a test tube and had her impregnated by means of a syringe. Lots of women have given me that impression. She also is seated in a chair, but that chair fits her exactly. Important, too. Capability. The daughter her shadow. I see an elderly woman with her gray hair drawn tightly into a bun. She has been handsome; never just pretty. The eyes, beneath thick brows, are as bright as those of a girl; but the lips resemble a half-healed cut. She is dressed in the leg of mutton sleeves and tight bodice of a past epoch, enclosing a mummified body which well accords with the stuffed birds and antimacassars. Were those lips ever a pouting wound to her husband's eager mouth? Although judging by the portraits of him all over the house, his must have looked as eager as a prison gate to let out convicts.

"William! You're not listening," repeats my wife, the tone rising a note shriller.

"What have you to say then, William?" repeats my mother-in-law.

Oh, how that "William" gets on my nerves! I raise my chin from my hand, sit back; regard Eve. I am really sad.

"I don't think I have anything to say," I reply wearily.

"What do you mean by that?" she queries sharply, my mother-in-law.

"What I say. You have done all the saying. You sit in judgment on me – by what right I can't imagine – and will neither listen to, nor consider, any opinion but your own."

"I speak by Holy Authority," she retorts, "whereas you have none."

"That again is merely a matter of opinion," I say. "A Catholic would not agree with you, nor a Presbyterian, nor a Church of England, nor a Mohammedan, nor – nor a Red Indian."

"William!" – she always pronounces that hateful name with an exclamation mark –"William! you're insolent and ignorant! I find it extremely difficult to forgive you as my duty commands."

She glares at me with fanatical and merciless eyes. A silly question bobs up as to whether Savonarola[61] had Scot blood in his veins.

"My duty," she continues sternly, "as a mother requires me to ask you a question to which it is your duty to reply truthfully!"

"Damn duty!" I mutter.

[61] Girolamo Savonarola (1452 – 1498), an Italian Dominican friar and fanatical fundamentalist. Dictator of Renaissance Florence in the 1490s, he inaugurated a reign of asceticism critical to secular art and culture. The phrase "a bonfire of the vanities" refers to the infamous bonfire of 7 February 1497, when his supporters burned thousands of "sinful" objects such as cosmetics, art, and books. Later condemned as a heretic, Savonarola was hanged and burnt in the Piazza della Signoria, in Florence.

"What did you say?" she demands sharply.

"Nothing," I assert cowardly.

"If you now find it impossible to fulfill the conjugal vows[62] you made to my daughter, why did you marry her?" she demands.

"D'you want a sincere reply to that question?" I retort, "although I don't admit that that has anything to do with you, or any third person."

"Answer!" she ordains.

"Very well. Your blood – or probably you'd say shame – be on your own head," I say, flippantly, unable to repress a slight smile, for I know that I'm going to enjoy myself – even in her presence for once. "Well, I married your daughter because I was in love with her – strange as that may seem to you. That is, her body strongly attracted me sexually (why do I tell that lie? flutters a thought. Just to annoy her.) Having denied myself

[62] Certain passages from Beadle's poem, "Small Body" (published in 1931 in *Readies for Bob Brown's Machine*) seem to refer to this horrific relationship. The poem also repeatedly highlights the terms "duty" and "conjugal." One such passage reads: "what is love + dreadful fear curiosity twined like lovers = white = sick = bed = shaded nights = off clothes = wanting run away = run = run = run + + what is love + + trembling = nausea = in bed = nightie tight to toes + pale curiosity dying + + darkness = powerful hand = muffled shriek = hungry wet slavering mouth + + god is this love + + horror unspeakable = dying = death fear = rushing darkness + love death horror = falling = lights = face madman = terrible hands = fighting fighting crazy = darkness + weeping = weeping = trembling weeping + + + + moon like mad woman running away thro forest white flowers + + + + no wonder = just horror + boredom + nights nightmares + duty = duty = conjugal rights = until death us do part + beastly = so beastly beastly + run = run = run + no conjugal rights." (And run, he did!) See Craig J. Saper and Eric B. White, eds., *Readies for Bob Brown's Machine: A Critical Facsimile Edition*, pp. 108-110.

sexual relief for love of her, I became as men do – and normal women also – intoxicated. I attributed to her all the mental qualities that I admired,[63] allowing naturally for her youth. I sought a life companion, sexually and mentally."

"You think of nothing but carnal desire," she snaps.

"I beg your pardon," I protest, "but I've just stated the opposite."

"That's nonsense. My daughter has had the best of educations," she defends, "so it's merely vulgar pretention to imply that she's not your mental equal."

"Education has nothing to do with mental qualities," I riposte tactlessly. "There are no greater asses than many professors!"

She glares at me. I had totally forgotten that her father and her husband were professors in Edinburgh University.

"Anyhow that surely is not a valid reason for refusing to obey your conjugal duties, William," she insists.

"Conjugal duties!" I exclaim, and in spite of myself, I laugh. "Well, it seems to me that Eve has always refused her conjugal duties, not I. Do you actually suppose that a man can cohabit with his wife whom unfortunately he loves, or did love – and lead what is popularly supposed to be the chaste life of a monk? Do you want me to go mad – or keep a mistress around the corner? I refuse to do either."

"Marriage, William," she says tartly," was not ordained for carnal purposes."

"For God's sake!" I exclaim, "what was it made for, then? In the marriage service you will find that magnificent phrase – by

[63] In the short story "NQO" (published in the December 1917 *International*) Beadle summarizes this notion in just three words: "sex projects romance." In "The Triumph of Tony" (published 1912 in *Windsor Magazine*), an irony-laden tale about a Victorian courtship that occurs aboard an ocean liner, the female protagonist is "suffering from an adolescent disease – romance."

King James' genius-streaked translators – 'my body I thee worship.'"

"The state of marriage was founded," says she severely, "for the founding of a family according to God's Will."

"Your prayer book," I retort, "explicitly states that marriage was also instituted to avoid the sin of self-abuse!"

"Not *our* prayer book, William," she snaps with cold fury. "That is the vulgar and heretical Church of England prayer book!"

"Oh, well," I say wearily, mechanically fumbling for a cigarette," what is the use of arguing? Each sect in every known religion condemns every other sect to hell and damnation. In any case this question concerns the man and his wife, and nobody else."

"Very well, William," says she, rising wrathfully, rigid as a Scot Dragoon on parade, "it is *your* duty[64] to make suitable provision *and compensation* for a wife who is too well bred to appease your carnal appetites. If in His wisdom He had not seen fit to take her father into His bosom, he would have known how to deal with – with such an unbelieving, feckless body."

Again I cannot resist a smile at the lapse from her rather pompous English into good homely Scotch. "Ah," I think to myself as I open the door, "so that was the motive – a problematical famous author with an assured comfortable income!"

My wife has buried her face in her hands on the arm of her chair. But I know that maneuver too well. How many times have her tears made me cede: forced me to continue this life of Tantalus?[65] My instinct is to take her in my arms to comfort her;

[64] Beadle might have enjoyed reading Modigliani's letter to his friend Oscar Ghiglia: "Your *real* duty is to save your dream."

[65] A fitting metaphor, as Tantalus was forced by Zeus to experience eternal hunger and thirst while standing in a pool of water near a fruit tree.

but I am too keenly aware of the reaction. Tears, lips and body, awaken desire; and I should be as weak as so many times before. For her sake as well as mine, this life together must cease. It isn't healthy.

I light the cigarette I have been longing for, as I watch Eve calmly, wondering if there is anything more disgusting than possessing a woman who does not desire you. My wife – or her mother – has inspired that beautiful thought. Inconceivable! Never again, I swear, and yet desire smolders which is agony.

"Eve," I say quickly, "it's no use crying. We must separate. Live your own life, and I'll live mine."

"Divorce!" Eve stops weeping instantly. She looks up. There is a gleam of positive hatred in her eyes as she says with unexpected firmness: "You know very well that mother will never consent to divorce."

"Damn mother!" I explode. "I married you, not your mother. Can't you for once assert [yourself], Eve? Tell me at least what you want to do. Haven't you any will at all?"

"You're brutal, William," she says, and turning her head begins to sob again. I can't bear to hear her sob, and she knows it. That too excites me sexually. I rise, seize my hat, gloves and stick, and bolt from the house …[66]

* * *

This vivid vision did not stir the faintest remorse for having left my wife; rather indeed served to remind me of the inevitability and the wisdom of the separation.

[66] This entire scene offers the reader various hints about how and why the protagonist – a sensualist and embittered romantic – has been transformed into a philosophical cynic who also possesses a sardonic sense of humor.

Back in my skull I again peeped onto the studio scene. The four of us were now lying on the divan, and Volodia was still playing in the garden. I decided to continue this fascinating game of dipping into magic memory boxes; to investigate all of them. I began with Volodia. His brain chamber was smaller than any I had yet visited. The heart gauge was jumpy and light colored, the sex tube empty; but the imagination bulb glowed – a little more than Francine's. The emotional needle, I remarked curiously, was extremely low, indicating, I supposed, feebleness of the affective qualities. I wondered what effect morphine had upon this man, so I took hold of the contact handles of the present:

* * *

Volodia: I'm seated on the parapet of the garden playing mechanically, wondering where on earth Georgette has got to. I'll bet she's too stupid to find where the swine of an Englishman's hidden the stuff. That last dose he doled out wasn't strong enough to make me feel good even. He's as mean as a Braila[67] innkeeper! And Georgette, the cow, she's no longer any good to me. What does she expect? No man wants to go to bed with a bladder of lard, and she will eat like a boatman. She said she could get this rich Englishman but he won't take any notice of her, and both his women are better than she, and his man lover, too. I could get along with him just as well without her. Strange my lovely body means nothing to him. He must be really a woman's man. He's no good, too, because he's a miser; gives me a few francs as if they were notes, and won't let me take my violin out because he lent me a moldy five hundred. What if I did spend it on drugs? What's that got to do with him? He should give me enough himself if he wants me to play every

[67] "Braila": A city in eastern Romania.

night – not that he understands music any more than any of his dog race. Oh, curse Georgette! I must have another.

I wonder if they've gone off yet, and I can creep through the studio? No, curse her! I can hear the French girl talking. Oh, how insupportably lonely I feel. If that brute had some jewels to look at, and none of his women have any worthwhile. The very image of a jewel makes my fingers itch. How I used to clamor for more light to be able to feast on necklets, bracelets, and rings glittering like wicked snake's eyes, and play, play, and play till I nearly dropped with fatigue. But they were fools, too, those women. What if they did pay for my studies at the Conservatory: hadn't they my lovely body to do with as they willed, to satisfy their silly lusts? Hadn't they my music to charm them and excite them afresh? The fools – fools! How they squalled when their precious jewels disappeared. And I didn't steal them, did I? I merely borrowed them to play to alone, to gorge on. Had I stolen them I should have sold them, shouldn't I? Well! Why, I wouldn't have parted with them – even for heroin. That's proof. Those silly women never had a conception of their beauty, such jewels. They only cared about their value in cash to make other women jealous. But they inspire me. Am I not one of the greatest violinists in Europe? Shouldn't I be the greatest if I were known? Didn't the professor himself say so? And then I'm not permitted to borrow a few jewels. Why, when they caught me in the cellar with them what was I doing? Why, playing to them set out in the light of an electric torch. They would never have discovered me if a filthy servant hadn't heard my violin. I hadn't tried to sell them, had I? I explained it all to the Chief of Police, but he just laughed, the brute.

And then they put me in that frightful prison where I nearly went mad for my daily shots. Oh, mother of heaven, what torture I suffered. No hell is there to compare to that. Yet not one of those women who had thrived on my body and my

genius, who had adored me, even tried to smuggle me a single pill to relieve my atrocious sufferings, and with their money they could have bribed every gaoler in the place. And when the torturers let me go, did one of them come to meet me? Not one. They let the police throw me the clothes I had worn and my violin, and chuck me out into the street in the middle of winter to starve. When I went to my professor, what did he do for the man he had himself said was the finest virtuoso in Europe? Set his domestics to chase me away, calling me an ex-convict. Oh, those nights and days of fiddling in the street for a little to eat, of sleeping on the floor of a filthy inn where a dirty boss gave me filthier food and drink to play Tzigane airs to his drunken customers. Oh, cursed city, where life was unsupportable! Oh, those low-class men and women; not one of them could appreciate my music, nor my lovely body; not one offered to help me. Only the aristocrats and very wealthy can do that, and down in the gutter what chance had I to meet such? Only could I think longingly of the Danube to carry my body back to my own homeland. Tears well into my eyes as I recall those days of my flight, walking and fiddling from village to village, footsore and often wet and hungry, towards freedom; towards Paris City of Light.[68] But I can't play anymore for I have no jewels to gaze upon. Now I can only fiddle, but that is good enough for brutes. Suddenly I feel very, very bad, that awful sense of life draining from you. I must have another shot.

I peep in the studio door. The Englishmen and their women are on the divan drowned in that beastly hashish stuff. Where is Georgette? I tiptoe across the studio. They would not notice an

[68] Based on this description, Volodia resembles one of the many nameless Romanian émigré violinists who busked on Paris street corners, hoping to earn their daily bread. Beadle's Parisian publisher Jack Kahane was himself the son of Romanian émigrés who settled in England circa 1870.

elephant. I creep upstairs into the bathroom. There is that cow Georgette stark naked, shoulders twisted as she sticks a needle into her enormous backside. She lied, the scum, when she said she didn't know where he kept it. I could murder her. Angrily I strike her across the face with my bow. The bow breaks and she screams. I curse her and say that if she doesn't shut up and give me a shot instantly, I'll kill her. I know that I couldn't, for the sight of blood makes me faint, but she is terrified by the look in my eyes.

"You're mad, Volodia darling," she mutters sulkily. "And look, you've broken the needle in my leg."

"Quick! Quick!" I command, "find another! Why did you lie to me?"

"I didn't," she denies, deftly plucking out the broken needle and wiping the place with iodine. "I found it hidden behind a bottle of bath salts at the back of the cupboard."

"Good!" I forgive her. "We shall at least have a night of peace."

Swiftly she adjusts another needle onto the syringe while with a trembling hand I take a treble dose. My hand shakes so that I cannot pour the precious liquid into the syringe. Georgette does it for me and I pardon her everything for that. I cannot wait to open my trousers, so I plunge the needle through the cloth and push home the piston. I sigh with relief as I feel the drug entering my body. Oh what solace! What joy! Only then have I the courage to take down my trousers and wipe the wound with iodine.

I glance at Georgette. She is beginning to look quite different. I was so angry with her. Yet I am fond of her in a way. She never bothers me about sex as all women do one way or another. Her large soft body pleases me, too, and I love to lie when I am tired and sleep with my head on her ample breasts – somehow that

always makes me think of mother, and sometimes I cry softly and deliciously.

"Georgette," I say gently, "I'm sorry I struck you, but I was mad for a shot."

"I know, I know," she replies sweetly. "I was too, that's why I couldn't wait to come down and fetch you. But I was coming as soon as I had had mine."

I know that she is lying and that she would have kept it all for herself, but then I should have done the same in her place.

"Come, my dear" I say. "Let's lie and dream on the divan and leave these hogs to themselves – and I'll play the Lamentation[69] for ourselves."

I take up my violin and go downstairs. Georgette follows and lies on the other divan. As I chin my violin I see that the bow is broken. I have forgotten that already. But I have no longer the energy to go across the studio to get a spare bow from the case, besides it isn't resined and I couldn't possibly undertake such a job now. A marvelous tranquility is enveloping me. I subside gently and my head sinks naturally onto Georgette's warm breasts. She smells so nice – like the pet goat I used to suck as a child. I see father sitting on a three-legged stool, swaying drunkenly as he plays the violin, and mother, who wants to sing, tears me from her bosom and dumps me beside the goat in a corner of the cabin. That was the only way to keep me quiet and she'd tell the neighbors that that goat had saved my life, for when she wanted to sing she couldn't be bothered to suckle me. I begin to cry softly, longing for the goat, and mechanically suck Georgette's breast, which soothes me instantly.

Vaguely I become aware of something bright over the curve of her udder. It changes curiously. Extraordinary colors flash. It's a

[69] Possibly a reference to the Lord's Lamentations (Romanian Orthodox Church Chant) and the Byzantine music of the Greek Orthodox Church.

jewel; huge, such as I have never seen. A diamond living! Emeralds scorching! Rubies burning! Oh! Oh! Opals seething! Look! Look! the most marvelous greens! Now I can play. But where is my violin? Strange, I can't move. What's that? A pyramid? I struggle. The pyramid remains wet against my face. Oh, it is the goat's nipple which I have forgotten to suck. But beyond is the marvelous magic jewel. If only I could rise I could play to it. Oh, sapphires – millions of sapphires! If only I could play. Tears crawl ever so sweetly down my cheeks. They are like voluptuous caresses, amorous like pearls. If only I could play!

A-ah! I *am* playing an Amati.[70]All around me are jewels. In the center that colossal, monstrous, gigantic tremendous jewel of opals, diamonds, sapphires, set in the night sky where the voices of the wind moan over the Danube. The violin, my own Amati, kisses my chin and sucks my throat as mother used to milk me. I am dancing, dancing madly as I play. The great jewel is in the middle. Faster! faster I dance and play. The jewel begins to turn, the diamonds to sweep through the sapphire sky. O-oh! I am becoming giddy, but my fingers scamper like frightened crabs on the sand of Sulina beach.[71] A voice cries: "he is linked to a great artist." Where, where is that voice? A low moaning of the wind over the marshes. Ah! the teller of fortunes that day in the village. She is there now, Narantsoula! I am in her arms. Her face is indigo and she has blue hair. She is loving me madly. I feel her belly sucking mine; her breasts, my chest.

"Take me, Volodia darling," she is hissing like a snake.

Black hair, black eyes and a smudged nose. "Take me, Volodia, I love you," she insists.

I don't understand. Her purple kisses annoy me.

[70] "Amati": A violin made by a member of the Amati family of Cremona, Italy.

[71] "Sulina": A town in the Danube Delta in Romania, on the Black Sea. The reminiscence further links him to a Romanian origin.

"No! no!" I shout at her. "Kiss me as mother did."

She strikes me on the face. I am astonished. Then I am angry. I wrench away from her vampire body and run. I hear her pursuing me. I run – run through the blackberries. The thorns tear my flesh. The plop[s] of the gouts of blood are in rhythm with the patter of her feet. They form into a melody in F sharp. I look back. She is well bloodied by the thorns which are my friends trying to stop her. I rush on. There is water – the Danube. I plunge. I swim furiously.

"Take me, Volodia darling," cries a loud voice. In the form of an enormous fish she surges upon me, Narantsoula! …

Where am I? I am staring at a great jewel. No, it is a small Japanese lantern on the staircase of the studio. Ah! I have been sleeping beside Georgette. Great God, that is where I am. And I thought – But I can't move. Why can't I move? The smell of goat again. Georgette's breasts. Ah! the needle is upstairs. Why did I leave it there? I peer cautiously around the mountain of a breast. *They* are still there. Sighs and moans. No danger. But why can't I move? I shake the vast bulk of flesh.

"Georgette," I call. "Give me another."

"Hoo! Hoo!" she says.

She must have had more than I. I am furiously jealous. But now I know where is the dope. I make another effort. No, I cannot move.

"Georgette!" I scream.

"Hoo! Hoo!" she murmurs gain.

How dare she mock me! I am violently angry. I beat futile fingers on soggy breasts. She does not budge. Even those on the divan do not stir. I cannot move. Ah! We are all dead. That is why. I feel very grieved for myself to have died so young. Yet again I try to scream. I perceive that the sound does not pass my lips. How silly of me! A dead man's voice wouldn't sound. But I struggle, for I do not like being dead. Against the light I see that

horrible pinnacle of the nipple from which I cannot escape. Wildly I beat on mountainous flesh that is suffocating me.

Oh, Holy Virgin! my violin! That, too, is dead. I see it in a coffin covered with flowers. Now I hate flowers because they cover my dead violin. I cry softly, always softly. There are long pallid figures walking about the studio, wailing. "Pearls! I have pearls!" They are the tears of my mother weeping for me because I am dead. Then they all fall on the floor. I struggle – oh, I struggle. I must save them. But I cannot move. That horrible nipple tries to bite me. It's a snake. I don't care. My pearls – mother's tears!

I lie exhausted. Then I reflect that I can't be dead. I can still see light and there is always the great jewel which is a Japanese lantern, and besides one can't suffocate when one is dead. I rejoice.

I move. I live. My body rises triumphant. But – where is my right arm? I can't find my right arm. I seek. I fumble with my left hand. Oh God, where is my arm? I have lost my right arm. I sit up swaying, sick with the fear that I have no longer my right arm. What shall I do with only one arm? My career is finished. I am done. Nothing is left but suicide. I wonder how I should commit suicide? I can't think of any other way but as I nearly did in Vienna – throw myself in the Danube so that my body would be carried back to my own country – and besides, even if the Danube were in Paris what am I to do without my arm? I can't bear to think of leaving my arm – I don't know where. My corpse would look so silly without an arm. "Look!" the people would say, "here's the body of Volodia who would go to foreign parts fiddling, and it hasn't got a right arm," and how they would laugh in the Braila inns. No! No! I sob. Then I wonder if I've only mislaid it, my arm? I could have held my violin with my left arm, but I couldn't have bowed without the

right, therefore I must have had it still. It must be somewhere on the divan.

Then comes a dreadful thought that if I have lost, or even mislaid my right arm, I may have lost my head, and that's why I can't think properly. My left hand feels my head and I sigh with relief. But how do I know that that is my own head? Perhaps it's someone else's? I put a finger in the mouth and bite hard. It doesn't hurt, but there is blood. Therefore it must be my own head, for another person's head wouldn't bite my finger just to please me, would it? But my dear right arm? I lose confidence in my left hand. I don't believe that it's doing what I want it to do.

"Idiot!" I scream." Where is my other arm?"

"There it is," says my left hand sullenly, and so it is, tucked underneath me. But instantly my joy is frozen. It won't move, my right arm. My left hand picks it up contemptuously. It falls. I tell it to move. It won't. "It is dead," I wail and begin to weep bitterly while my silly left hand keeps on lifting my dead right arm and letting it fall like a leg of mutton …

* * *

This experience had interested me enormously. The hints of the boy's – for he was little more, perhaps twenty – past intrigued me. I had estimated him as having a mental development not much above a child, which is frequently the case with musicians. Volodia had, for me, quite a streak of genius in his playing – when he was stimulated. He had some imagination portrayed by the jewel fantasy which accorded with the comparative brightness of the imagination bulb, corroborating an hypothesis that drugs give nothing in that way, but merely incite whatever such powers are innate.[72] Sexually of course, he was an impotent for reasons which were

[72] Beadle expresses a similar view in *Artist Quarter*.

fairly clearly implied. I immediately plunged into the memory mechanism:

* * *

Volodia: "M'rci, m'sieu! M'rci, 'dame!"

I am very angry as I walk off the terrace, my violin and bow tucked under one arm, my cap in the other hand containing a few coppers and a fifty centimes piece, not enough to buy a cheap meal! As I shove the change into my pocket I glance at the crowd, comfortably installed in overcoats and furs before glowing braziers. "Beasts! Ugly fat toads! Imbecile women full of food and wine, and I've had nothing to eat all day, except a cup of coffee and a crescent,"[73] I mutter furiously. "Swine, who don't appreciate anything but eating and drinking. I'd like to give them something of what I am feeling."

Then I catch a sparkle upon a large diamond on a woman's hand. Ah! now I can play something that would move a frog to tears. I button my jacket, for the wind is cold, and savagely I play the lamentation of my people, pouring all the pent-up nostalgia and hatred of this hard city through my fingers, fascinated by that magic glitter of the jewel. As I play I lose myself. I am listening to the voice of my mother rising against the moaning of the wind across the great plains. I finish on a long-drawn chord like the hunger howl of a distant wolf.

I wake up. There is still the silly crowd chattering unconcernedly. They have felt nothing – nothing. As with a mechanical "M'rci, m'sieu, 'dames" I turn away, someone taps me on the shoulder. A man in uniform is at my elbow. I start away frightened. I fear men in uniform. But he is only a chauffeur, and I hear him saying:

[73] Crescent rolls are a form of bread, made from yeast; croissants are a pastry, made from dough.

"A lady wishes to speak to you. Come this way."

A large car is drawn up by the curb. In the glow of the café I see the glimmer of a woman's face inside and the glint of jewels.

"Get in, please," says an imperious voice as the chauffeur holds open the door.

I glance around at the huge, luxurious car, the jewels. I would follow jewels to hell. They are rich. I obey.

"Here!" says a man's voice, and I sit in an armchair. The car starts immediately.

"What was that piece you were playing?" demands the lady's voice.

"It is the Lamentation of the people of my country, Madame," I tell her surprisedly.

"Where did you study music?" she continues in the same commanding tone.

"Vienna, Madame."

"Would you like to play for me?" she inquires more gently.

"If Madame wishes," I reply.

I try to see her face in the lights of passing lamps, but I cannot distinguish anything clearly, except that she is young; also the man with her. And she has lots of jewels. I know too much to bargain what price she will pay me. She says no more to me, but speaks several times to her companion in a language I don't know, English, I think – not German or Russian. Presently the car glides through big iron gates of a private hotel. As the chauffeur opens the door I step out hurriedly and wait. A manservant ushers them into the house. I follow into a large hall with a marble staircase. I am in luck – at last! I think – for she must be very rich. In the light I see that she is tall and very beautiful, blond with blue, blue eyes. The man too is handsome. He has long sleek black hair cut like the saints you see in cathedrals. She says something to him and he beckons and leads

me through a door. As we pass he switches on the lights. In a glow from concealed lamps I see a big studio with a large gallery at the end, and tapestries and Persian rugs on the wall and floor. As I stand with my violin under my arm he suddenly turns on a big light which nearly blinds me. He regards me carefully from head to toe. I am ashamed of my worn and dirty clothes. But he eyes me with a queer smile.

"If you play as well as you look, you'll please Madame," he says. "Now go down to the end of the studio and play that same piece, just as you did in the gutter!"

I obey again, and play with all my soul. When I have finished I hear her voice from the dark gallery, saying:

"Very good, Max."

He comes over to me.

"All right," he tells me in a friendly tone. "Now the first thing, you'd better have a bath. Madame doesn't like unperfumed people about her."

He conducts me across the studio to another door which leads to a lavatory and a sunken bath.

"You'll find everything there, but I'll send a valet," says Max, and leaves me. I look round. On glass shelves are all sorts of crystal bottles with perfumes and powders. The bath taps are not nickel. I peer closely. They are of solid silver! She must be very, very rich. An American, no doubt. I turn on the hot water. To have a bath again! To move among aristocratic and wealthy people once more! Am I dreaming? Shall I wake up shivering with cold and hunger with ice in my bones? No. I put a hand into the water. The heat is real. I tear off my horrible rags, fling them on the floor, and take up a scented soap and step into the bath. After a soft knock the door opens. A Japanese servant enters, carrying an evening suit and underclothes.

"Madame hopes that these clothes will fit Monsieur," says he solemnly, and deposits them on a chair. "Monsieur will find

studs and links. If Monsieur requires assistance will he kindly ring once?"

I am nearly ill with the joy of the hot water and the clothes. Just as I am drying myself a knock sounds again, and a stranger comes in. He, too, is handsome and very well made. He has almost white hair and a young face with sharp, queer eyes. He looks at my naked body critically as he politely excuses himself, and explains that he is Madame's doctor and that she has a horror of diseased people. Will I permit him to examine me? He taps me on the chest and listens at my back as I say "Ah"; examines my penis, and squeezes my balls gently.

"Very good," says he with a smile, and goes. I am a bit bewildered, for I have never had such an experience and I wonder if he is a fairy? I shrug my shoulders. I shall find out no doubt. I try on the clothes. They are not a perfect fit, because I am very slender, but, by tearing a dirty handkerchief in half and stuffing each part into either shoulder and tightening the waist on the trousers from behind, the effect is not bad. And such underclothes! All pure silk! I look at myself in the glass and I am pleased. Ah, how good it is to be rich! I hunt through the pockets hoping that – perhaps – But no. As I brush back my hair carefully I recollect that I am very hungry. She might anyway – No! I understand. Madame is a great lady. It would not occur to her that anybody was hungry just after the dinner hour. I know great people. I take up my violin and bow and press the button. The Japanese servant appears.

"I am ready," I tell him.

He leads me along a side passage and up a flight of stairs into glaring light, and I find myself in the gallery over the studio. At a table near the door are seated several people – a fat man, red necked; a large woman very décolleté with double chins; and a dark saturnine man with a black-pointed beard. On a platform at the back is a Negro orchestra. The young man Max comes up.

He invites me to sit at the table which is loaded with a wonderful supper.

"Put your violin on the chair," he says. "Now tell me what you propose to play? The Lamentation, of course, but Madame wishes you to keep that for the last item."

As I reply I feel the fat man and the large woman staring at me superciliously as they go on stuffing and talking in German which I pretend I don't understand.

Below the gallery in the studio are many people, all in evening clothes, lying about on divans and cushions. The women are wearing jewels. I feast my eyes upon them. Japanese servants serve everybody with drinks. Another fills my glass with champagne which I drink thirstily. I look at the many dishes, caviar, lobster, rollmops – which I adore, and my stomach contracts. But – I dare not eat. I know that once I start I shall have my fill and I cannot play well on a full stomach. I shall not be able to get that famished melancholy for the Lamentation which so pleases Madame, as I shall not feel hungry. I drink more champagne and smoke a cigarette of which there are quantities in silver boxes. They fascinate me, those silver boxes, they glitter like jewels. I begin to wonder whether I can slip one into a pocket. The temptation is great, only that saturnine fellow keeps watching me. Besides these are not my clothes and perhaps I shall have to give them up. I feel sad at the thought of parting with them. The silk is like lovely caresses on my flesh.

Max appears, smiles at me as he bends to speak to the fat man. The lights go dim. Max walks to a bay in the gallery. Spotlights shine. Max looks very handsome, almost like a woman, as he introduces Herr Ludwig of the Berlin Opera. He bows and retires to the piano. Ludwig takes his place, and does his act, a Lied.[74] He looks like a fat fish about to burst. There is medium applause. Then he sings Trinken. He has a deep, rich bass and

[74] A German art song, especially one from the nineteenth century.

gets right down to the lower G with ease. A storm of applause. I glance at the accompanist in the dim light behind.

Max plays with a virile touch. I begin to hope that he is able to play up to me. I peer over the rail. Lovely bare arms and shoulders float in a vague light. A large jewel on a white throat smolders like a sultan among the rings and bracelets of other women. I drink more champagne to stop the craving of hunger.

I am happy, slightly drunk with the sight of so many jewels and wealthy, well-dressed people. Exquisite food and drink is before me. Presently I shall play – ah, as only I can play! I have a thought. As the Herr from the opera comes back to the table I felicitate him. He bows ceremoniously but condescendingly. He is right to be haughty. He is known. But wait. I, Volodia, too, shall be known – as once I should have been known if I had not have been a fool. But this time!

The Negro band starts up. Below they dance, the rich and aristocratic. I take some old brandy and wriggle to enjoy the silk underwear against my flesh, wonder how long before I may eat, and try not to hear the terrible jungle sounds of the saxophone and the drum, lest it destroy the divine rhythm in my head. I notice that the Herr and the fat woman are discussing me in German. They are indignant that I, an unknown, should be allowed to play at the same concert. The woman hoists her shoulders and says that it is an eccentricity of Madame la Baronne. I wonder what the silent, saturnine-faced man does. Then Max calls him. He is an American who tells funny stories, half in French and half in English. They should be very clever by the laughter he wins, although I can only understand one side.

I drink more brandy and I cannot resist a caviar sandwich to stop the gnawing in my stomach. Fighting against the jazz band I dream and smoke. Images flit before me. Is it the effect of the sandwich, or the brandy on a twisted stomach? I see my father,

tall, lean, with a face like a gargoyle I've seen in Paris, fiddling madly as if possessed by a demon; and my mother, with braids of blond hair hanging down over a red bodice, and face uplifted, resembling a wolf howling at the moon as she sings the Lamentation. Again I hear the rain on the roof which so sounds like applause … A big, beautiful woman is lying on a divan. Others are about her. All are naked except for gems. She says: "Go, Volodia, play your Lamentation, for I want to weep." And when I have finished she gives me a jeweled ring from a finger and kisses me, and they all kiss me. Ah! those days … Once more I feel the rain lashing on my face as I drag my weary limbs along among rocks and shrubs hugging my violin under my ragged jacket, fearing each moment that the frontier guards will shoot. But now … I reach for the brandy. Max is before me. I glance at his eyes. Oh, I know I am not well, I tell him, ask if he can give me "something"? He glances at me keenly, smiles, and bids me follow him.

A-ah! force and courage spurt through my nerves as I return clasping my violin. I step into the light, proudly tossing back my hair, and bow, certain that I have already triumphed. Fixing my gaze on a large diamond on a woman's breast, I play a nocturne of Chopin. I am well received, but not too much. Then I give them a wild Tzigane scherzo. That warms them. Now I'll make them cry. I mutter. Eyes closed, I summon the image of my mother singing to the fiddling of my father in a peasant hut in the swamps, belly sticking to the backbone on a cold, starving day of pain … I awake on the last long-draw chord of the famished wolf.

The applause rises like a storm over the Danube delta. I bow – bow. Vaguely I catch a glimpse of my hostess smiling. She is proud of me. As I return to the artists' table the fat Herr rises to congratulate me ceremoniously, and the Fräulein smiles. Even they accept me now.

But hunger swoops upon me. I start on caviar and follow with lobster mayonnaise, and I can hardly wait to get at a wonderful game pie. As I am eating, the Fräulein, who is an Austrian contralto, asks me all sorts of questions to which I reply all sorts of nonsense, and when I have my mouth free for a moment I inquire who is our hostess. She stares; and I tell her with my mouth full again, that I was hired by an agent and didn't catch the name.

"Why," she responds, "she's Madame la Baronne de Volnier, the wife of the ex-minister and daughter of Monsieur le Comte de Bézues."[75]

"Oh?" I say. "She must be very rich then?"

"Oh – oh! one of the richest families in France."

"Has she children?" I ask for something to say.

"Oh no, pardie![76] She merely needed a distinguished husband and he needed a distinguished and rich wife. There!" she indicates vulgarly over the rail of the gallery, that's Monsieur le Baron with that good-looking boy." I see a tallish man with an eyeglass, wearing decorations, crossing the studio with a slender hand on the shoulder of Max. The contralto giggles as she adds:

"You understand? And they say she always takes away his boyfriends. They say that they have Roman orgies here." She shrugs. "Oh, they're notorious. But what would you? They are rich enough to do as they like." And she gives me an ogling look as much as to say, you'd better look out for yourself.

[75] Bézues-Bajon: A commune in the Gers department of southwest France.

[76] Pardie (archaic): A mild oath used in the sense of "verily" or "indeed." From Middle English *pardee*, from Anglo-French *par Dé*: by God.

But of course I can tell what he is, and I begin to wonder what la Baronne intends to do, and whether there is a way to make money out of them.

I sigh with relief as I finish a marron glacé. I haven't eaten very much, for when you've been starved for many days your stomach shrinks. I drink a green Chartreuse and light a cigarette, and peer down below. The crowd has thinned. My fellow artists rise to go. Max beckons to me. I make formal farewells to the three and follow him. He leads me to a small room furnished with violet leather cushions and stools. He smiles again, that mysterious smile, as he opens a cabinet let into the wall, a small bar, saying:

"You will find everything you need there. In a little while Madame will send for you."

I look at Max and make a sign of sniffing. He proffers a snuff box to take another shot. After he has gone I find that I am thirsty still, and open a half bottle of champagne. I lie on the cushions smoking, and speculate on what the game is, and how I can profit. I know from experience as well as the medical examination that they need my body for an orgy. Perhaps, as often has happened, to play to them too, for music I have noticed, always has an exciting effect on women. Max has an allure of a fairy, but the doctor looks a male. Are they lovers? And Madame? Is it a ménage à trois? And the homosexual husband? Am I booked for him? I recall the remark of the contralto that she usually takes away his boyfriends.

My gaze, wandering about the room, is attracted by a glittering object in the cabinet. I get up and discover a crystal flagon with a sapphire stopper. I examine it in the dim light and long to slip it into a pocket. I love sapphires, although not so much as diamonds. Then I open it to see what there is within. Dope, of course, but what? A thick dark liquid which has a smell that I don't recognize. Opium it looks like, but the odor is

different. I taste it on the tip of a finger. It is bitter. Hashish, I decide, although I have never seen it in liquid form. But hashish doesn't interest me. As I am admiring the stopper and longing to possess it, I hear a voice, and hurriedly push the flagon back and pour out another glass of champagne.

But nobody enters the room. Madame is speaking in the room adjoining. I slip out and listen at the keyhole. Madame is saying:

"But, my dear Herr Professor, naturally as a Teuton you are confounding aesthetic principles with sentimentality. You admit homosexuality and tribadism,[77] but only on the condition that that is diluted with – I should say poisoned by – sentimental love. No Gaul could have written Werther. A perfect example of the Teuton wallowing in the mire of sentimentality. You are unable to dissociate an act from the past and the future. With us an act is a thing-in-itself having no relation to any other act, preceding, or following. That act only exists in the frame of the present. Directly it is over, don't you see, it has become the past, and therefore is not necessarily of any consequence."

"I confess, dear Madame," says guttural tones, that I see your point of view, but I cannot accept it. For me it is impossible to comprehend a sexual relationship between a man and a man or a woman and a woman without – well, mutual admiration – cerebral, if you like – and not solely on a physical plane, any more for that matter, than normal sexuality."

"Naturally. That is the everlasting Werther of the Teutonic soul. Tell me, dear Herr Professor, is sex a physical or psychical phenomenon?" says Madame.

"Basically physical, I grant you, dear Madame, but there is much of the psychic involved," contends the professor.

"Merely to the extent that the psyche is relieved by the emptying of the glands," states Madame, "just as the same

[77] "Tribadism": A form of sexual activity between women in which the external genitalia are rubbed together.

psyche is solaced, or irritated, by the functioning or nonfunctioning of the excretory organs. Constipation frequently produces headaches, ill-temper, melancholy, despair, even in some cases leading to mysticism or suicide: all purely psychic troubles induced by physiological causes. Now observe, dear, Herr Professor, that these same symptoms are typical of those provoked by deprivation of sex – disappointment in love, I presume you sentimentalists would baptize it. I am positive that had Werther relieved his pent up emotions, otherwise his overcharged glands, by means of another woman he would have felt much better physically, and therefore psychically, and would therefore have had no need to sublimate in erotic dream fantasy!"

"But, my dear Madame," protests the professor indignantly, "surely you must admit that to Werther that woman, and only that woman, was capable of satisfying his love, that she represented to him the ideal woman; and that therefore, any other female was ipso facto displeasing."

"That is to say, dear Herr Professor," mocks Madame, "that Werther was attributing to that lady's genital organs a magical property? Surely you will not insist upon that as did primitive humanity when genitalia were assumed to possess such miraculous powers? What reason is there that two or more people who have enjoyed each other's sexual attributes should 'know' each other socially – which is an entirely different plane – on the morrow?"

"But surely the possible result – a child, should –" began the professor.

"We are not discussing children. Breeding, although a total[ly] neglected science, except for animals and plants, has nothing to do with aesthetic pleasure." Madame laughs a low chuckle. "As for your contention that mutual admiration, sentiment or cerebral, is sine qua non, please remark that one may have a

great admiration for the cerebral, or social, qualities of a person, but find that he, or she, is unsupportable physically as a sexual partner; and on the other hand, someone may be an Adonis, or an Aphrodite, and as unintelligent as a domestic, yet may serve as a delightful instrument. Au fond you are a Christian poisoned by the doctrine of original sin – magic again! – and the sole way you may excuse yourself to your taboo is to doll up your desire in the rags of sentimentality. It's the aesthetic only that counts in sex. The instrument must delight the eyes; the quality of the flesh, the touch; the odor, the olfactory organ. During and around the act the mental state is purely primitive, the sense ends are involved, and not the cerebral, the utter annihilation of the thinking individual into the animal."

"Madame!" the professor nearly shouts. "You wish to say that lovemaking is purely animal?"

"What a blow to your sentimentalists, dear Herr Professor," jeers Madame. "But reassure yourself, man's title to the rank of the superior animal is that he applies aesthetics in the approach to, and variety in, the act of love, and the duration of sensation augmented by the invention of alcohol and the discriminate use of drugs!"

"Yet you spoke just now, dear Madame," says he, "of the utter annihilation of the thinking individual?"

"Quite so. Any person who, during the apogee of orgasmic sensation, is consciously aware of his, or her, environment is certainly not passionate; is incapable of abandoning the self to Eros. I have indeed heard tell of such beings, women who, apparently, while being possessed, catch flies, or add up the laundry list, but really such creatures seem fabulous." Madame chuckles again as if teasing the professor. "The deed is, or should be, dear Herr Professor, accomplished for the love of the deed, which lives and has its being in that isolated moment. An individual is merely a flight of acts resembling volts of electric-

ity along a wire, each volt is a being in itself. An act utilizes us as an instrument to its own pleasure-need, and passes on, leaving us the prey to the next act."

"But," objects the professor, "no matter how soon the next act seizes its prey, as you so charmingly put it, dear Madame, there is always a pause between."

"Granted," retorts Madame, "but so is there a space between two electrons as between every other object in the known universe, although in life such is practically imperceptible to us."

"We agree on that, anyhow, dear Madame," says the professor, making a grunting noise which I take to be a laugh. "And if it gives you pleasure I will cede on other points of your psychology of sex, but with reservations; that we all have sexual prejudices – just as a homosexual cannot endure the smell of women, nor lesbians the odor of men."

"Quite," agrees Madame. "But in those cases, as with normal people, the person is not a whole. Only an androgyne – such as myself – is that."

I haven't been able to understand much of their talk, nor have I ever heard of the word "androgyne," and I wonder [what] kind of a vice that is, although I thought I knew them all.

"Although I will admit," Madame adds, "that even I have a sexual prejudice. I cannot support actual penetration. And as a matter of fact such an act is a nearly physical impossibility, for my clitoris is so abnormally developed that I am almost the perfect hermaphrodite."

"Extraordinary!" exclaims the professor. "The only personal case I have ever encountered."

"Oh," says Madame, "I've merely told you so that you may add me to your collection of odd creatures. I hope you'll have a special cage for me in the Berlin Zoo, my dear Herr Professor. And if you are interested in other freaks of my acquaintance

come round after Tuesday, as I'm always incognito from Friday to Tuesday morning."

I hear the slither of feet approaching and slip back into the room. Max, in a yellow kimono and sandals, invites me to follow. In the bathroom he orders me to strip and put on an emerald kimono. Politely he offers me another sniff and takes one for himself. He then conducts me to an alcove curtained off from the big gallery by a Chinese tapestry with an enormous dragon embroidered in gold. The room within is suffused with a faint light, and is heavily perfumed by incense. On a large divan lounges Madame. Beside her is the doctor fellow. Both are nude and are drinking Russian tea and smoking cigarettes. I bow to Madame and await her pleasure. She glances at Max who lifts off my kimono. I stand naked before them smiling, for beautiful is my body, so that I am not ashamed.

"Turn around," she commands.

As I obey she rises on an elbow to examine me critically.

"Very good," she says.

Max leaves, turning off the bright light as he goes. In a niche in the wall I notice a strange statue about six inches high. A naked girl on her knees has her arms about a huge penis and is kissing the top.

"Are you civilized?" inquires Madame

"I don't know, Madame," I reply respectfully, not knowing what she means.

"A civilized person," she says, "is one who is above all prejudices – that is taboos, sexual or superstitious. Do you understand?"

"No, Madame," I admit, more bewildered, for I have never heard the word "taboo." I keep wondering what an androgyne does.

"You're interested in that statuette," Madame continues. "Does it shock you?"

"No, Madame. Why?" I venture to ask, not comprehending exactly what she means by "shocked," although I have never seen such a statue before.

"Admirable!" exclaims Madame.

"A natural!" says the doctor. "The mind of a child before it is poisoned. Quite civilized, really."

"No, Leon," contradicts Madame. "It is necessary to be poisoned in order to become civilized by expelling the toxic by the antitoxin produced by the intellect. Do you know what that statue signifies?" she questions me.

I gaze at her more bewildered than ever. It is so obvious.

"That statue," Madame continues, smiling at something that seems to amuse her, "represents a god worshipped by an ancient civilization, which is still worshipped by all humanity, but in secret."

"Why in secret, Madame?" I inquire, still not quite comprehending.

"Perfect!" she says, and laughs. "I'm sure you will amuse us – for a while. What is your name? Volodia!" she repeats, mouthing the word as if it were candy. "Charming. How old are you, Volodia?"

"Eighteen, Madame," I reply, watching the statue which makes me think of my mother.

"Eighteen! A wonderful age!" she says and, stretching out a hand, feels my sex. "Rather small, but no matter," she adds, caressing me. "Well, now you are my guest, Volodia. I shall not let you go until Tuesday; but if you are – satisfactory, you may stay indefinitely. You shall have ample time to practice the violin during the week – which, by the way, you need, for your technique is weak. The reason I understand well, and you will have to work very hard, Volodia, and then I will see that you get the best of engagements in Paris – in fact, I will launch you – if you do not disappoint me. Will that please you, Volodia?"

I bow as I reply:

"If that will please Madame."

"Volodia," she says, and I notice that her eyes change, "there is no Madame until Tuesday morning. I am Theodosia. This is Leon. Max you already know. Now lie beside me, Volodia – or perhaps you would like this first?"

Leon, the doctor, who has half risen, is holding a hypodermic syringe.

"Now tell me, Volodia," she says, smiling pleasantly, "what is your normal dose?"

I tell him, adding that I have been deprived for many, many months.

"Good. Then this will suit you to begin with."

Deftly he injects the heroin into a thigh.

Gently Theodosia pulls me upon my back. I realize now that an androgyne is merely a vampire woman like mother and others. As she begins the effect of the drug pervades me. I sigh with content. How lovely to be again among the rich and the aristocratic! Fascinatedly I gaze at a diamond earring which glitters deliciously against the pallid white of my belly. Leon is caressing her with his tongue and, at the same time, myself with his hand. My nostrils dilate to inhale her odor which is like almond flowers. I stretch in luxurious abandon. Silently Max enters, places the crystal flagon of hashish on a side table and, smiling mysteriously, leaves. Just as a far distant sensation commences I hear the opening chords of a Chopin nocturne …

* * *

I released the tape with a sense of shock. The "Theodosia" of Volodia's adventure was my Roman empress of the Bal de l'Internat, she of whom I had dreamed for years as my ideal woman. The coincidence that I had given her the sobriquet

which she, evidently, had herself chosen, was indeed strange. Actually I had never found out who she was, but in this occult experience I had recognized her name – which I had often heard and read – that of a quondam wealthy dilettante and well-known poetess who had left society to bury herself in a Tibetan convent, according to report. Ah, I reflected, how bitterly I should have been disappointed had I never met her in the flesh. At least sexually, for her mind seemed as brilliant intellectually as I had imagined. But it is ever that way with ideals! The statuette, which had failed to shock the naive Volodia was, of course, one of the Egyptian cults of the phallus. I remarked again the curious phenomenon that while I was experiencing in the person of the subject in question, I understood no more than he did, nor less; but that when I had returned to my proper ego the whole was perfectly comprehensible. From these weird probings into the past of the boy[,] I perceived clearly enough why he was a hopeless drug addict and the cause of his sexual decadence as registered by the empty sex tube on the instrument board in his cranial chamber.

I selected Belle, who was lying with head on Eddie's shoulder, and a seraphic smile upon her lips, as the next experiment. The fo'c'sle lantern was low, and of a greenish tinge; the imagination bulb no brighter than Francine's; the sex tube low; but the emotional needle was steady on the "adoration" side.

* * *

Belle: A queer delightful feeling is all over me coming from one point. Even my hair tingles. I want to scream. "I can't stand it! Oh, darling I can't stand it!" But I hold my breath. It is so delicious! The exquisite agony becomes unbearable, I try to push her head away, but fierce hands clutch my bottom. Then a groan is wrenched from my bursting lungs. I am so dizzy I

don't know where I am. I can only moan in joy and relief. Dimly I see half-lidded eyes, a mass of hair and a wet mouth. I recognize Betty.

"Oh, darling!" I breathe, "I didn't know there was anything so wonderful in all the world."

Betty laughs as she smoothes back her reddish-bobbed hair with a slender blue-veined hand and sits on the bedside.[78]

[78] In 1938 such remarks (and the passages that follow) would have been considered utterly censorable and would have prevented *Dark Refuge* from appearing in any Anglo-Saxon country. These conditions remained largely unchanged in the United States until the 1961 publication of Henry Miller's *Tropic of Cancer*, which led to a 1964 Supreme Court ruling that declared that the book possessed significant literary merit and was not obscene. (*Tropic of Cancer* was first published in 1934 by Jack Kahane's Obelisk Press in Paris.) In 1968 the London publishers of Hubert Selby's novel *Last Exit to Brooklyn* – a book that contains graphic depictions of homoeroticism, illicit drug use, prostitution, and rape – won a court battle in England that resulted in the complete transformation of British censorship laws.

Beadle, Miller, and Selby were all fighting a righteous battle for freedom of expression and for a more vital, authentic, honest rendering of human sexuality: a point that is now often overlooked by the fundamentalists of political correctness, who take issue with the use of certain vernacular expressions in these novels and who prefer to throw the baby out with the bath water. In my 23 July 2015 interview with Nabokov biographer Robert Roper, he expressed a similar view when he said, speaking of Nabokov and *Lolita*: "The Thirties through the Sixties is a period of great sexual awakening. Of bringing sexual material into the scope, the unashamed scope of serious writing. So, he was with that; he was with that enterprise.... Nowadays, a lot of people who hate the novel and still want to ban it say that this kind of thing should never be written about. But back when he was starting to write about it in the late Forties, there was nothing like that agreement: that this was somehow beyond the pale.

"Well, now, my delightful child, you're beginning to live," she says, lighting a cigarette. She looks down at me tenderly. "You'd better have a pick-me-up," she adds.

She rises and goes to a table to mix cocktails. I still feel muzzy and exhausted. I watch her lithe body and long legs. She is lovely. She has quite a big brown mole just below the crease of her bum. I am still bewildered because I have never had such curious sensations. Somehow I feel lighter; much better than I did. I don't yet understand why. Still there are lots of things I don't understand – I mean I'd always thought that only a man and a woman could – well, I can't recall exactly what I did think. Hazy. I knew how a man was made, of course, but I never did comprehend what happens, nor how babies are

---

So, he was, in a way, doing what he thought was noble work, to write about that." (See Rob Couteau, *More Collected Couteau*, New York: Dominantstar, 2020, pp. 353-354.) Sometimes courage runs in the family. The novel *Lolita* was first published by Jack Kahane's son, Maurice Girodias, under the Olympia Press imprint.

Only Kahane would have had the courage to publish *Dark Refuge* – filled as it is with such censorable material – as early as 1938. The explicit rendering of drug-fueled orgies, bisexuality, and homosexuality would have made it impossible to publish anywhere else but Paris (and even there, this was made possible only because it was in English). Literary historian Hugh Ford sums it up nicely when he writes: "Only war and the publisher's death [in 1939] finally toppled the Obelisk, but by the time those calamities occurred Kahane's Obelisk logo had been affixed to some of the most controversial books of the past half century, many of them branded as pornographic and obscene or serious or all three, depending upon the tolerance and understanding with which one could view works that were ofttimes abrasively forthright in style and subject." See Hugh Ford, *Published in Paris: A Literary Chronicle of Paris in the 1920's and 1930's*, New York: Collier Books, 1988, p. 345. One wonders if *Dark Refuge* would have fallen into such obscurity if Kahane hadn't died only a year after its publication.

made. When Eddie kisses me a long time on the mouth he makes me feel woozy and funny, that stifling kind of feeling. But oh, nothing like this! And another thing – now I understand things I hadn't before – I mean among women. I'd noticed that several girls in our troop were continually kissing and mauling each other. Some of the men, too. The girls said they were queer – beastly. Now I can't help wondering what men do to each other. I'll ask Betty.

"Betty," I inquire, as she comes over with two cocktails, "what do men do [to] each other?"

"What!" she gasps.

She stares at me in surprise, and then laughs.

"What, for heaven's sake, put [that] into your head, you wonderful child?" she queries.

"Oh, the girls say that Micky Tepfer and John Paynon are 'like that,' and I was wondering what they could do to each other."

"Well, don't, darling," says Betty, putting a lighted cigarette between my lips. "That's beastly. Doesn't stand talking about."

"Why?" I insist.

"Why? Oh, you baby, you! Because it's unaesthetic. Love between women, or between a man and a woman is beautiful. But between men – Ugh! don't! You make me positively ill!"

"Do you love your husband, then," I ask curiously.

"Of course I do, silly! But I love you, too. I'm bisexual. Aren't you?"

"I don't know," I say, wondering whether I am or not.

"I love several men for that matter," adds Betty coolly.

"Besides your husband!" I gasp.

"Naturally. Just as one man loves several women. I love one man for his brilliant mind, another for his lovely body; although he's as stupid as a coal heaver, he's an Apollo. So does my husband love several women. I was crazy about his favorite

mistress. We had a ménage à trois for some time, and had a perfectly spiffing[79] time."

"What?" I breathe, "you all three slept together?"

"Not much sleep, darling," laughs Betty.

"You see, you sweet infant, we're civilized and therefore not jealous. Jealousy is a brute instinct. Fidelity to one person is psychologically impossible and physiologically dangerous. Love is a glorious, beautiful pastime. There's nothing occult or sacred about the sexual organs. Nobody but a fool, or a fanatic, would maintain that every time a man or a woman needs sexual relief a child should result. Good Lord, my darling, we should breed like rabbits! Love is a glandular affair, if you understand what that means. Have you never had a man?"

"Good heavens!" I exclaim, shocked. "You don't until you're married!"

"M'm," says Betty, smiling amusedly. "Now that is a strange idea in these days. Why not, pray?"

"Oh," I reply confusedly, not liking to admit that I have always been taught that a girl should keep her virtue for her husband, for fear that Betty will laugh at me, "oh well, I mean, you might get a baby and then – then if he won't marry you, you're ruined."

"Oh, you're too precious for words," says Betty, pealing laughter. "Your mother ought to be ashamed of herself, turning you loose in the theatrical world as ignorant as a child of ten. You mean to say that you've been nearly a year dancing and you've never gone to bed with a man?"

"No," I deny, firmly, and it's true. "I – I promised once, but – Oh, I couldn't at the last moment."

"Little welsher!" exclaims Betty, laughing still more.

"Well, he – I mean, he tried to make me tight, but I was so ill I couldn't and – and afterwards I was glad I hadn't."

[79] "Spiffing": British slang meaning "excellent, splendid."

"Why?" she persists.

"Oh, because – and besides I was glad I could still tell Eddie I hadn't."

"Your fiancé? Is he a nice boy? Intelligent?"

"Oh, yes," I tell her proudly. "You'll see him. He's coming round to take me to dinner before the show."

"Never been to bed with a girl either, Belle?" says she, teasingly.

"N – no. Well, I mean only once – at school."

"What did you do?"

"Oh, only – only stroked each other."

"Did you enjoy it?" queries Betty curiously.

"Y – yes," I admit reluctantly, I don't know why. "But – but nothing like – just now."

"Darling!"

Betty kisses me on the lips.

"Is that your fiancé?" she asks, rising to look at a portrait in a silver frame. "Looks quite civilized, too! I'm sure I shall like to meet him. Do your people know?"

"Oh, yes," I say. "Mother's very pleased because he's a marquis, you know. Oh, I don't care a hang about that! I add hastily, offended at Betty's laugh. "But mother is a snob. I mean, that's why she's forgiven me for running away on the stage. Anyhow, you married a lord!"

"Naturally," retorts Betty, "as I believe in marrying into one's own class whatever one does outside."

"Oh!" I exclaim, astonished. "I didn't know you were – what d'you call it? – I mean had a title of your own."

"By the way," says Betty, looking at the portrait again, "I hope your man is really civilized and won't want to snatch you away from me?"

The anxious way she says that and the look in her eyes frightens me somehow. I feel that I don't want to lose Betty –

now. And I wonder whether he will make me as happy as she did. But I daren't ask her, for I know she'll laugh. I glance at the gold bracelet watch which Eddie gave me. It's nearly six now. He will be here in a few minutes as he's always on time. A dread seizes me, and again I can't imagine why. I start up, exclaiming:

"Good heavens, I must get on my things!"

"There's no hurry, darling," says Betty coolly, and rising, she picks a small gold box out of her bag and takes out a white tablet.

"Oh, darling!" I exclaim, as she squirts soda into a glass. "Have you got a headache?"

"No, this is not aspirin," she tells me. "It's heroin. Bucks you up."

"Oh!" I gasp, horrified. "*You* don't take that horrible stuff?"

"Why not? And it isn't horrible," she says. "You think so, little goose, because fools have told you so. Alcohol is horrible – if you take too much. So is love," she adds, laughing. "Try one?"

"Oh, no, no!" I refuse, recoiling.

"Yes, darling – just one – to please me," she insists. "Come, baby, this will make you feel good – to meet Eddie."

"No," I say, but she persists, and after all one can't do much harm if she takes it, too, and I wonder what it will feel like. Obediently I swallow a tablet with soda water.

"Now," she says gaily, "we're all set to meet him."

"Heavens!" I exclaim again. "He'll be here in a tick![80] We must get our things on."

"Don't be silly, darling!" says Betty. "He'll like you better like that. But lend me a kimono, or a dressing gown, will you – as I haven't met him yet?"

"But – but," I gasp. "Aren't you going to dress?"

[80] "Tick": A small amount (in this case, a brief duration of time).

"Oh, I'll just slip on something and we'll give him a surprise," says she, smiling funnily.

"Oh, I don't know what he'll think," I say in dismay. "He might suspect something awful to find us *both* like this."

"Oh, he won't, if he's a civilized man, as you say," says Betty, opening a wardrobe. "Oh, the cerulean blue is a peach! Just my color too, my dear."

She slips it on, and she does look lovely with her green eyes and reddish hair. I have been so upset by her suggestion that I have forgotten to put something on myself. The flat bell rings. As I just scramble into a dressing gown a wonderful sensation comes over me – as if I were drunk, but different – excited and wildly happy. I hear Eddie's voice speaking to the maid and dance into the sitting room as he enters. I kiss him madly. He looks slightly startled and glances across the room to where Betty is standing in the bedroom doorway, smiling. Her eyes are glittering, and the kimono is half open, revealing most of one white thigh.

"Oh, Eddie, darling," I say, and my voice sounds queer, "this is a dear friend of mine I want you to know. Lady Betty Mommond, the marquis" – I begin, and then confusedly recollect that that's all wrong. I start again: "The Marquis Delorme –"

But Betty, clutching the kimono with the cigarette hand, advances smiling, holding out the other hand.

"Good evening," she says with that drawl she always uses with strangers: "Delighted, I'm sure. Belle's been telling me wonderful things about you."

"A friend of Belle's is already a friend of mine," says Eddie, and, bowing in that wonderful way he has, takes and kisses Betty's hand.

She sinks onto a divan, her lovely, long jeweled hand inviting him to sit beside her.

"Delorme?" she drawls. "Re-ally? I believe we're some sort of cousins? My grandmother was a Delorme. Oh, Belle darling, don't you think we might have some cocktails?"

Somehow I find myself standing there not quite knowing what to do. I mean, Betty seems in some way to have stepped between us. Eddie starts to say something – I don't know what – and I scamper into the bedroom. Then recollecting that there isn't a third glass and no ice, I rush back and ring. That wave of mad happiness swirls over me, and I just can't help dancing up to Eddie and kissing him. He laughs and takes me on his knees.

Betty modestly covers her thigh as the maid comes in with glasses and ice. I am so crazily happy clinging to Eddie. He smiles at Betty as he takes out his gold cigarette case with arms on it, and proffers a cigarette to her.

"They're special," he says. "Possibly you would like one?"

She looks at him quickly, smiles, and takes a cigarette. He holds a lighter, and she inhales deeply.

"Yes," she remarks with a rummy smile, "I like that brand," and they both laugh, but I don't understand.[81]

Eddie lights two more cigarettes at the same time, and puts one between my lips. I imitate Betty, and draw the smoke deep into my lungs. It tastes queer and has a funny kind of perfume. Eddie places me on the divan beside Betty and mixes the cocktails.

Another and stranger sensation comes over me. Betty suddenly seems quite a way off, although she's just beside me, and Eddie appears handsomer than ever. I love to watch his slender white hands as he is shaking the shaker, although he does appear to be doing it so slowly. But I don't care as I am feeling happier than ever. Suddenly a fit of the giggles takes me, for Eddie looks so comic as he pours out the cocktails, and I laugh till I cry. Again the two exchange glances, but neither says a

[81] "That brand": Most likely, either marijuana or hashish.

word. I am still gasping with laughter when I notice that the chink of the ice sounds like bells ringing, and a passing taxi makes a noise like a train.

Betty is lying back watching Eddie, and her nostrils are quivering just as they did with me – before. He hands me a glass. I never knew a cocktail tasted so delicious. It trickles down my throat for a long time – lovely and cool, like a caress. Then Eddie sits beside me, and they talk, but I can't listen. Their voices appear so far off, and I'm too happy! Eddie's hand tickling my thigh is exquisite, and I feel woozy with delight. We all smoke another of Eddie's cigarettes and have another cocktail. In a mist vaguely I see Betty whispering to Eddie.

"Eddie darling!" I call, holding out my hands.

"In a minute, dearest!" he replies from a long way off, and very, very slowly goes into the bathroom. I can't understand why he wants a bath now, nor why he walks so queerly.

"Better come to bed, Belle darling," says Betty in my ear, and again I can't understand why she speaks so loudly. But I don't care because I'm so intensely happy. She picks me up and carries me onto the bed, throws her kimono on the floor, and takes off my dressing gown. Then she begins kissing and caressing my body more delightfully than ever.

Suddenly I recollect Eddie, and there he is, quite naked, but that doesn't seem strange at all. Then he opens my thighs and begins to kiss me as she did, but – but it's ever so much sweeter and goes on and on and on. I'm gasping, yet I can't. A long way off I hear a low moaning. I no longer know where I am, nor who is there. I feel as if I'm going mad. I can't stand the sensation any longer, and wrench my body away suffocating and everything goes black.

I must have swooned. Slowly I make out Eddie and Betty sitting up beside me smoking cigarettes. I stare at them both and something more than I can bear makes me burst into sobs.

"What's the matter, darling?" I hear Betty ask.

All I can manage to whisper is:

"Oh! Oh! I don't know what's the matter, but I do so love you both!"

"Our own darling Belle!" says Betty, and they both kiss me tenderly.

* * *

Smiling at Belle's naive character which corresponded so well with the Belle I had personally known, I took up the "present" controls, curious to discover what was passing through her mind as she lay beside myself-that-was under hashish only.

* * *

Belle: O-oh! how I am exquisitely happy! There is soft flesh all about me, delicious, so soothing. A long way off is a slow thudding which sounds hollow. Vaguely I wonder what it can be? Hazily I think that it must be someone's heart beating. I am with some people, I recall dimly, but I can't remember exactly who they are. Eddie? – or is it Betty? No, I don't think Betty was in the party, but that doesn't really matter for I'm so, so happy. But I love Eddie. So I hope that it's his heart beating. Or perhaps it's Francine's? Oh, yes, that's true, now it all comes back! And Bill. I love Bill too, but not like Eddie. I adore Eddie! O-oh! someone moves, and it feels like an earthquake. A finger – or is it a tongue? – is caressing my clitoris. Oh, it's lovely! Just fancy that I didn't know I had one till Eddie told me, and what its name was. It's that that makes that heavenly sensation – even nicer than being had – and Eddie does it wonderfully, and so did Betty, and when they have me both together – Oh, that's divine! I wonder whose it is? But I don't care really, because I'm

happier and happier. Still I hope it's Eddie – or Betty! Oh, yes, Betty isn't here. I keep on forgetting that. O – oh! there's that earthquake again! I hope Bill isn't going to have me once more. He'll wake me up, and I don't want to wake up. And besides he always hurts me up top afterwards. Not like Eddie. I wish Eddie would kiss me again. Nobody kisses as he does – except Betty, and she isn't here. I feel very sad and want to cry. Then that sensation begins again, but oh, so far off, far off! Perhaps it is Eddie, I mean the finger or the tongue or whatever it is. O-oh! it's marvelous and I'm too perfectly happy to bother who it is. Then slowly, slowly it fades away; I mean the sensation. And – oh, what's that? Bright lights and a funny sound which I know so well. What can it be? Oh! oh! the house is clapping! Fancy, I'd forgotten! There's Betty in the orchestra stalls and a man is handing up a great basket of orchids from Eddie who is smiling at me. I feel so proud and happy. There's nothing so wonderful in all the world as success. Now I shall have a contract and my picture will be in all the papers and mother won't dare to – Oh! there's the earthquake again! And oh! that sensation beginning once more – such a long way off – Oh, I'm so happy – happy –

* * *

An utter blank as if the current had been short-circuited. She had fallen asleep, or into a coma. Evidently, I reflected, the two experiences, present and past, revealed that Belle did not have any typical illusions of hashish or heroin: either drug merely intensified and prolonged sensations; produced a state of stupefied *bien-être,* coinciding with the feebleness of the imagination bulb. In the latter she had had what might have been a normal memory dream suggesting ambivalent emotions towards Eddie, which made me ponder a moment on her real state of mind –

whether she was not obsessed by a hankering after the glories of the stage?

I flew down her nose and observed the four of us sprawling on the divan. Yes, Belle, her head upon Eddie's chest, seemed slumbering heavily. The head of myself-that-was rested on her thigh, and Francine's upon my belly. The eyes of both Eddie and myself were wide open, staring with that fixed otherworld expression. I wondered what we were dreaming about. I hesitated; then chose Eddie.

The imagination bulb glowed rather dimly, not quite so murky as his wife's; the heart gauge was steady but slow, which was natural under the effect of the drug. The sex tube medium. Just as I was about to grasp the "present" controls, a whim urged me to investigate the memory index.

* * *

Eddie: A violent pain grips my skull beneath a heavy weight. I am sitting deep in the grate of a fireplace. Single white beds stretch down on each side of the big room beneath the windows A crowd of boys in flannel nightgowns are prancing and shouting before me. One smacks the thing on my head, crying:

"I crown you member of the Syme's House, and may you have the spunk never to funk!"

Another leaps forward yelling the same doggerel as he slaps harder. The stab of each blow wrenches an "Ow!" My eyes are full of tears of pain, but I know that I must not blub. Others dance by, each one hitting. Writhing I put up my hands to ease the object on my skull. Immediately my wrists are seized and voices scream derisively.

"No! No! That's not done! Funk! Funk! Cowardly custard!"

The chanting goes on. Every boy crowns me after his fashion. I am forced deeper into the grate, my legs sticking in the air. I

long to squeal, "Mother! Mother!" But I dare not, for I know they'll mock me if I do, and hit the harder. The torture seems interminable. A boy, taller than the others, lets me off with a light tap of the fingers as he repeats the formula, laughing. I like him. He appears kinder. In spite of my pain I watch that boy. He is strong and has blue eyes and fair hair and laughs all the time.

At last the ordeal is over. I try to struggle out of the grate, but I have sunk so deep that I cannot move. Roughly, laughing and shrieking with delight, the boys wrench me up onto my feet, and pluck off the object on my head. It is a piss pot. I slink away as they thrust another new boy into the grate to be crowned a member of the house. Nobody takes any more notice of me as I crawl into my bed holding my splitting head. I hear screams of pain and laughter, but I am too cowed to care what they are doing to the other victim. Presently I peer out resentfully. Over the fireplace I see a large shield on which heraldic arms are painted. A crowd of boys are holding down a lad in the fire grate. He howls wildly amid hoots of derision. I feel proud that I didn't yell like that. I try to sleep, deciding that I'll run away next day and tell mother that I can't stand it. The torturing goes on. Then there is a tempest of squalls and laughter. The boys scatter. The ceremony is over.

Peeping, I see them pulling the covers from their beds, and I wonder what they are up to. Each boy drapes a counterpane over his shoulders, more or less toga style, and in a line they begin to dance along the aisle between the beds, howling in unison:

> "Boyibus kissibus sweet girliorum,
> Girlibus likibus wanti some morum!"

Suddenly the leader throws himself onto the nearest bed and, holding the counterpane cloak fashion, as if concealing a victim, violently imitates the movements of a cock treading a hen, while the other[s] shriek. Then the game starts once more with the next boy in line playing the lead.

As I watch this strange performance all the clothes are whisked off my bed from behind me. I sit up, angry and confused. A dozen or more small boys about my own age prance about screeching. As I leap out of bed to go after the clothes someone seizes my nightgown, and rips it right up. I turn, dragging the bedclothes with one hand, and trying to cover my nakedness with the other. My pillow is chucked across the room. A boy trips me. Half a dozen others jump on me as I sprawl on the floor and tear the rest of my nightgown to ribbons. Hands pull my genitals and smack my bottom amid squalls and howls of mirth. Screaming and crying with rage, somehow I manage to get to my feet, and rush at my nearest tormentor. He dodges. I go for another. As I start to punch him my arms are caught from behind by a bigger boy. I struggle madly as again I am smacked and pinched all over. Then the boy releases me and as I, crazy with fury, turn on him, he leaps over a bed laughing. Sobbing, I pull out the pot from under my bed. As I raise it my wrist is grabbed. I wheel furiously. He is the big, blue-eyed boy.

"Good lad!" he says, laughing, "you've got spunk. But that won't do. You'd put someone in the sick bay and get a swishing in the morning."

Sullenly I let fall the pot which breaks.

"Silly little ass!" he tells me. "The matron will dock your tuck money[82] for that. How much d'you get?"

"A pound, sir," I say, sulkily.

[82] "Tuck" (informal British): A shop, often located in schools, that sells confectionery, sweets, snacks, and soft drinks.

"You don't say 'sir' to me. I'm not a prefect and never shall be. I'm only the junior rugger[83] captain."

The small boys have formed a group around us, giggling. He wheels on them.

"Hook it, you kids, and leave him alone, or I'll lam you! You two, Pexton and Boggy Tertius, help him to make his bed."

The kids scatter, and the two boys named drag back my bedclothes and my pillow. I feel the big boy eyeing me all over as I stand naked and uncomfortable.

"Who's your father?" he demands.

I tell him proudly and defiantly.

"Oh ho, so we've caught a lordling this term." He laughs, but not unkindly. "My guv'nor's only a moldy baronet. Thorpe Primus is my name. How old are you? Twelve? You look about ten. But you're well made. I'll turn you into a jolly good half." He runs a hand over my belly down my thighs and calves. "Bantam," he adds, laughing again. "But built like a racehorse. Come, hop into bed!"

As I obey he smacks my bottom, saying, "Good night, Delorme!"

"I'll tell Phillips Sextus!" pipes a voice.

"Who said that?" snaps my protector.

Only snickers answer him.

"Don't go too far, Thorpe," says a bigger boy's voice down the dormitory, "or I'll have to report you to the prefect's room again."

As one of the boys pulls the heap of clothes over my body I hear Thorpe Primus reply:

"Right ho. But if you do, you know what'll happen when I catch you out of bounds, skinned onion!"

There is a gust of laughter. Someone shouts softly:

"Cave!"

[83] Rugby.

Patter of naked feet as boys rush to their beds, my new friend among them. The dormitory door opens. There is silence, except for a few prodigious snores. I peer from under my higgledy-piggledy clothes, fearing that the housemaster will notice them. But he walks down the aisle as if seeing nothing, saying mechanically: "Good night, my lads!"

He switches off the light as he goes out. Immediately whispers start up from all sides.

"I say, Dexter," I hear from across the room near me, "d'you know why Croft Quintus isn't coming back this term? Breaking up day ole Jewy Clack caught him humping the needlewoman,[84] Nellie, the pretty one –"

"Where? Where? How?" come excited voices.

"In the linen room. He'd have been expelled, of course, but that would have ruined him for Sandhurst and the Head knows his governor, so he let him off on condition that he didn't return. He's going to a crammer's[85] instead."

"Shut up, you kids, or you'll get a hundred lines a piece!" comes the monitor's voice from the far end. A moment's hush and the whispering recommences in a slightly lower tone.

"Hasn't Nellie come back?"

"Of course not!"

"P'raps Croft's going to marry her," says another.

"Don't be a silly ass!" jeers someone amid a ripple of giggles.

"Jolly good job he isn't coming back," declares a boy.

"Fortners won't crow in the House matches this term!"

"Sssh!" a sibilant whisper runs as the light in the judas window[86] of the housemaster adjoining the dormitory, goes on.

[84] A seamstress or woman who does needlework.

[85] A school that prepares pupils for an exam, especially students who have already failed an examination.

[86] Judas window or judas hole: A peep hole in a door (an expression still employed in France today).

Eddie must have been a lovely boy, I reflected, as I dropped the tapeworm end, a Gito, as sweetly innocent looking as a choirboy in a surplice – which awoke a personal memory of how choirboys of my time too, were often made to stand on a table in the prefects' "common room" or a study, and sing the most Rabelaisian parodies of the anthems we had been caroling in chapel, compositions by one of that august body, receiving a lick with a cricket stump if we forgot our lines; an embryo author, who I recalled, had since become a famous poet.

That glimmer of Eddie-that-was made me remark the curious phenomenon of a memory within a memory, a dream of a dream, provoking an image of those multiple Chinese boxes each within the other. I also had had similar experiences at school.[87] We were like pups playing around under the dawning impulse of sex. Even strenuous sports, compulsory without a medical certificate, and long hours of study, were not enough to absorb the vital energy of healthy adolescents. No doubt there was the danger of perversion, but after all that was biologically correct. If the active male force was weak then the subject eventually became homosexual, a nonbreeder, and by nature unwanted. These musings regarding my own childhood incited curiosity anew to know what that myself-that-was was dreaming under hashish. Quaintly enough I – that is the self-that-is in the present illusion – noted with pleasure that the imagination bulb was brilliant. Of what I had dreamed that night I had no notion. Eagerly myself-that-is seized the controls of myself-that-was.

* * *

[87] The passage about Eddie's abuse at school is so vividly rendered that one wonders if it may actually be an autobiographical reminiscence on the part of Beadle.

Myself-that-was: I am very bad-tempered and fed up with strolling about Paris alone. I mutter with perfect bad taste lines from myself:

> I cannot think,
> I cannot dream!
> I can neither enter Heaven nor Hell,
> but lie like a chewed star
> spat out from God's yellow teeth
> on the dusty carpet of the Infinite![88]

And that's just what I do feel, by God! The jostling, scurrying crowd annoys me. Why did I come out? To get away from myself. Bah, I mumble savagely, if only my wife had been a reasonable person – but she isn't and never will be. That's finished, past. Queer, she seems to have produced in me a loathing of all Englishwomen. Every time I meet an English girl I see Eve and fear she's going to begin: "Now, William!" That's what drove me away from London to settle in Paris, I realize bitterly, although I tried to kid myself that it was to study the French character, to isolate, to work – and now I can't write a line. What the devil's the matter with me? I turn into an arcade which leads I don't know where and don't care as long as I escape the gnashing, panting streets. I pause irresolutely to glance at an antique shop. Antiques always interest me. I stroll

[88] In a letter written to his niece Isabel on 19 February 1931, while in the midst of complaining about difficulties related to his daughter's estate, he writes: "I can't dream / I can't think / I feel like a chewed star spat out by God's yellow teeth on the tattered carpet of the infinite. Zut alors!" The missive is composed on a letterhead from Le Normandy Café-Bar, located at 1, Place Grimaldi, Nice. (See my Afterword for more commentary about these letters.)

over. In the window is a porcelain statue of Ahriman. Looks a genuine piece of ancient Persian work. His ugliness is positively beautiful in the cruelty and lust of the expression. There is a hole in the crown of the head for burning incense. He would be splendid in the studio before a mirror and soft light, a fuming devil to inspire macabre hashish dreams. As I am wondering how much the fellow asks, the reflection in the glass of a passing girl distracts me. She stops beside me to stare in the window, too.

Covertly I regard her. The face is lovely; beautifully modeled with tempting lips cut like a cameo. She is slender; tall; has that length of limb, the narrow pelvis, that pleases me. Well dressed, but evidently not wealthy, she hasn't the allure of a cocotte,[89] nor of a working girl, nor of the middle class; something of all three. As I ponder whether I dare accost her she raises her head to look at some object high up, exposing a lovely line of throat.

"Wouldn't you like to mousle[90] that dimple," whispers a voice in my ear.

Indignantly I glance around. A face as black as a stage Othello's is leering at me.

"Damned cheek!" I mutter, frowning, and regard the girl apprehensively, hoping that she hasn't overheard, or at least doesn't understand English.

"She'd be lovely nude with her hair down!" whispers that damned nigger[91] once more. I shift my shoulders squarely upon

[89] "Cocotte ": Prostitute.

[90] "Mousle" (obsolete): To toy with roughly.

[91] Beadle was born on a Merchant Marine ship (his father was the captain) on 26 or 27 October 1881 – the same month and year as Picasso. By 1899, at the age of eighteen, he was serving in the British South African Police in Cape Town. During the Second Boer War he was a member of Morley's Scouts. By 1902 he was employed by Transvaal Customs, as the assistant compound manager. After making

him and continue to watch the girl who is still absorbed in antique rings. I, too, like antique rings. But I remark that that black brute is right; she hasn't shingled, or bobbed hair.

"Wouldn't you like to wrap those long limbs around you?"

---

a brief trip to Paris in 1904 (at the age of twenty-two) he remained in Africa until about 1911. Given such a colonialist background, it's no wonder that the author was imbued with many of the typical racist attitudes promulgated by the blood-thirsty British Empire during this period. We can witness some of this mentality as late as 1941; in a passage in *Artist Quarter* he questions the sophistication of African artists (at one point even using the term "raw nigger"), thus contradicting the views of his contemporary, Pablo Picasso, who collected African art and who regarded African artists with the highest esteem.

In his insightful essay included in the 2007 reprint of Beadle's *The City of Baal* (Castroville, CA: Off-Trail Publication, 2007), publisher John Locke writes (speaking of the author's adventure fiction): "Most of Beadle's characters are Englishmen in the employ or ex-employ of the Empire, and the word 'nigger' was common in the British Empire as a description of dark-skinned peoples. Of note, the epithets do not appear as verbal abuse from a white to a black. Instead, they are descriptions shared between whites, a seeming affirmation of their common understanding of racial superiority." And we might add that in Beadle's pulp novels the narrative voice often refers to native Africans as "black" or "Negro." (See, for example, his most commercially successful novel, *Witch-Doctors*, published in 1922.) But clearly this is not the case with *Dark Refuge*. While Beadle's views on race were, as Locke points out, "complicated" (e.g., in Locke's words, the stories often feature a "blurring [of] the line between 'white rationality' and 'black superstition'), nonetheless he was obviously a product of this period.

In any case the repeated use of this derogatory term casts a stain over the narrative of *Dark Refuge*, which in so many other ways remains far ahead of its time, both conceptually and stylistically.

That blasted fellow again right at my elbow! As angrily as I turn around in the opposite direction to her, the creature seems to walk right through the plate glass window. I am startled. Then I mutter: "Oh, the reflection, of course."

Furious at being interrupted I move away from the shop. Step by step he walks by my side. I stop. He stops.

"You're a fool!" he murmurs. "We can easily pick her up, and we'd have a wonderful time in bed. I'll help you."

That was the limit. *He*'ll help me, the black swine!

"Who the hell d'you think you're talking to?" I demand wrathfully.

"Look!" he says, leering. "She wants you as much as we want her."

In spite of my anger I can't resist looking back. I catch a glimpse of the girl's eyes reflected in the window, watching me. I start. Beside her is a Negress stark naked who has her head turned ogling.

I stare dumbfounded. But she isn't a real Negress; for her face is a replica of the girl's, except that she's soot black. And the expression is different – frankly lecherous. As the white girl moves from the shop the black double winks vulgarly. I am struck by the loveliness of the body; the same form, the same limbs – but black, black …

"Oh, come on!" urges the monster at my side impatiently. "They invite us. Look!"

The girl's actual gaze encounters mine. There is indeed a sketch of an inviting smile, but not that horrible lewd leer of the double who is making obscene signs. I can't understand why none of the passers-by remark such a strange exhibition. A hand pushes me forward.

"Go on, brother!" says the ebony incubus. "We need a woman."

"'We' again!" I exclaim furiously, turning on him. Then to my horror I see that he too, is naked and, moreover, obviously excited sexually. Violently I try to push him off, but my hand goes right through him.

"Oh, my God, I'm going mad!" I gasp.

I hurry on. In step he follows. I break into a cold sweat of fear, and run. He runs with me.

"Go away!" I cry frantically, trying to dodge from him in the crowd. "Go away, damn you!"

In my terror I have forgotten the girl and her Negress. I bump into people. They protest. I strike at the beastly nigger, but my fist hits air. Wildly I shout in French:

"That nigger, he's naked! Can't you see? He's disgusting! Call a policeman! Arrest him!"

Some of the crowd stop to stare.

"He's mad, name of God!" says one.

"Delirium tremens!" says another.

"He's a dope fiend!" asserts a third.

"Send for an agent!" urges a fourth.

"Oh, my God, what a pity! Such a handsome young fellow, too," exclaims a shop girl.

Frantic now, and fearing to be taken for a real madman, I rush out of the arcade and across a main street; miss a taxi by a grass blade; nearly crash into a cyclist. I spot a policeman on point duty. I pull up sharply. He is watching me; thinks I'm drunk, no doubt. But no, it must be the awful nigger stark naked. He's mad, of course, I realize suddenly, and stand still. The policeman is still observing. But why doesn't he arrest the nigger? Then I have a bright idea how to get rid of him. Boldly I walk up to the policeman. I glance to see whether that has scared the nigger off. No, he's right at my elbow grinning, the black swine, but he isn't so indecent as he was.

"Why don't you arrest this man?" I inquire.

"Who?" queries the policeman.

"Why – this beastly naked nigger!" I exclaim indignantly.

"What nigger? Trying to be funny?" snaps the policeman, regarding me sharply as I indicate the black beside me.

"Good God!" I add, aghast.

Alongside the policeman is another black as stark naked as mine who is signaling with one hand as if directing the traffic while the fellow is talking to me. Silently I turn away, dreadfully convinced that I must indeed be mad.

"Nuts!" agrees the policeman from behind me, "but harmless."

Then I perceive that each person on the street has a black alongside him or her. Several of the Negresses are making indecent signs to black bucks. Yet some of the males, I observe, are walking sedately beside their white doubles with brows contracted as if working out a problem; others have anxious, even desperate expressions. An errand boy is grinning at a little girl who clings shyly to her mother; but the lad's black is gesturing with a finger and the small Negress is giggling.

"I'm mad," I mutter. "I'm mad indeed."

I long to run, but I dare not. I stop. If *I* am mad, then they are all mad, too, I argue, for they've all got nigger doubles! That seems right and cheers me a little, I don't feel so peculiar. Yet something bewilders me. No, that can't be so obviously, for the policeman couldn't see his nigger or mine.

"No, no," I murmur, dismally. "I'm mad all alone."

I glance despairingly at my awesome companion. He leers and points to an adjacent bar. Oh! now that's *just* what I do need, a stiff drink. I rush in; sit on a stool at the bar. My incubus does likewise, only there isn't a stool there; he is sitting up in the air. Stuttering, I order two whiskies. The barman looks at me queerly. As he serves us I get still more worried, for the nigger beside him also serves two whiskies, which makes four.

"Kinder thirsty?" suggests the barman, indulgently.

"You're crazy," I tell him. "I didn't order four whiskies. And anyhow, why two siphons?"

"What two siphons?" he demands suspiciously.

"Why, these two!" I state, indignantly. "And I ordered two whiskies for myself and – my friend."

"What friend?" he queries, harshly.

"Oh, my God – Nothing," I mutter; hastily pick up the first glass and gulp the contents. My now taciturn Siamese twin does the same. Still feeling that my nerves are on edge I grab for the third whisky – but my hand clutches air! I grab the rail. I must be mad, as I had decided. Seeing niggers was bad enough, but trying to drink whiskies that aren't there is too much. The barman is watching me derisively.

"Feeling ill?" he inquires, gruffly.

"Feeling!" I exclaim. "Oh, hell, give me another – but one this time."

"Another?" he snorts. "But you haven't drunk your second yet?"

"I must have," I protest, "for it isn't there."

"What's this then?" he growls, shoving a whisky towards me.

"Oh, that's – that's – my friend's," I stammer. "We always drink alike. For God's sake give me another!"

"No," says the barman, firmly. "You're so drunk now you can't see a glass in front of you."

"I can see it," I protest, "but it isn't there."

"That's enough in your state," says he.

"What state?" I repeat, irritatedly. "What kind of a state are you in anyhow, when you and your nigger serve me four whiskies and two siphons instead of the two whiskies I ordered?"

"What nigger?" he sneers; then severely adds: "Four whiskies for two, and two siphons for one – *that* I can understand. I've

been there. Rats and snakes too, I've seen, but never niggers. You're real bad with D.T.'s" and he turns his back upon me, muttering something about alcoholic foreigner and the queerest drunk he ever met.

I light a cigarette. My plutonian horror does, too. I try to be calm; to reason. "Now," I say to myself, "you see this nigger and other niggers, and nobody else does. Well, you're mad number one count. You see four whiskies and when you try to take the third it isn't there. Ergo: found mad on two counts."

"I'm going," I say indignantly, and pull money from a pocket. My damned nigger pays his damned nigger too, although neither has a pocket. I want to cry with vexation; although I notice that I seem to be getting resigned to a white man's black burden,[92] as everybody else appears to have one. All the same, I make a despairing effort as we go through the swing doors.

[92] In February 1899 Rudyard Kipling composed "The White Man's Burden: The United States and the Philippine Islands," a poem in which he urged America to assume the "burden" of Empire à la Great Britain. Vice President Teddy Roosevelt read the poem after it was published in *McClure*'s magazine and regarded it as "rather poor poetry, but good sense from the expansion point of view" (the latter phrase referring to the imperialist philosophy of "Manifest Destiny").

An example of Beadle's complex views on race may be found in his second novel, which was also titled *A White Man's Burden* (London: S. Swift and Co., 1912). As Michael Diamond notes in his book, *'Lesser Breeds': Racial Attitudes in Popular British Culture, 1890 – 1940*:

> Ignoring the black man's sexuality could also cause problems. In *A White Man's Burden* by Charles Beadle, a white woman in a state of undress thoughtlessly asks a black servant to help her on with her dressing gown, and he assaults her. He must suffer the death penalty because the blacks would treat mercy "only as evidence of weakness in their rulers and as a direct

"Look here," I say, "how much do you want to go away?"

But he isn't even looking at, or listening to me; he's winking at a slim woman, or her Negress, I don't know which, passing. The whisky seems to have done me good; I am soothed; can reason better. Evidence says that those niggers aren't there, but my eyes tell me that the street is swarming with them. I look in the shop windows. There is the crowd, but not a single nigger! Now I begin to feel very, very sad; realize that something is radically wrong with me. That other whisky that I left on the counter – or did I? As I glance reproachfully at my black nightmare he grins; says "Let's have another drink."

I feel I need one, too. But does he want one, or two, drinks? That seems an important question. I decide I won't offer him one at all, and then maybe he'll go away. I've known white men like that. We enter the nearest café. Now I'm wary of barmen, so I choose a table with one chair in a corner. My companion sits comfortably on air. The waiter has a limp, and a bald head; so has his nigger and, as he's nude, I see a false leg from the knee down. I light another cigarette. My fellow follows suit.

"Oh, for God's sake don't do that!" I snap, for it is irritating to have all one's movements mimicked. The waiter brings a

---

incentive to crime." In his heart the husband, a government official, feels that "he and all Europeans who persisted in treating a native as a thing of wood or brass, an automaton, anything but a human being, were really to blame." This is humane and perceptive, but he goes on, "a savage, nearer to the animal, has stronger passions and control weaker than the civilized races, yet the fact was ignored – because they were natives, a conquered people." The "savage" has been in domestic service for ten years.

See Michael Diamond, *'Lesser Breeds,'* New York: Wimbledon, 2006, p. 180 (quoting from Beadle's *A White Man's Burden*, pp. 264-265).

whisky and his double another one; that's two, but still better than four. Cunningly I quickly gulp the one that the waiter served, but then my black – I remark that he's becoming quite "mine" now! – drinks from the glass that isn't there. "Yet," I argue, patiently, "that's quite logical; a being that isn't there has a perfect right to drink a whisky that isn't there, particularly if I don't have to pay for it. I ask the waiter how much I owe him. He charges for one whisky, so that's all right. But then I feel annoyed because again my black pays his black, although neither are there, which seems senseless.

After this last whisky I feel more philosophic. If he's there, this damned nigger – well, we'll discuss the matter. Maybe he's intelligent. Mechanically I proffer a cigarette, which he accepts. Then everything goes muzzy again once more; for how can something that isn't there take something that is there? No, no, that won't work. In exasperation I ask him:

"Now tell me, are you there or not?"

He grins, puffing smoke.

"Oh, yes, I'm here," he asserts. "I've always been and always shall be. You'll never get rid of me!"

"Oh, good God!" I exclaim in dismay, and add sharply: "Just what do you mean?"

"Exactly what I say," says he. I glare. This state, whatever is the state, I'm in, has got to be elucidated. If I'm mad, as I appear to be, perhaps, if I can discover the cause I shall be able, on Freudian principles, to cure myself. I look at him doubtfully. He's so like me that I might be gazing in a magic mirror that turns you black.

"Are you educated?" I inquire, in order to find out on what ground I can attack.

"Oh, yes," he returns calmly, "as you are, only more so; for I know things that you won't know, and remember things that you don't want to recollect."

"What the devil d'you mean?" I query, intrigued by this curious reply. "Who are you anyhow?"

"I'm your subconscious," he states, solemnly.

"What!" I gasp.

"What!" he apes. "You don't seem to like your subconscious. Most people don't. Everybody tries to dodge him because they're afraid he isn't quite – a gentleman. But I'm always there whether you like it or not. The trouble is," he went on more seriously, "that I know what I want and you don't – or rather, won't acknowledge it; for what I need you need. I tell you what we – for I am you – need, but you don't want to listen. You're always frightened of something; of being found out, of being punished. Sometimes we get what we want, but oh, our hairy aunt![93] I have to lie so hard. We need a woman. If I say so, you shrink and stop your ears. But when I lie really well, and tell you that she's your soul mate, that you love her purely – whatever that may mean, but you love the phrase, soothing, I suppose! – that your ambition is to hold her hand in yours for the rest of your life and the sound of her voice is the song of angels, I can get you going. Then you kiss her and wriggle and squirm with desire, but you pretend that you don't know such a vulgar fellow. But her sub leers at me and wonders why you don't take her. And when I shout at you so loud that you cannot

[93] According to Jonathon Green's *Dictionary of Slang*, "my hairy aunt" was an early nineteenth-century expression of mild surprise, a euphemism employed (along with several other "aunt" expressions, such as "my giddy aunt") to avoid blasphemy. Beadle employs one such expression is an essay on writing: "My hoary aunt, I actually made money! Not much, but real money." See Beadle's essay on the writing process published in the forum "Contemporary Writers and Their Work," *The Editor: The Journal of Information for Literary Workers*, 25 February 1920 (reproduced in the Appendix section, below).

fail to hear, you are shocked and begin to mumble mumbo jumbo about the sacredness of virginal purity and holy matrimony, but you can't see what grimaces of disgust and disappointment her double is making. But I can. Then if I drive you really hard you commence to make advances and her sub writhes with delight, but the girl also denies that she can hear her, and repulses you, saying: 'Oh, you mustn't! Oh, I can't! Not until we're married, darling,' and her black self curses and rages with balked desire. You part, but *we* torment you both and won't let you sleep, or work peaceably, until you take out a license, just as you do to drive a car, a permit from the Secretary of the United Taboos Union, to go to bed with the girl and satisfy both of our dark selves. When I-you get tired of the same woman, or she-her of us, or perhaps we discover that they can't satisfy us, or us them, and I point out a neighbor's wife, or daughter, whose double is making similar signs of distress, you won't listen, or start your mumbo jumbo about 'duty,' 'fidelity,' 'family,' 'what will the neighbors say?' or that neighbor do. That's why it's such damned hard work to get what we subs want. No wonder we get really mad sometimes and torture you until you're ill, or crazy. Then we have to invent more silly stories in which a blind duck wouldn't believe; that the neighbor's wife, or daughter is ill-treated, misunderstood, overworked, by her husband – or father – who's just such a hypocritical idiot as you are; and that your wife is cold, stupid, or crazy, or all three, and that you're a poor martyr. Then triumphantly you produce your taboos impaled on a skewer, and say now that it is obviously your 'duty' to give her what her subconscious is nearly ill and mad for. Then we subs have a good time for a bit, and you think you're happy – until we get tired of the farce, and want a change. So the human comedy goes on, just because you won't meet us face to face, sit down, and have a roundtable talk over the matter. You're just as

annoying as all the humans. Even you can't have a drink without boring me by saying: 'Oh, of course I don't *want* a drink because I like it, but I feel so faint that –' 'That disappointment was such a shock to my nervous system that really I need a little stimulant!' 'Oh, well, I'll have another just to please Jack – or to show my wife I'm master,' ad nauseam! You've had these two drinks because the shock of seeing me was so great that – you need another. Go on, have one, then."

I wince. I had as a matter of fact felt that this tirade was such a blow to preconceived opinions that I did need another one. I order one more, and he grins delightfully.

"I knew you would," he exclaims triumphantly. "because that's just what I needed."

As the waiter serves me I stare perplexedly, but I don't say anything lest he should come back; for the wooden-legged double is not there, and I'm served one real whisky. This I feel is some progress. Thirstily I drink half, covertly watching my sooty alter ego. This time he doesn't imitate me; in fact doesn't appear to have noticed. I am relieved; more cheerful. After all, he isn't such a bad egg, my subconscious; rather amusing.

"Well, subby," I say, "so you like drinking too?"

"Sometimes, conny," he retorts, impertinently, "that is the only way to obtain some relief from that pretentious prig of a conscious. I don't like to be continually tormented by your ridiculous taboos. Alcohol, or any drug, is a refuge; puts your taboos to sleep, and leaves me a little freedom to do what I want – or at least dream of it if I can't obtain."[94]

He chuckles.

[94] "Conny": The dark figure now coins the nickname "conny" when referring to the "conscious" layer of the psyche. An overcoming of taboos is the final – and principal – theme of this chronicle; and the use of intoxicants to do so is the "dark refuge" that "puts your taboos to sleep."

"Well, I wanted that girl in the arcade, and so did you, but you wouldn't admit that that was so. If you had had half a dozen drinks, or a few shots of dope, you'd have listened to me. But your sober conscious is muzzled and hobbled. She wanted you. You saw very well how her black double was inviting us, although on her actual lips only a slight smile appeared through the muzzle."

"Yes, I see," I answer irritably. "But she was so virginal, respectable, that I daren't accost her –"

"What's that got to do with it?" he inquires contemptuously. "She's got to lose her hymen sometime, hasn't she, even if she had such a thing?"

"And she might have been married," I protest.

"Conscious!" he guffaws. "You call your part of us the conscious, and you, conny, aren't even conscious that you're lying! You'd have just stalled, and waited for me to hatch out some absurd lies to appease what you term your principles which are merely an acquired set of taboos! O-oh! our hairy aunt!" he sighs prodigiously, "you really work us subconsciousnesses to a shadow![95] Positively," he adds sarcastically, "you shock me so that I need another drink!"

[95] The Swiss psychologist Carl Jung (1875 – 1961) coined the term "shadow archetype" to describe this psychic process of repression and projection. For example, in his 22 October 1937 appearance at the Terry Lectures at Yale University, Jung stated: "Unfortunately there is no doubt about the fact that man is, as a whole, less good than he imagines himself or wants to be. Every one carries a shadow, and the less it is embodied in the individual's conscious life, the blacker and denser it is. If an inferiority is conscious, one has always a chance to correct it. Furthermore, it is constantly in contact with other interests, so that it is steadily subjected to modifications. But if it is repressed and isolated from consciousness, it never gets corrected. It is, moreover, liable to burst forth in a moment of unawareness. At all events, it forms an unconscious snag, blocking the

I order one and resolutely drink it myself. But he seems quite content, and I suppose he's right, if he is me and I am he! Economical anyway, I reflect.

"Quaint, isn't it?"

"What is?" I snap, peevishly.

"That drink, or drug, always attacks taboos first and sex last. In vino veritas,[96] eh? and a drunken woman's an angel in bed, what? But of course she is, for she's got all taboos hog-tied and her Negress can have a good time."

"But, after all," I say loftily, "you're only the primitive part of us. The conscious invented civilization."

"Hypocrisy, you mean," he sneers. "'*L'hypocrisie est la plus belle fleur de la civilization,'* [97] as some Frenchman wrote. By not listening to me your conscious takes to crime, which is merely an offence against a taboo. We're frank; you're false. I say I want to go to bed with a woman; you begin to blather about duty, but eventually you obey my will; for I torture you until you're ready to poison, or shoot, the husband, or whatever obstruction is in the way of my desire. And mark me, conny," he adds very solemnly, wagging a black finger at me, "taboos *eat* taboos! and if that isn't primitive! 'Thou shalt not kill' is one of your pet taboos, but the ban against taking another man's wife, adultery, swallows that up without remorse if necessary to attain my le-

---

most recent attempts. We carry our past with us, viz: the primitive and inferior man with his desires and emotions, and it is only by a considerable effort that we can detach ourselves from this burden. If it comes to a neurosis, we have invariably to deal with a considerably intensified shadow. And if such a case wants to be cured it is necessary to find a way in which man's conscious personality and his shadow can live together." As quoted in the *New York Times*, 22 October 1937.

96 "In wine, there is truth."

97 "Hypocrisy is the most beautiful flower of civilization."

gitimate satisfaction. If I want wealth and luxury you'll rob and murder to get it; if I crave power you'll lie to your fellows; play, prompted by me, on their weaknesses and passions, bamboozle them into slaughtering their kind in the name of patriotism. What we want you've got to do, or be tortured until you're ill or crazy. We're implacable. Be kind to your subconscious and your subconscious will be kind to you."

"Still," I persist obstinately, "we conscious are responsible for modern progress."

"Mechanical only," he retorts. "You know but little more of yourselves – us, that is – than you did ten thousand years ago. You're still scared of taboos and try to shove us farther down in the dungeon of your mind."

"For a reason, as Freud maintains," I remind him.

"Freud's a fool!" says he, categorically. "He declares that my motive is solely sexual. It isn't. We require to be satisfied physiologically, an hygienic need, just as eating every day and the daily indignity."

"Daily Indignity!" I exclaim. "I've never heard of such a paper. Socialist, no doubt."

"No, very unsocial – fortunately," he giggles. "I referred to the necessity to evacuate the intestines, as you prefer to call a spade an agricultural implement!"

"That is not at all funny," I reprimand him. "But how do you know about Freudian theories?"

"Am I not you?" he ripostes unpleasantly. "All that you read with which you, or your silly taboos, don't agree, you conveniently forget. I don't – as I told you."

"If you are my subconscious," I query, haughtily, not liking his low sense of humor, "why are you black? You don't pretend that I'm a descendant of Ham,[98] I suppose?"

"I'm not a Negro," he points out. "I'm merely dark."

"Why dark then, if you're [my] alter ego?"

"You'd be dark too, if you had to slink about in the cavern of your mind. And to think," he adds bitterly, "that without me you're nothing. I try to teach you wisdom in dreams, but you won't listen because your taboos distort them into symbols which you pretend you don't understand. You were right; we are primitives. Satisfy us, food and sex, and we'll work for you, if you have a problem you can't solve, I can do it for you – if I'm contented and you rise in the morning with the solution, and flatter yourself it's yours. Although you have had an inkling of that truth revealed by your popular proverb to sleep before making a decision – consult your subconscious. You wish to wake at a given hour during the night? I have no clock, but I get you up to the tick. Neither has your stomach a watch, but I know the dinner hour. Writers, artists, scientists, financiers, what would they do without us? "Oh, I've got a brain wave," you say. Idiot! I gave you that idea. A woman has an intuition that her husband has a girlfriend. Her sub told her so. And then I'm not even allowed to show myself."

"Well, you have this evening," I snap, "in that obscene state!"

"Because you were in that 'obscene state,'" he retorts, chuckling, "although you wouldn't have thought it obscene if you had been alone with the girl."

"Damn you!" I growl. "Anyway, nobody could see that I was."

[98] The narrator is referring to a seventeenth-century theory that the name Ham (the youngest son of Noah in the Old Testament) derives from a Hebrew word meaning "burnt" or "black."

"There!" he taunts, "that's the unbearable prig of a conscious. And for that matter nobody saw me, except yourself, for I gave you the vision –"

"You mean you've put these crazy ideas into my head?"

"You didn't think you'd invented them yourself, did you?" he queries proudly. "I'm imagination!"

I stare at him dubiously. I had often wondered where a happy idea, a phrase, a line, came from; although I rather resent his stealing my fireworks. Still, indubitably he is very valuable to me; a far better friend, as he stated, than an enemy.

"You're very interesting, subby dear," I flatter him. "Now tell me, a lot of people find a refuge in religion instead of alcohol or drugs. What do you poor birds do then?"

"Well, conny dear," he replies, smiling pleased, "we sublimate – and sometimes we don't."

"What d'you mean?"

"Sometimes they chase the devil – that's me – by starvation to enfeeble the physical motor force, and also by minor drugs such as lime juice, camphor, and sometimes we find other ways and means."

"What?" I demand curiously.

"Oh," says he, giggling, "we persuade the conscious to fall in love with Jesus, or Mary, or any old saint will do, or even the idea of God, and continuous prayer may lead to a state of exaltation that frequently ends in a physical orgasm. There are cases who are so obsessed by sex that they become what you term 'mystics,' and rave in speech and prose about invisible spouses, even – rarely – write beautiful poesy to some phallic symbol, such as the Song of Solomon. But, of course," he adds judiciously, "all these methods are not very satisfactory, and I'm always very sorry for those subs who are certainly out of luck. But that subject depresses me. I need another drink."

"You want to make me drunk?" I accuse.

"I do, conny dear!"

"Why?"

"Because you're getting boringly serious, and your stupid prejudices prevented me getting the woman I wanted."

"You see," I point out, "you think of nothing but sex, as Freud maintains."

"Not at all," he defends. "Satisfy my natural desire, and I'll have leisure to think of other things."

A couple of women enter the bar and select an adjoining table.

"Look, conny, the dark one's nice and plump," exclaims subby, excitedly. "Pick 'em up. I'll help! Upset your whisky and pretend that you've splashed her skirt, apologize and invite 'em over, but for heavens' sake, get to bed quickly! We haven't had a woman for weeks and our glands can't hold out much longer."

"Shan't!" I refuse sulkily, ordering the other drink. "She's not my type, and she's fat and as ugly as a fried fish. You've no aesthetic sense, subby."

"Aesthetic fiddlesticks!" he snorts. "What's that matter in bed? All cats are gray in the dark."

"Strange, too," I remark, "you haven't either any sense of voluptuousness."

"A starving man isn't bothered by gastronomical finesse," he retorts. "Only the well-fed may be gourmets. I'll bet you that if you have enough drink your fussy principles will be drowned, and I'll get you to bed with that bitch, and so have some relief."

"That would be a lot of use," I reply. "I should be so drunk that I should be incapable of satisfying you."

"Oh ho!" he chuckles. "Don't you recollect that girl, conny, at the Reserve whom I persuaded you to invite to dinner – after four cocktails – and you didn't remember anything after the old brandies until you awoke in a bed in a strange hotel with a woman's stocking under your pillow, and wondered whether

anything had really happened? I knew for I had had a wonderful time – and so had she. "

"You swine, you!" I exclaim, indignantly.

"Bah, you're merely jealous because you can't remember the pleasures I had."

"But why did she bolt then, if she had so enjoyed herself?"

"Why?" he snickers. "Because when she awoke she recalled everything, and her taboos started squalling, so she fled in shame. Hoo! hoo! hoo!"

"That's enough," I tell him, sternly. "Subconscious or no, I'm not going to be bullied. I'm going for a walk."

"He! he! he!" he giggles. "And I'll come too. And then we'll see."

"If you do," I warn him, "I'll go straight back to bed."

"If you do," he mocks, "I'll make you dream and get a poor satisfaction that way."

"Disgusting brute!" I snort.

"Yourself!" he ripostes.

"Look here," I ask, exasperatedly, "what in hell am I to do to persuade you to let me alone?"

"Get me a woman! One that is full of bloodied passion. That's what we both need."

"I know," I admit, disgruntled, "but I can't find one who pleases me."

"That one in the arcade," he suggests. "She's beautiful, just the long limbs and slender body you like to satisfy your confounded aesthetic tastes, and full of lechery to suit mine."

"How do I know," I object, disconsolately," she may be as stupid as a fish."

"What's that matter?" says he, selfishly. "She'll give us more erotic joy than any woman you've had. I know. And I don't mistake. Remember that I didn't urge you to marry your wife. I saw that she had a low-powered sub and was too cluttered with

taboos, and see what a mess your silly conscious has got you into."

I do recall, to be just, that during my brief courtship of my wife, the carnal attraction had been very slight; reluctantly I am compelled to recognize the fact that my silly vanity had directed my actions.

"And listen," my sub went on eagerly, "you haven't been working well lately; haven't had any ideas, you've complained. If you get me that girl I'll throw you up the best ideas you've ever had in your life. I'll give you my word of a sub, which never lies."

"All right, if I can find her again," I agree.

"That's a bet," says he, and vanishes.

* * *

How extraordinary, I reflected, that I had totally forgotten that hashish hallucination! Promptly I suspected that the taboos of that "pretentious prig" of a conscious, as dear subby had put it, were more active than I had supposed; had indeed remorselessly suppressed that memory. My intellectual vanity, I remarked, had, even in the dream, been slightly wounded, evincing a strong resistance to admit that whatever talent I had was due to my swarthy unknown part of me – kind of took the gilt off whatever gingerbread I was disposed to hand to my conscious self; and my intellect had jibbed at the inference that reason was another sovereign dethroned by a dictator. Still I was obliged to avow that, in the light of years of experience, subby had expounded the situation the more rationally; and that since I had revolted against sentimentality after my marriage and had worshipped Eros more philosophically, I had gained much time and energy to devote to intellectual pursuits; and had consequently led a happier life.

Francine had been the girl of the arcade; so obviously I had kept my promise to – myself. And again, dear subby had been quite correct in his diagnosis of her charms; moreover I could recall that he, too, had kept to the bargain, and that after she had joined me I had had a spate of literary ideas.

Had I, I mused, left Francine by force of circumstances, as my conscious pretended, or had that been a pretext thrown up, as he would have said, by my swarthy alter ego who had wanted a change? As I pondered on the subject of my next exploration, I remembered the departure of the comic triplet, Cecci, Izzy and Vee. I decided to look them up. Instantly I was a gnat winging through the open window across the garden and into the Place[99] which gave an impression that the hour was late in the middle of winter. This appeared strange, for all the scenes I had experienced in the studio and the garden had been evidently in midsummer. But I perceived that my astonishment was puerile – even absurd, considering that I was dwelling in a state where time is a curve. Delusion and reality had become so interwoven that there was difficulty to distinguish one from the other. No doubt, I reflected gravely, I had hit one of those famous kinks in time.

This was confirmed by the sight of a couple on a bench beneath a leafless acacia who, wrapped in cloak and overcoat, were twined in an equivocal attitude. The girl I recognized as a waitress for whom I – or rather my quondam self – had had an errant libidinous fancy; possibly averted by the fact that although she had had almost Athenian features and a body desirable, she had been knock-kneed, too broad in the hips, and short in the legs.

I continued on the trail of my three specimens.

[99] A reference to Beadle's home at 7, place du Tertre.

Just as I came to Vee's house[100] the garden gate in the wall creaked and was thrust violently open. A powerful sigh sucked me willy-nilly into a nostril redolent of cheap alcohol. Nearly asphyxiated, I found myself in the brainpan of the stranger. The chamber was smaller and the roof lower than any I had yet visited. The heart gauge was rapid and strong; the nerve needle sluggish; the sex tube low; and the imagination bulb was as dim as a night-light. Keen to know who this person might be I seized the "present" controls:

* * *

The Chauffeur: Heugh! Heugh! Easy meat these Anglo-Saxon cows! Drunk as a market woman! Shoves her pals – both of 'em fairies and one dead drunk – into a room together and offers me brandy – Courvoisier, too, sacred name! Would I! Been a lively bit of flesh in her time, I'll say! Oui, 'dame! Gulps her drink like an American – maybe she is for all I know. Heugh! Heugh! they came staggering out into the Place with the little bald rat trying to hold 'em both up. He's an amateur of coke, anyone can see that. "There's your game," says Mother Loulou. She was, but not what the old girl guessed. Thought I had a Montparnasse bunch, but no, sir, a hundred yards down the street. Pity, except for the little rat they wouldn't have known whether they lived at Malmaison or Le Touquet.[101] What a chance missed! Still, I caught up on that, heugh! heugh!

And when I pinched her breasts – a bit long in the fall – and she was skinny even on the floating rib for one who likes 'em well lined – she cackles like a hen and falls on her back. I've had

[100] "Bea" Hastings was then living in Montmartre at 13, rue Norvins.

[101] Le Touquet-Paris-Plage: A French commune on the Opal Coast, adjacent to the English Channel. Rueil-Malmaison: A western suburb of Paris.

'em longer in the tooth, but not much. Well, a thick of beef stolen by a dog from the gutter at the end of the market, and a hundred francs for doing a man's duty. Heugh! Heugh! That's what comes of having dope fiends for pals who can't even rise to aid a lady. I'd better come back to see her, for maybe she'll need another stroke or so, and at that price I'm on. Shall I call it a day, or roll down the hill and take a shot of red at father Tintin's! Thanks to the good God she didn't stink of foreign scent, or Fifi 'ud start hunting flat irons when I do get home. Come, my beauty, you can get a move on down the incline without spending gas …

* * *

A light was in the first room inside the garden; I heard the swishing of water. As I flew between the closed curtains Vee flopped heavily onto a crumpled bed. Her disordered blouse was torn and her bodice unhooked. She was trying futilely to take off her drawers, crying the while.

On a round table was a pile of books, a Shelley, a Besant, a Mahabharata, a volume on Syndicalism, and a few pamphlets and weeklies.[102] Beside the table was a bidet into which had fallen a thesaurus and a bottle of ink, turning the water deep blue. On top of the pile of books was a douche can; the red rubber tube coiled over the pillow across the bed onto the floor.

The fo'c'sle lantern of the brain room was very dim. I could scarcely make out the instrument board. The heart gauge was

[102] Annie Besant: British socialist and theosophist, who adopted Jiddu Krishnamurti and proclaimed him the new Messiah. Syndicalism: A worker-based organization that advocated the right to strike. Mahabharata: A philosophical Sanskrit epic. These represent some of the predominant interests of Beatrice "Bea" Hastings, upon whom the character Vee is based.

heaving tumultuously; the nerve needle violently quivering. The bulb of imagination fairly bright; the sex tube pretty high.

* * *

Vee: Oh, damn the fool! why was he so drunk? He should have known. It's that beastly cocaine that the little brute gave him – or Bill, blast him! Oh, but I'll make Cecci stop that though, or else he won't get any paints and stuff. I know men! Look at Jerry getting the money out of me to start that paper and then chucking me out! And my lovely husband! Jolly good job Arthur did drink himself to death, or else I'd never have had a penny left. Oh, Cecci darling, so cruel of you to make me thirsty and then lie like a log with that horrible pederast friend. I wish I'd let him go home now, but I thought – Oh, I can't remember now – hup!

I'm a free woman anyhow and I know what I want. There're plenty of other good-looking men around, even if they don't pretend to be geniuses – and what's that matter in bed? He was nice, too, that shuffer.[103] Just crazy about me. I could see that. Oh, I feel so bad. Bother the thing, it's split! I don't care, I haven't any remorse. Pooh, a lover the more! I'm the woman of a thousand lovers – and proud of it, which is more than most women can say!

I'm free. I won't be bullied by men. Bah! instruments to a woman's pleasure – and to make babies, that's all they are. Hup! Oh damn, now the lace is torn. Still I have got nice legs. That's what Jerry always raved about – legs, my legs! Now that shuffer chap, I shouldn't know him if he came in tomorrow. Did he have moustaches? I'm hanged if I know. But he was very strong, didn't give me half a chance, raped me, the swine. But I like 'em like that. It's more exciting. But he was too quick. Why,

[103] "Shuffer": chauffeur.

I'd only just got started! Most men never think of a woman's fun. Just rotten egoists. I wonder what Cecci is like as a lover?[104] How I want to kiss that lovely body. I'll go and see if he's awake now, and what that beast, whatever his name is, is doing to him. What did he say, the filthy pederast? Oh, that a woman's love was a matter of intestines. Well, it's true physiologically – so's a man's. But what of it? After all, a flower's a plant's sexual organ, the stamen – Why, a phallus is just like a big sweet pea with two bulbs instead of one like a crocus. Hup! Anyhow, a flower's a flower and guts are guts. Just a different system, that's all. But a flower may grow on a dunghill and the union of intestines produces the sweetest pleasure that humans know. Hup!

Oh, I've got such a terrible indigestion. I knew that those kidneys were bad for me and that I shouldn't mix cherry brandy with gin. Hup! Oh, I'm going to be a vegetarian. Yes, I recall that Flossie Barton turned vegetarian and she told me she never had the hiccoughs again. But then of course, she had to, for she couldn't sing on a concert platform and have the hiccoughs at the same time, could she? Ah, thank God, I didn't forget this time, so there's no chance of my having a child by that shuffer. That would be too awful! I'd have to blame it on Cecci. Yet I'm sure it wouldn't resemble him in the least. His would be a darling with those lovely sooty eyes. Oh, I'd love to have a baby by him. Oh, why did I start to think of babies? I simply can't stand being reminded of my lost darling! And to think that he should have to be murdered by his own father, the drunken brute, the swine! Oh, why didn't I have the pluck to kill him immediately. Any jury would have acquitted me. Oh, but I would have if that would have brought back my little darling. Oh! Oh! he'd be eighteen now. Oh, God, God!

[104] Hastings and Modigliani met in Paris in 1914; their tumultuous affair ended two years later, in August 1916.

Sobbing I roll over on the bed, burying my head in the pillows. Somehow the bed jumps again, and I hit my temple against the table. That hurts like the devil. I reach for the bottle of brandy, but the silly thing tumbles on the bed and spills liquor all over my face, so I rub it onto my poor forehead. A good drink would do me good. But I can't find the glass. Oh, yes, it broke itself, that's true. I stand up. My legs feel like twisted blankets. I find a cup – no, it's the soap dish. Oh, damn. Then something falls with an awful clatter and I'm so worried because I can't think what it can be.

Oh, God! I scream and squirm across the bed, frantically clutching at a red snake coiling around my body.

Oh, that gave me a turn! It was the douche can that had fallen and the tube had got twisted around me. Again I struggle to my feet. I must have a drink. Oh, where has that cup gone? I can't drink out of a soap dish, can I? Vaguely I glimpse a woman in the long mirror who hasn't got any drawers on. Who on earth can – Oh! it's my own reflection, te he! he he! Oh, but I do look funny! But supposing someone came in. I can't think where they've gone, my drawers, I mean. Hup! Oh, damn these hiccoughs! Oh, yes they're around my feet. Just fancy! How funny I should have forgotten them! But I can't get them up for when I stoop everything goes round. I try again. I fall on the floor. I clutch at something to help me get up. It's the bidet. The nasty thing jumps at me, and soaks me. Oh! Oh! I'm all blue! What can it be? I sit and stare in dismay. Then I see a bottle of ink upset on the floor. I can't understand how it could have got there. I struggle to rise, but collapse again. Perhaps I had better stop here. It seems safer. Panting, I sit in the wet, but it's so uncomfortable.

But I want to see my darling Cecci. He may be awake now and quite all right. And anyhow he looks beautiful asleep. But I can't go like this, and I can't get my drawers on, and besides they're

all wet and blue. And my hair's undone and I don't know where my vanity bag is. I look in the bidet, but it isn't there. If the ink bottle, I reason, and a book fell into it, why shouldn't the bag? Anyhow, I couldn't possibly go like this, even if I could get up – Oh, not with all my clothes off. That wouldn't be decent. Oh, I do feel bad. If only I could have a brandy, that would make me feel fit. Where on earth is it? Ah, here's the cup on the floor beside me. How nice of it. And there's the bottle on the edge of the bed. Isn't much left, but –

My confounded hands wobble so that I lose half. O-oh, that's good! Yes, I do feel better now, oh, much better. Maybe I can stand now and wipe myself? Very carefully I clutch the end of the bedstead and hoist myself gradually right onto the bed. I lie back, thinking of poor Cecci. If only he'd drink alcohol and not touch that beastly drug which makes a brute of one so that you don't know what you're doing, and let anyone do what he likes with you. Ugh, nothing could ever induce me to try it. O-oh, how lovely the neat brandy feels deep down inside – deep, like a lover, te he! he he! That would make a gorgeous poem. Where the devil has the pen and ink gone? Oh, yes, the ink's all over my drawers! Oh damn!

I wiggle my feet off the bed cautiously, but when I try to stand everything goes blurry and I fall back on the bed. Oh, hell. I know I shall forget the image if I can't put it down. What was it? Oh, I've forgotten already. No. The nectar of the grape like the hot desire of Priapus, as intoxicating as the transports of Aphrodite! No, that's not quite right. Something like that. I'll have to turn it into Alexandrines tomorrow, or – hup! – Oh dear–

* * *

The reference to her murdered baby piqued my curiosity. Drunk or sober I had never heard Vee talk about her past as so many women bore everybody; except when she was very tight she'd sometimes have crying fits and mumble about her "lost darling." I decided to have a dip in the kind of lucky bag of memories. As I hesitated, the idea occurred to me to think hard of my hashish god who was squatting, I hoped, in my own skull, asking for guidance. Instantly my finger seemed attracted by one particular tape which obediently I chose.

* * *

Vee: I am panting slowly, conscious of the most blissful sensation I have ever known. Every muscle is relaxed, every soothed nerve absorbing beatitude. My cheek cuddles satin flesh. The throb of a violently beating heart seems to penetrate my intestines, the heave of the chest to control my pulse. His breath lightly stirs a strand of my discovered hair, each one of which appears jealousy to seek the caress. An arm lying across his stomach rises and falls like a ship on the swell of the ocean. I do not want to move – ever! just to wallow in the cradle of bliss, sucking, like a thirsty flower, the dew of delight. A movement terrifies me – threatening to destroy my celestial world.

"Don't, dearest!" I murmur imploringly.

"But my arm's gone to sleep," says he.

I laugh, yet for a second I am displeased at the reminder of a mundane state. Just like a man, I reflect a trifle impatiently, as he draws the arm from under me. He sits up, slides his legs over the edge of the bed and, smiling at me, rubs the circulation back.

"Darling!" I whisper, raising my lips. He bends and kisses me, but oh, it isn't the same as it was before! I sigh and sit up, too. As he takes a cigarette from a side table I watch him curiously as well as amorously. I have never seen a naked man before.

When coming to bed my husband always puts out the light; besides he wears pajamas. Now I am not a bit shocked that my lover is naked, and that I am only in my undies. Before I should have been horrified, but now it is so natural. My lover is beautifully made. His body might have been sculpted by Phidias,[105] I think, as he sits there nonchalantly smoking. The flanges of the chest are cleanly carven, the flanks descend in a ceaseless curve to the groin where his sex resembles a strange white bird sitting in a golden nest. Life has changed – forever changed! I was so frightened to take a lover. Now I am glad, so glad and proud, so proud. Romance, which had so little stirred me, is a pallid sham. No hint of the wonder and the beauty of this – yes, this miracle of nature – was ever whispered. Incredible that such an act should be considered obscene. But now I understand. My husband is obscene, and those like him have obscene minds. Anger stirs when I realize all that I have been deprived of by these worse than liars and that beast of a drunken husband. True, he had procured me the pleasures of maternity, but any clod may be a father. Those joys were mine of which he knew nothing and cared less. What he termed love had never been for me more than a disgusting operation to which a wife is bound to submit. A wave of sheer gratitude surges towards this boy. Impulsively I stoop and gently kiss, sacredly kiss, the organ which has afforded me such unique pleasure and solace. As I look up I am startled by the expression on his face. Have I unwittingly shocked him?

"Gerald, darling!" I murmur.

"You shouldn't do that," he says, severely.

"Why?" I query, hurt. "Don't you know that I love you, and your lovely body too?"

[105] Phidias (circa 480-430 BC): A Greek artist known for his Statue of Zeus at Olympia, considered to be one of the Seven Wonders of the Ancient World.

"Yes, Victoria," he admits, "but that – oh, that isn't done."

I look at him, distressed by his lack of understanding. "What d'you mean, Gerald darling?"

"Oh – oh," he says, looking very embarrassed, "you wouldn't understand, of course, but – why – oh, well, only French girls do that."

I stare at him, puzzled.

"What *do* you mean, Gerald?" I persist.

"Oh, nothing," he mumbles.

He appears to be ashamed, as if wishing he hadn't spoken. I can't think what he can mean, nor what French girls have to do with it. Then I recollect that he is a youth, younger than I am.

"You great, silly, darling boy!" I whisper, taking him in my arms as if he were a big child, and somehow I feel as if he were – mine! "Kiss me, and tell me that you love me."

He kisses me, but not passionately. I feel as if I were repulsed, as if I had encountered something in him that I can't understand, and I so long to comprehend.

"Gerald, dearest," I inquire, anxiously, "don't you realize what you are to me now?"

My hand instinctively caresses his shoulder and down his back as I cling to him.

"Oh, God, yes!" he exclaims, and clasps me ardently.

I give my lips and sigh with delight as his arms tighten about my body. That suffocating sensation begins once more as I inhale his breath thirstily. I am conscious of his rising desire.

"Ow!"

I start convulsively away at a violent pain on my ribs.

"O-oh! you are clumsy!" I tell him, angry for the moment at my pleasure being interrupted. "You've burnt me with your cigarette!"

"Oh, dearest, I'm sorry," he whispers, contritely. "Let me kiss –"

"No, no," I refuse, petulantly, still rather annoyed, yet mollified by his gesture. "Now I can see that you do love me."

He frowns as I avoid another embrace – and the cigarette. Again that longing that he shall comprehend me wells.

"Gerald darling, do you really and truly love me? Tell me the truth."

"Of course I do!" he exclaims, impatiently, and pitching his cigarette stub into an ashtray, takes me in his arms passionately.

"No, no," I insist, pushing him away. "I want to talk to you. Go on smoking."

"Oh, damn!" mutters Gerald. But at that moment a clock strikes.

"Oh, goodness!" I cry, "it's half past four! Boysie and nurse will be here any moment. Quick, get on your clothes, for heaven's sake!"

He tries to grab me, but I dodge, and rush into the bathroom. As hurriedly I dress, the clothes seem to cover and smother all the joy that had been mine. I feel as if I had been somebody else – myself perhaps – for just a little while, such a little while. Now every garment appears to be a piece of my other self, Lady Arthur Manzen, wife of – oh, horror! – Sir Arthur Manzen, Bart, of Lakedean, mother of Bernard, six years old. All the responsibilities and fears of that unhappy person envelop me as I click a diamond brooch my husband gave me upon our engagement. I am violently conscious that I have been unfaithful, have broken my vows – but what could a kid of barely seventeen know she was swearing? Why did I listen to Gerald? Why did I yield? I don't know, except that the temptation was irresistible in my loneliness. I couldn't help adoring him – even if only in contrast to my husband. In that moment I positively hate Gerald. Sharply I call through the door:

"Go into the dining room. There's whisky in the sideboard, if you want one."

I hear him mutter something and his footsteps leaving the bedroom. Then the clink of glass as I powder my nose. Suddenly I recall the condition of the bed. I turn scarlet as I rush back to put things straight. What a state! Crumpled pillows and the coverlet on the floor and torn, too! Good heavens, even Arthur would have noticed, even if he were as drunk as usual.

As I hastily remake the bed a curious flush gushes over my body like a salvo of all the sensations I have experienced on that bed. Again I feel his body against mine, his lips on my lips. My love for him surges back. Now I don't care if I have been unfaithful to my husband, and don't care what I have done as long as I can keep Gerald. I scurry out into the dining room. He is sitting in an armchair with his long legs crossed, smoking, with a glass of whisky at his elbow. He is so elegant and handsome that I can't quite believe that – that he is my own truly, truly lover. I almost leap at him.

"Kiss me, darling!" I command him, laughing, "but don't burn me."

"No fear – now!" says he smiling. But his kiss is chilly to what it was a few minutes ago. I plant myself on his knees. For fun I sip his whisky.

"Ugh! horrid stuff! How you men can drink that muck I can't imagine." Then I put an arm around his neck, and say: "Gerald, I want to talk to you seriously." An expression of slight apprehension flits across his face. "You do love me – truly, Gerald?"

"Yes, of course," he says, "otherwise – Well, I shouldn't be here, should I?"

I don't like the tone, and glance at him anxiously as he inhales his cigarette. He appears so absurdly young. A queer sensation comes over me, as if he really were my son – not passion, but a great tenderness.

"Oh, dearest, I do so want you to understand me," I go on, "all that you mean to me. I don't suppose that you ever will really, because you're a man, and that's different, isn't it?"

"I suppose so," he retorts, smiling, "but I don't know, for I've never been a woman."

"Don't be silly," I admonish him, a little vexed at his flippancy, but he always was like that, and then I used to rather like it, instead of the awful solemnity of my mother and husband, the only beings with whom I had had to live intimately. "Now, what I want you to understand, Gerald dear, is that you're everything to me – now. I've gone too far, I've passed the Rubicon, I've burned my boats. Too late now to return to what I was. There never will be any other man in the world for me, except you, Gerald. "

"But –" he begins, as if uneasily, "your husband –"

"Oh, my – husband doesn't count. He never did – and he was always drunk and now – well, there's never been anything between us since the birth of Bernard six years go. You see, he drinks so, and always has. Oh, I don't know – I'm only too glad."

Again I look at him anxiously. He appears puzzled.

"No, I don't quite see how –" he says slowly. "I mean, it doesn't seem natural. After all a husband –"

I can't bear to meet his eyes. I nestle my head on his shoulder and continue:

"Let me try to make it as clear as I can, Gerald. You see, I was married when I was scarcely seventeen. Mother brought me up in her own way – as thousands of other girls are – in our class. But anyhow, I wasn't allowed to go to boarding school, for fear of moral contagion, she said. So I always had a governess. Dad never interfered, had always let her run the house, and me, as she liked. All he thought about was his research work. He lived in his library. That's why I didn't miss much other girls'

company, for I had that huge library to feed on. That made me queer for a normal girl, I suppose. I wasn't interested in young men, only books, like father. Mother always sneered at me because I scribbled verses. One thing dad said was good, and that encouraged me naturally, I began to think that I was a real poet. Don't be alarmed, Gerald, I've never written since I was married." Involuntarily I sigh. Gerald squeezes my hand and I kiss him out of gratitude, because I think he understands. "Well, then mother would go on at him, saying that he was making a bluestocking[106] of me and that I'd never get a husband. One morning at breakfast she knocked all my unreal world to pieces by saying in her abrupt way, as if shouting at father to wake him out of his dreams:

"D'you know, John, the child is sixteen? That's a dangerous age for a girl. The sooner she's married the better."

"Oh?" said dad, and peered at me over his glasses as if I were some unknown specimen of coleoptera[107] or something.

"Why, my dear, is she in love then?"

Mother snorted disdainfully. But the idea had startled me. What exactly marriage meant I hadn't the slightest notion except that it usually resulted in children. I had never thought about the subject. I had never understood, nor liked, romances. They made such a fuss about love, and then stopped, and said that the couple was happy. But why or how they were happy, was never explained. So they bored me. I took the whole thing for granted, and didn't bother about it anymore. But all that – Oh, God, when I married and found out, I cursed all the novelists that ever lived, the dirty liars! Ah, Gerald!"

"But I don't understand how –" he interrupts me.

[106] Bluestocking: An obsolete term for a woman having intellectual or literary interests.
[107] Beetles.

"I know you don't, darling," I say gently. "That's what I'm trying to tell you. Let me go on. Once mother had an idea in her head she could not rest until she had got rid of it, no matter what it was. Being thorough, she called it. She was keen on all social things with which father wouldn't have anything to do. Her choice for me – of which I knew nothing at the time, was – my husband. Why, heaven only knows, except that he had a title and this place and a good deal of money – which even at that time he was doing his best to get through. She insisted upon "bringing me out" as she called it, at a Hunt Ball. At first I didn't want to leave my books to go, but natural curiosity stirred, and I should have to go anyhow once mother had decided that that was the proper thing to do. There, of course, I met him. He was handsome in a florid way and fairly slender still – not the monster he is now – and he had a hearty manner, jovial, which seemed good natured. Almost any kid of my age would have been impressed. From childhood I had heard about the family of Sir James Manzen. The son, Arthur, was scarcely ever seen in the countryside until after the death of his father. I was still more impressed by his hunting kit, and thought he must be a very important person indeed.

"Later mother calmly announced at breakfast – I never knew why, but she always had 'announced' things then, I suppose, before father got immersed in his books and was inaccessible – that I was to be engaged to Sir Arthur Manzen. Father, I recall, peered vaguely as usual and mumbled: 'Oh, really, Bernard Nansen? Quite an estimable man, I believe. Didn't he write a book on anthropology or something? Very profound, I've been told. Hope you'll be happy, Victoria, my child.' That was father all over. I believe he'd have let mother give me to the king of the Solomon Islands with no more interest. Poor dad, he died in his library, of heart failure, six months after my marriage. Thank God he never guessed the misery I was going through.

"Mother was the real criminal, although no doubt she thought she was doing the best for my happiness. God knows what the relations must have been between my father and mother. I never knew him except as a bookworm. He was an egoist, I suppose, and not a good father, for he should have at least, taught me something of the dangers of the world, and have tried to guide me. That's what I shall do for Bernard – Oh, but you're not interested," I add quickly, noticing that Gerald is pouring another whisky. And suddenly I realize that I'm talking more to myself trying to justify my love in my own eyes rather than his.

"Yes, yes, I am. Go on, dear," he says politely.

"Well," I continue, a little hurt all the same, "we were married. I didn't see Arthur for the first three nights. He was ill, I was told. The last I had seen of him after the wedding breakfast he was reeling drunk, but I was too naive to understand then. Well, he did come to me – still drunk – Oh, I can't tell you."

No, no, I can't tell him. I'd rather die. Not that. Oh God, how vividly I feel again that nightmare start on awakening to see my husband in gray pajamas swaying slightly above the bed, smiling foolishly. "Shorry I'm sho late, darlin'!" he says, thickly. I stare dumbly, fascinated with fear of I don't know what. He fumbles for the switch. Darkness. I hear his heavy breathing and slight movements. The clothes are pulled down. A hand is plunged between my thighs. I struggle frantically, biting my lips not to scream. A huge signet ring he wears hurts me. He seizes a wrist and forces my hand upon him. O-oh God! a shriek is stifled by his stale whisky-stinking mouth. I attempt to pull away my hand from what feels like a warm toad. Something begins to move, to grow. Frantically I tug. He forces my fingers to clasp and caress violently this horror. I wrench my mouth away, try to squirm loose. He growls like a wild beast. Suddenly he lets go my neck, tears open my legs. I wilt. Again he

growls menacingly. I am trembling with terror. Thrusts of pain. He's murdering me. I shriek wildly. A butchery –

"What are you thinking of, dear?" inquires Gerald, tenderly. "You look so sad."

"Nothing, Gerald," I choke and burst into sobs on his shoulder. Clumsily he tries to comfort me. I make an effort to gain control. I know that he can't understand, poor boy.

"You see, Gerald," I whisper, as he strokes my hair, "it was like that – always. Yet he was extraordinary in a way. During the hunting season he'd be blind drunk at night and in the saddle at six in the morning. That's all that he thought of – horses and drink. He'd strike and curse me like a stable lad. Once he was thrown off his horse and broke three ribs, but as soon as he was out of plaster he was just as bad. Of course he was drunk all the time he was in bed. At last I told mother. She was shocked – genuinely, I believe – and said she'd talk to him, but she might as well have talked to a madman. He is, as a matter of fact, alcoholic mad. You've seen how he goes queer, sometimes, and that's nothing to when we're alone. While he was having delirium tremens mother died and so, after, I was absolutely at his mercy. He started again as soon as he was out of the nursing home, although the doctors had said he was cured. He'd disappear to London for weeks on end – as he has now. But I'm only too thankful to be alone. For a while I didn't know, nor care, what he was doing, but I do now. All his money went, and other property he mortgaged to the hilt, and half my money has gone, too. Oh, Gerald, Gerald, you don't know what I've suffered! Tell me, don't you believe that I'm justified in loving you?"

"Of course you are, dear," says Gerald, gripping me tightly. "Married to a brute like that! Haven't I said so?"

"Yes, yes, but I wanted to tell you everything. You don't blame me, do you, Gerald? Swear you don't?"

"No, no, of course not, dearest, but – but –" He hesitates. I can't see his face above my head. I wish I could. "But – one thing I can't understand is – if he was like that – your little boy – "

"Oh!" I exclaim, grasping what he means. "Why, he was like that when Boysie was conceived. Don't you understand now how I've got to look after him with such a father? He's so delicate. He may – Oh, it's a nightmare. Don't leave me, Gerald! Stay near me to help me bear it!"

"Don't worry, sweetheart," says Gerald sweetly, kissing my wet eyes ... I will, I swear. I'll never leave you at the mercy of such a drunken sot."

A noise startles me. I jump off his lap. That's nurse and Boysie coming back for tea. I dash for the bathroom to do my eyes. When I return, nurse is standing by the table, smiling. Bernard is on Gerald's knees. I start *My* place! Then I catch my breath at the thought; if only Gerald were his father! But I stifle an almost hysterical laugh. Six years old is Bernard. Why Gerald was a kid in knickers then!

"Hello, Mumsie!" Bernard calls and rushes into my arms. As I kiss him, a terrible fear leaps that the child may have smelt my odor on Gerald! But that's silly, I know.

"Oh, Mumsie, you do look funny!" exclaims Bernard, as I let him go.

"Why? How?" I ask, uneasily.

"Why, Mumsie, you look heaps younger!" he states, joyously.

"Nonsense, Boysie," I reply, glancing apprehensively at nurse. Has she, too, noticed something different – although it doesn't seem possible? I dare not look at Gerald.

"Oh, nurse," I say, hurriedly, "do ring for the tea, will you? You must both be dying of hunger."

"Oh, no," declares Bernard. "Nurse and I went into Rappel's, and nurse gobbled three crumpets all alone!"

"Oh, I didn't, Master Bernard," says nurse, laughing.

"Well," insists Bernard, "you galloped up two – and a tart!"

"What's that?" I say, starting violently. A loud, raucous voice comes through the open window, a voice I know too well, singing:

> There's a fox in the woods they all say!
> We'll all go a-hunting to-day!
> Tra la la la! tra la la! …

I stand petrified. Arthur has come back from London! and of course, he's been drinking at every pub on the road. I hear the chauffeur, Hutchins, trying to calm him. Thank heavens, Arthur doesn't seem in an ugly mood. Gerald has risen. Glances at me. I shake my head. It would never do to let him meet my husband as he leaves the house. The maid comes in with the loaded tea tray. At the sound of scuffling feet and oaths Bernard looks at me.

"It's your father, dear," I tell him stupidly.

"Oh," says Bernard, "I can *hear* that!"

"Sit down to your tea, Boysie," I say as calmly as I can, knowing that sometimes the presence of the lad has a soothing effect on his father, if he isn't too far gone. "Draw up a chair, Gerald. Do sit down, nurse, and pretend you don't notice – as usual," I add, a little bitterly.

At another bellow from my husband my heart begins to thump. Strange, I do not feel embarrassed about Gerald. I have forgotten that he is my lover. I sit before the silver tea urn and start to pour out. The noise increases – Hutchins' voice mixed with belches. They appear in the doorway. Anxiously I peer at my husband. His eyes are pouched and bloodshot, his hair is plastered in wisps over his half-bald head. He must have fallen down for his clothes are muddy.

"Lemme go, you silly bastard!" he mumbles at Hutchins who, behind him, shakes his head ominously.

"Hello, Arthur," I say, feeling as if my tongue were glued to my mouth. "Why didn't you wire me you were coming home?"

"Why the bloody hell should I?" he demands querulously. "My home, ain't it? Don't I know my old bitch is waiting there to snap at me?" he adds, glowering around the room as Hutchins forces him into an armchair. "Where's my bloody son?"

"I'm here, father," pipes Bernard bravely, for he's used to it, poor lad.

"Oh, there y're! Why'n hell didn't ye say so?" Arthur growls, his bleary eyes trying to regard the boy. "Stuffin' again! Go on, stuff then! If ye don't put on too much weight we'll make ye a jockey in a couple of years. Heh, missus, wash thish?" as his myopic sigh takes in Gerald. "One of Meron's whelps, the string-haltered gelding ha! ha! ha! Takin' tea wi' the ladies, pretty cretcher? B'christ ye wouldn't be here if ye were a man! Bah! none of the Meron stable 'as enough spunk to serve a mare, ha! ha! ha!"

I am scared. Imploringly I look at Gerald whose eyes are tight angry. Arthur's hand upsets a cup of tea which crashes on the floor.

"Huh," he goes on, "what's this horse piss? Where's my bottle, you bitch? And you – where's that bloody gelding gone?" His half-blind eyes peer about. "Heh, there y're! Ye're going to drink tonight wi' me, d'ye hear? See if ye're a man!"

I sense the rising violence. My knees tremble. I dare not tell nurse to take the boy away, for that would I know, provoke a frenzy. Little Bernard watches his father with the terribly candid eyes of a child, dread, contempt, mixed. I get up almost staggering, put the decanter and glass before him.

"Where's the geldin's trough?" he shouts.

From behind Gerald I pass a glass over his shoulder, whispering: "For my sake!"

My husband lurches, waving the decanter across the table, striking the tea urn, which nurse deftly catches in time. Sullenly, Gerald proffers his glass, into which Arthur slops whisky. I see the rising temper in Gerald's eyes, and bless him for his self-control. The only hope now is to ply my husband with liquor until he collapses. He reels back in his chair and unsteadily pours himself out half a glass. Nurse adroitly takes the decanter from him as he vainly seeks the level of the table.

"Heel taps!" he roars, as he spills whisky down his throat and his waistcoat. Gerald slyly empties his drink into a tea cup. Arthur crashes his glass onto the table.

"Thash way a man drinks!" he shouts. "And you, ye bloody gelding?"

Obediently Gerald holds up his empty glass.

"Oh, but he poured it into a tea cup!" exclaims Bernard.

For several seconds there is a dreadful silence. I hear the intake of nurse's breath. My husband's eyes goggle bloodshot as the meaning penetrates his sodden brain. My throat contracts and bursts into a silly giggle:

"Tee he! he! he! Tee he! he he!"

Comes a growl like a wild beast.

"Ye bloody fuckin' welcher!" Arthur bellows.

He hurls the decanter across the table. An edge catches Bernard who is sitting beside Gerald, on the side of the head.

I shriek. Blood is welling as Gerald picks up the boy from the floor. Something crashes. In a haze as I continue screaming I see Arthur sprawling over the table vomiting on the cloth …

* * *

I came out of this trance almost ill with the repercussion of the shock of the scene. Now I understood much of Vee's hysterical character, evidently conditioned by this tragic accident.[108]

But the experience that impressed me the more forcibly was the voluptuous delights of a woman in coition. I smiled as I recalled the Greek myth of Hermaphrodite summoned before the gods, as the only being who had been man and woman, to give judgment on the comparative pleasures, declared that the female had seven times that of a male, and now I could well

[108] Beatrice Hastings was the seventh of sixteen children born to John Walter and Catherine Jane Doorly. Her father was a merchant and a wool trader. She grew up in Port Elizabeth, South Africa, and at the age of twelve attended a boarding school at Hastings, England. Upon her return to South Africa, attempting to gain her freedom, the eighteen-year-old Hastings embarked upon what would prove to be a terribly unhappy marriage with Edward Tracy Chamberlain, who soon died of a heart attack. (Since Beadle was also raised near Hastings, attended English boarding schools, and later served – at the age of eighteen – in the British South African Police, they shared a common cultural background.) It was also somewhere around this time that Hastings may have given birth to a child that didn't live very long. (One of her first published poems was a sonnet titled "The Child's Burial.") Hastings was romantically involved with a boxer, Lachlan Thomas, with whom she toured around England, accompanying him to his various pugilistic matches. According to her death certificate they were married. By 1906 she returned to London, where she met Alfred Orage. Besides serving as the model for "Vee" in *Dark Refuge*, Hastings is portrayed by H. G. Wells as "Mrs. Harrowdean" in *Mr. Britling Sees It Through* (1916); while Katherine Mansfield portrays her as "Beatrice" in the story "Poison" (1920). In Francis Carco's *Les Innocents* (1916), a novel about the Montmartre demimonde, she again appears as "Beatrice." And in Cocteau's *Le Livre blanc* (1928), she assumes the guise of the domineering "Mlle. R." For more on her biography, see Stephen Gray, *Beatrice Hastings: A Literary Life*, Johannesburg: Viking / Penguin Books, 2004.

believe it. No wonder that love was all in all to a woman and the world well lost.

Vee I had never considered seriously; her work merely academic and uninspired, herself ridiculous rather, particularly her hen laugh; but after I had lived her story I had more sympathy for her – or should have had had I known at that epoch.

The next room was larger. On a divan in a corner was Cecci asleep on the flat of his back, the soot-fringed eyebrows closed as he breathed rhythmically through pomegranate lips. The hands were folded upon his chest, strangely white hands for his twilit body, broken and dirty of nails. On each temple a tuft of thick hair had been twisted into the semblance of horns which, with the pallor of his face, suggested a faun in stone upon a tomb.

On the far side of a large square table sat the gnomelike Izzy, queerly resembling a monk in a cell at work upon an illuminated parchment. Before him was a medley of papers and a mess of wet ashes in a saucer. Pen in one hand and a cigarette in the other he stared with diamond bright eyes at his friend, a malicious smile upon his cup-rimmed mouth.

I chose him first. The dome was unusually high and vaulted like the roof of a cloister. The heart gauge was tumultuous. I was surprised at the warmth of the credulity bulb and the lowness of the sex tube. The imagination bulb glowed almost incandescently. As I grasped the contacts I had the sensation of touching live wires before I faded into himself, reading what he had just written:

* * *

Izzy:

> O, my friend, thou art more beautiful than the concept of time: whilst thy soul lies in the scintillating arms of a virgin son of the poppy and the hemp, more wondrously beautiful than the dark of the moon which is an illusion!
>
> O, my friend, more beautiful art thou than utter death, for thine is the dreadful charm of the lowered rhythm in abeyance, the declutch of the intellect from the passions of the body which is asleep, that beauteous abysm of chaos where creation beds destruction from which is born art!

Good. Very good. I am in form tonight. This youth has that rarest of minds in a jewel of a casket that stimulates the intellectual rhythm that I need. Great Lord, what it is to be a god! These clods that circulate about us like cosmic dust a planet, are meant but to serve the needs, and minister to the desires of such as we. Bah! that woman! Women are the lesser of the species – sacks of dung, as Cluny calls them. How to embrace such! In place of intellect is a primitive system of sense ends reacting to physical demands – hunger, sex, maternity. Who shall be as vain as a she-cat in rut? Yet withal a lowly organ is destined to a great end – Man! Love? – an intestinal metamorphosis! Ah, you gentlemen, the great romancers, the stories of Antony and Cleopatra, Sheba and Solomon, Heloise and Abelard, Dante and Beatrice – intestinal attractions! Friends betrayed, parents abandoned, empires overthrown, millions slaughtered, for what, great God? – for the coupling of a few inches of guts!

God's death! I must note that for canto cxxi of my magnum opus, The Metamorphosis of the Monad. Ah!

I dab a finger in the wet ashes and draw on the bare table the profile of my dear friend, using a burned match to finish the

details.[109] Name of forty Gods, that is good! I must find a way to preserve such. But how? Ah, my genius glows as ever! For ashes I'll substitute cement which will harden in a few minutes. Ha! ha! ha! that is excellent! Thus I may draw on a café table and nonchalantly slice them off with a penknife to present to my dear friends. Ha! I shall tell them that I am like their dear good God, for did He not take dust to make a man? Ha! ha! a bon mot of Izzy which the newspapers will snatch at. That will buy many sons of the poppy and daughters of the hemp for goodly mating. Yet that is a mere nothing. I rub out the drawing with a finger and light another cigarette.

Ah, apropos *that* female – why do all Englishwomen look like badly dressed children about twelve? Because their minds are but twelve – and their men fourteen. Who else could think of nothing but whisky and sport? Tcha! It is disgusting! "Women, Jews and Anglo-Saxons," scoffed Weininger, "are inferior races," but he was a Jew himself, the renegade swine![110] "Genius

[109] As mentioned earlier, the penurious Max Jacob utilized ash as a drawing medium: "André Salmon once made an inventory of Max's palette: Chinese chalks, at a sou a piece, a blue carpenter's pencil, some cinders, charcoal, and a few pastels in ochre and pink, all the blues and a delicate green. He had also a brush, several watercolor tablets, a tube of zinc white, and a bottle of Chinese ink. On his table he kept a small pot to collect cigar ash, another medium for his extraordinary paintings." See *Artist Quarter*, p. 54.

[110] A reference to Otto Weininger (1880 – 1903), a Jewish Austrian philosopher who converted to Christianity in 1902, a year before his death by suicide at the age of twenty-three. In Weininger's book *Sex and Character* (1903) he regards Christianity as the "highest expression of the highest faith," while he calls Judaism "the extreme of cowardliness" and equates it (pejoratively) with "femininity." (Not surprisingly, some of his work was later utilized by the Nazis.) The narrative significance of Weininger's appearance here becomes clear once the reader understands that "Izzy" is closely modeled upon Max

is a return to childhood," wrote Baudelaire. Maybe so, thus the English cannot produce genius, for how can one return to what one is? Beel? Yes, I like Beel much. Very sympathetic. But surely his mother must have cheated his father – for he cannot be pure English! Ah, I must tell Beel that. How he will laugh! Still, some of them were poets – a few. Shelley, Ben Jonson – truly I love M'sieu Jonson when Beel he translates. He is very amusing. And that Walt Whitman. Yes, he is American. But the good God knows what blood they have in their veins. Shakespeare certainly. But he must be of Norman descent, otherwise it is not possible. The best of them is Norman. But what is that to Villon, Ronsard, Rabelais, de Lautréamont, de Gourmont, Flaubert, and Isidore Ginsberg![111] I laugh! There is again that English woman poet, whisky and men, a bag of fermenting sex, and she says she is a poet. Oh, to make me laugh!

Jacob, himself a controversial convert from Judaism to Christianity (who claimed that Christ appeared to him on a movie screen in Paris). Jacob announced his decision to convert while sitting in the Café Rotonde toward the end of November 1914. Soon afterward he informed his cousin Jean-Richard Bloch (who was also Jewish): "I'm not rejecting anything. I had no religion and I'm choosing one." In the percipient words of Jacob's biographer Susanna Warren: "Max Jacob wanted magic, mysticism, fantasy, love, and a personal God, and he thought he would find them in the Roman Catholic faith." She adds: "Jacob turned even the sacrament of baptism into his own mythology, and if the ceremony converted him to Roman Catholicism, it is just as true that he converted Catholicism to his own purposes." Warren, *Max Jacob*, pp. 226, 231. Picasso will later feature Max as a monk in his two oil paintings of the *Three Musicians*, completed in 1921.

Weininger is also briefly mentioned on page 209 of *The Esquimau of Montparnasse*, when the "Esquimau" protagonist remarks: "Women, as Weininger said, are divided ... into wives and courtesans."

[111] Here, for the first time, the author reveals Izzy's full fictional name.

I look at the sleeping Cecci and sigh. Ah, that beautiful body that I must share! Have I not taught him eclectic secrets that he should thus betray me, return to me stinking of women? Ah, what sadness that he was born bisexual and therefore imperfect. That is his own fault if women shall destroy his art. Still, he is young. I may still win him wholly to me. Only must he live for his art – neither money, nor women, nor fame shall caress him.

Yet that kind of a she mule – she may be of use to him? She has money to buy him stone and paints and – artificial paradise. Ah, must I yet again make this sacrifice for sordid ends? No, no, not sordid, for is it not for his art? Yes, yes, and that she-camel may be made to be of use to me, too. She can perhaps translate my work – the good God knows how, but what matter for those barbarians, who pay so much? In America there are more than a hundred million of them. Formidable! They will not understand Isidore Ginsberg, but what do I care? Advertisement! An American, a most amusing man, once told me that in his country of God you could sell moonbeams – if the advertising was good. Ha ha, what a country! Yes, she is to be considered. I must make her many compliments, tell her that her writings, which I cannot read and do not wish to, resemble – who? Shakespeare? Yes, he is their god of literature, such as it is. Or perhaps she would prefer a modern? I must find out from Beel the most fashionable. Shaw, I have heard them talk about. He makes much money, they say. But too much of flattery? Oh no, she – one has but to look at her – will lap up quantities of the most fulsome flattery like a dog his vomit.

Also it is true I shall have to make love to her. Every foolish woman expects that – even the French. Peugh, that disgusts me! Now what can I tell her? That she is more divinely beautiful than Helen and writes better than Madame de Sévigné? I bet she will cackle like a hen that has just laid an egg. Ah, I have it! I shall write her a poem with a double meaning which she will be

too stupid to comprehend and when she proudly shows it to her French friends they will wet themselves with laughter, ho, ho!

Ah, it is the hour already. That is a thing that dear Cecci has never learned to bear in mind: That the dose should be weighed scrupulously and taken regularly as if prescribed by a doctor – not to abuse the gifts of the gods, sniffing and swallowing like small pigs in a gutter. I will take a sniff and then write that she-camel the poem in her own house while she lies dead drunk with alcohol. The Muse asleep? Maybe. How we shall laugh! From my Napoleon snuff box I ladle with a nail file a small portion of the powder into the crook between the thumb and the index finger and, standing before the mirror, absorb in two strong sniffs. Ah, thought quickens like a motor when one steps on the gas. I smile happily at the flux of the sense of power that wells through all my being as I step over to my dear friend. I feel his pulse. It is feeble but regular.

"You have taken too much, you woman-tainted animal!" I whisper softly. "Ah, you should never take alcohol, a vulgar poison for brutes. It is as if one were to eat jelly with lamb as do the barbarian English. Ah, now the muse surges!"

Gently I kiss him on his beautiful cold brow which is as voluptuous as if he had been dead for days.[112] Then I go back and pick up my pen …

* * *

On leaving I noticed that the imagination bulb was more incandescent than ever; and the light from the fo'c'sle lantern might have been electric. I entered Cecci's cranium anxious to examine the mental state under complete exhaustion from

[112] Perhaps a foreshadowing of Modigliani's premature death at the age of thirty-five, on 24 January 1920.

alcohol and drug. The chamber was very dim; the imagination bulb extinct; the nerve needle stationary at zero; only the heart gauge moved perceptibly. I took hold of the contacts. Nothing registered. Evidently then, I reflected, the subconscious was not dreaming as I had thought might be the case. On former visits I had been too excited by my strange discovery to give more attention to the interior mechanism. Now I wished to find out what were the functions of the various bulbs and gadgets, but apparently without the assistance of my Virgil, I could not comprehend their uses. In this Chamber of Cecci I detected a veinlike protuberance that ran from one instrument to another; in places were seemingly varicose swellings which resembled, on closer inspection, a kind of foreign excrescence, a fungoid growth,[113] but what that signified I was unable to guess.

The gloom of the chamber suddenly was less dense. I turned away from the instrument board to seek the cause. Squatting tranquilly as if he had come in answer to my secret wish, was the hashish god. The two eyes were as ever fixed in eternal contemplation; the middle orb had the same friendly twinkle touched with irony. A telescopic arm shot out; the long nailed index finger lengthened in jerks; touched some object behind the "box of memories." Obediently investigating I observed in the dark of the corner another apparatus connected by fleshy cables, clammy cold to the touch. Again a cover or skin rolled back, or contracted. I could feel another mass of tapewormy ribbons. The long, polished nail of my occult guide lifted one which I took:

* * *

Cecci: I am gazing around an enormous room triumphantly. No one dares to confute me, and they know it. Nobody dares

[113] Modi died from tubercular meningitis.

any longer to argue with me when I state that there is no modern art except mine. Not a single man even attempts to contradict among the thousands in the huge café. Ha ha! Ho ho ho! Look, there's Picabia, Matisse, Fugita, Degas, Bourdelle, Derain, Rodin, Mercier, Utrillo, Soutine, and ho! ho! there, skulking in the crowd – Oh, Suze, look! – the old fellows! Rembrandt, Leonardo, Michael Angelo, Titian, El Greco, Fra Lippi – all of 'em! Why, they're too scared to say "baa" like a sick sheep![114] Oh, I know it! And here's my old man Serge as drunk as a sailor! He knows it, too, you bet, as well as I do, that I'm the only man who can paint and sculpt, and the pig won't buy me stone because, says he, I'm too well known as a painter, Pouah! Two years more and he can go and play with himself, and I'll go to sculpting again, and show then what the world has never seen. Buy me another, Serge?

Oh, shut, up, you make me sick [in] the stomach. Wo-ow! Well, then give me an advance on next week's? What if it is already exhausted? You give me a moldy thousand a month in doles like a child and make tens of thousands out of my work every day.[115] And on the top of that you want to tell me how to

[114] On page 85 of *Artist Quarter* Beadle relates that, according to the poet and journalist Louis Latourette, "Apart from Picasso, the only painter Modigliani admired was the douanier Rousseau."

[115] "Serge" is modeled upon the Polish poet Léopold Zborowski, who decided to serve as Modi's art dealer after they befriended each other in 1916. All this involved a great deal of personal and financial sacrifice. When no other dealer would take Modi seriously, Zborowski and his wife Hanka supplied him with painting materials, models, the use of an apartment, and a steady provision of alcohol. Zborowski also arranged a monthly stipend for the artist, but Modi spent much of it on drinking and drugs. In *Artist Quarter* Beadle says that "From Zborowski he had a fixed allowance of 300 francs a month – about twelve English pounds at that period – with canvases, colors, and studio provided, as well as his share, less the monthly advances,

live! You're worse than that English kind of a poetess who made me sell the paints she bought me to get just a little artificial paradise, or a drink; and then expected me to work well. A man of genius requires these things, name of God! And then she'd bed with anyone who came along when she was drunk, and that was mostly always, and then lecture me afterwards because I'd had a little bit of tail on my own. She was as egoist as that little Jew Izzy[116] who'd make a scene if I as much as slept once with a woman. Great God, haven't I the right to go to bed with whom I like? D'you hear? I'd go to bed with an ape if I thought I would. Ha, but that kind of a poetess! She had no dignity. Madonna, was such as I to sup out of the same dish as every waster in the quarter, the whore defrauder! All right, Suze dearest, I know, I know that the subject excites me. But it's all Serge's fault because he won't let me have another. Wo-ow!

Then as swiftly as I make a brush stroke, I empty the dregs of every glass on the table, ha ha ho ho! Ho ho! Bah! you're all like young girls. Don't know how to drink! Hey, garçon; No, I shan't

---

whenever a picture was sold. In the hope of checking excesses he was paid weekly, but long before the end of each week he was invariably penniless." He adds that "Zborowski is the real hero of this story," and concludes: "Without Zborowski he would probably have died almost unknown as a result of throwing away money on drink and drugs." See *Artist Quarter*, pp. 324-325, 337, 341. It was thanks to Zborowski that Modigliani first started to paint nudes: something that Zborowski insisted upon as part of their business arrangement.

[116] If these were actual words spoken by the artist, they would have been uttered with a sharp sense of irony, as Modigliani was quite proud of his own Jewish background. The artist Nina Hamnett recalls that when she first met Modi in February 1914 he introduced himself by saying: "Je suis Modigliani. Juif. Jew." He also single-handedly confronted a group of Royalist anti-Semites in a Parisian café and denounced them after revealing his Jewish identity. (See *Artist Quarter*, p. 88.)

shut up. Wow! They've all become three now. Three Matisses grinning! Three Rembrandts snickering! Three Rodins laughing! Yow! they're all beaten, three at a time! I don't care if the patron is looking. He's only an old pig sitting at his desk like God on a soap box. Yes, he's watching me, the insolent one! Thinks he's going to get another sketch for a drink and sell it for a hundred. Never again! The whole quarter's been living on me for years. Hoarding 'em until I'm dead.[117] Oh, I know! No, Serge, my old camel, I shan't shut up. Bah, for the flat feet! Besides he daren't send for a cop, the swine! They know me too well. Why, M'sieu Le Commissaire bought a picture. I don't care anyhow, because I have a rendezvous. No, I shan't tell you, Suze, or anyone else. Ah, the blessed angel! Oh, the thrice beloved! What are you grinning at, Suze? No, I won't come home. You're an imbecile, and you're only charming because you know it. No, I won't be quiet. Why should I? I'm the only one who can discourse beautifully. I'm an orator. Damn the glass! What if I did upset it? Great God, haven't I the right to upset a moldy glass if I want to? Hey, garçon, bring me another! Oh, Suze, go away! Your face is all tied up in knots and you know that that makes me ill. And I'm tired of you. No great man can stand a woman more than a few months. Besides, I can't keep on painting the same nude. And you're getting fat, and you've got wrinkles around your belly. Child? What child? How do I know it's mine anyway? Besides, I've got hundreds of children. I merely have to look at a woman and she's in the family way. Bah! they'll all be rich when I die.

Hello, Izzy! You've been there all the time? Why, I've never seen you this evening. How's Jesus? What, you don't remember when you met him on the steps of the Butte? Ha! ha! Why, you

[117] Upon receiving news of Modi's demise, within twenty-four hours the Parisian art dealers scrambled to locate his paintings and jack up the prices – and the prices continued to skyrocket in the years ahead.

told me yourself. And he converted you, and you're going to be a monk. Ho ho! All the same, you can write, dear Izzy. He's the son of Baudelaire, Izzy. Hello, there's Vee making faces. She can't see me now, but she was always blind even when she wasn't drunk. She's a camel! Never knew enough to appreciate me. Thinks she's a poet à la Madame de Noailles.[118] They've both got literary diarrhea.

"For the love of God, Suze, get your husband home, or Emile will have him pinched again!"[119]

[118] Anna, Comtesse Mathieu de Noailles (1876 – 1933), a Greek Romanian poet, novelist, and author of an autobiography, who befriended Proust, Rilke, Paul Valéry, Jean Cocteau, Pierre Loti, and Max Jacob. (She was French only by marriage.)

[119] In the winter of 1916-17 Modigliani briefly became involved with Hastings' close friend Simone Thiroux (c. 1892 – 1921), a blonde French Canadian medical student who began to pursue painting. On page 246 of *Artist Quarter* Beadle writes: "Simone was an orphan who had inherited money at twenty-one from her parents: the father was a Canadian and the mother French, hence she was known as la Canadienne." But "by the time she met Modi very little, if any, of her small capital was left." In 1917 Simone bore him a son, Gérard Thiroux, who was given up for adoption and whom Modi stubbornly refused to recognize. (On 21 April 1981 the French newspaper *Le Journal de Dimanche* discovered that Modi's son Gerard was living in Milly-la-Forêt, a small village near Paris, where he was employed as the parish priest.) The phrase "How do you know it's mine?" might lead us to believe that Suze is based on Simone. In 1921 Simone died of tuberculosis at the Hôpital de la Charité in Paris. On 29 November 1918, Modi's lover Jeanne Hébuterne (1898 – 1920) gave birth to Modi's daughter, also named Jeanne (1918 – 1984), an event that was celebrated by the artist. Hébuterne was considered to be Modigliani's common-law wife, so the phrase "Suze, get your husband home" might indicate that "Suze" is based upon Hébuterne, who committed suicide by leaping from a window the day after Modigliani's death. Or

Oh, shut up, Serge! Yes, I heard you. Leave me alone. I'll go when I like. Where's Izzy? He's the only one who ever understands me. I want Izzy! He's got some stuff – always has now. Charming man, Izzy. Take your paws off me, Serge. What do I care for the patron? I'll kill him if he says a word. I'd like to kill someone tonight. I don't care who. Maybe I shall. Cut his throat and suck the blood, and at the same time slit up his guts with a Japanese knife until you hear them fall plop like a horse's in a bullring. Hi! Hi! Who wants to meet my friend death? Nobody wants to die? What a shame. Don't worry. You never were born, you hairy kind of abortions! Where's Izzy gone? I like Izzy. He's a Jew too, even if he did kiss Jesus on the stairs of Montmartre. What? All right, I'll [have] some if you'll give me a sniff. No joke?

What's the matter with you all? Your faces go together like a concertina and look like a stew. God, what ugliness! I'm coming, but why d'you want to make such a noise, like a lot of seagulls? No, I don't want a coat. It isn't raining. You're drunk, as usual. Can't you see God's crying out of jealousy? Can't you taste the salt tears? Holy Saint Catherine, and you're Christians and you can't taste God's tears! I'm not shouting, Serge. You're all yelling like idiots. Of course, the less you have to say the more noise you make, dirty politicians! I'm not coughing, Suze.[120] It's the smoke. Leave me alone. If you don't go away, I'll beat you.

"Slip off, Suze, and I'll take him to Rene's. He's quite crazy tonight."

That's that imbecile Serge again! Of course I'm crazy. It's great to be mad. Only great men are mad. Baudelaire was mad, Lautréamont was mad – Rimbaud, Gauguin – all of 'em! Only

---

"Suze" may be a composite of these two figures. Modi is said to have fathered at least two other children.

[120] Another reference to Modigliani's tubercular meningitis.

fools are sane. Hark to their hee-hawing. Oh, I know the trick. You're going to get me there and then pretend you haven't got any. To hell with you! Besides I've a rendezvous with life. Take your hands off, idiot. If you touch me, I'll knife you. There, I just push him and he falls into the gutter. I could just push them all over with one finger tonight. What a fuss they're making about him! What's it matter if he is dead? He's good for nothing. He [n]ever created anything, as I have. Just tell God I killed him, and that'll be all right. Oh, I'm going to the lavatory. Yes, yes, Serge, I'll come back. You don't think I'm going to sleep there all night? Well, then? No, it isn't too late. I tell you I don't want a coat. Oh, to please you, then.[121]

Some of the thousands on the pavement put a coat over my shoulders; and a hat on my head, and I laugh and run back into the café. Amédée is piling up the chairs.[122] The patron glares at me, suspiciously.

"No more drinks tonight," says he. "You've had enough."

Insolence. But I've got something far better than his moldy drinks. I laugh, showing my beautiful teeth. He thinks I am not so drunk as he thought I was when I tell that I am only going to the lavatory.

"Quickly," he grunts. "We're closing."

The fools! I simply slip through the other room of the café and out into the other boulevard, laughing to twist my guts. Nobody knows that I have a rendezvous. The coat and hat

[121] The absence of quotation marks indicates that this extended rant occurs in the form of an interior monologue.

[122] Beadle is perhaps amusing himself by naming the waiter Amédée, since it is *Amedeo* Modigliani that they are hoping to eject from the café while Amédée piles up the chairs around him. Both the French *Amédée* and the Italian *Amedeo* mean "lover of God" or, more correctly, "for the love of God," and thus endow the subsequent passages with an especial irony.

annoy me. How silly! I throw them away as I run, for I know it is late and I'm frightened that my beloved will not wait. God is crying harder than ever, and I suck in his tears. How funny it must be to [weep]! Only gods, women and weak men, weep. Very silently I laugh as I hurry on and on. How angry Serge and Suze will be when they find out that I've tricked them. But do they think that I'm a child – me? I stop suddenly because a policeman is watching me, the fool! But then everybody always looks at me suspiciously, merely because I am not like anybody else. How should I be – me? I'm the unique, the only me. Beel used to say that, but then he was just conceited and had no right, as he was no genius. Beel went to America, or the moon, I've forgotten which, and it is of no importance. Poor Beel, he was so stupid like all Anglo-Saxons. Is that a shadow, or the policeman following me? No, it is a woman. I must run again because I am late, but I must have just one. I always keep some hidden from Serge and Suze.

Good, there is a door ajar left open by the concierge who has been bribed by someone. I slip inside. My hands are wet with God's tears, but that doesn't matter. I lick the powder that remains on my fingers. Hah, that is better, my old man! Strength, marvelous strength surges through my body, the very life breath of the gods. Now could I run fifty miles without stopping. Gaily I step out, singing a love song of my country, for am I not going to a bridal feast?

A-ah, there she is, my beloved, awaiting me on a bench! Oh, the sweetest of all humans! I greet her as I sit down as I would a princess. "Why have you kept me waiting for so long?" I ask the loveliest of saints. She mutters. She is adorably shy, of course. She is pure. She has never known a man. Ah, how beautiful she is! I try to embrace her. Oh, misery, she repulses me. But yet that is part of the feminine game to excite me more. All women do that. Do I not know women? What? I am drunk? Of course I am,

beloved, drunk with you. Let me look upon your wondrous face more beautiful than the houris of Paradise! I lift her chin into the light of a street lamp. She has cancer of the left nostril. I adore cancers. Rare is the beautiful woman who has also a cancer, and this is a very lovely cancer. I attempt to kiss it, but she beats me; sweet, sweet blows which she knows that I love. How lovely is she, and I am so strong! She has, I am sure, a body more beautiful than an archangel's face. In sculpture too, I shall make her immortal. I tell her so.

"Poor boy," she says, "but you have no coat and hat! You're soaked through and through, Holy Virgin! You'll catch a death cold. Haven't you the price of a doss?[123] I ain't had any luck tonight, or I'd to warm you a bit. Ain't got a room neither, or I'd take you there. Now, don't be silly! Great Lord, I'm old enough to be your mother. Oh Jesus Mary, you're trembling and burning with fever!"

"You're the silly one, darling," I tell her, hugging closer. Then a pain darts through my chest. God, she's stabbed me! I choke …

* * *

I merged back into the skull chamber. Cecci must have swooned, I reflected. The heart gauge and the instruments in general were exactly as I had left them to take over these new mysterious contacts. I was puzzled. Had I tapped a record of subconscious dreaming which the usual "present" controls had failed to give?

The large room through which he had fled to the other boulevard I had recognized as the Café de la Rotonde although unaccountably altered; but the annex, vast in Cecci's drugged

[123] "Doss" (British): A crude or makeshift bed. She assumes that Modi can't afford a flophouse fee.

vision, did not exist. Next door to the Rotonde was a butcher's shop. Was the experience the record of a dream in the subconscious provoked by a fear of illness, probable, as he had a weak chest? And the consequence of drug taking of which he had been frequently warned by friends anxious to break him of the habit? I turned to interrogate my queer preceptor, but he was no longer present.

Pondering, I recalled the scene. The faces of Vee and Izzy – they too, had changed; grown slightly older. Also many of the others whom I well knew. Solve this mystery I must. Fumbling in the newly discovered contraption I picked up the continuation of the same tape.

* * *

Cecci: A vast figure in white is towering over me holding a tiny object which glitters. Vaguely I stare at white walls and ceiling. Then gradually I become aware of a long off, insupportable pain in my chest. My slow breaths seem like streaks of fire at which I wonder for a long time. The pain draws nearer: becomes insufferable. Something moving attracts my gaze. Behind the white colossus hazily I make out a blackness that is all about me, yet does not go up to the ceiling. A screen it seems to be? I feel another presence on my other side. But I am much more interested in observing my fire breaths again. The pain becomes enormous inside me. It is huge and distorted like an early Italian primitive and it stirs like a newborn calf in a blanket. A distant rumbling comes from above me. I recognize the sounds as words, but I am too tired and indifferent to comprehend, and the pain is screaming so loudly. "No hope, sister, as I diagnosed. Riddled with tubercular lesions as well as double pneumonia, on the top of alcoholic and drug poisoning. Pity."

The murmurs twine away into the screaming of my pain. I too, try to scream, but I choke with fire. The enormous figure appears again holding something of glass in his hand. He smiles and his lips move.

"That will soothe your pain, old man."

Immediately strength rushes into me and chases away that monstrous pain. The fire flashes go out, but I am choking. A woman's face swims about above me. I cannot imagine who she can be. Ah! Ah! She has slitted eyes and a fluted nose – her throat! It is she! Mama! Mama! I try to raise my arms …

* * *

Very slowly, as if greatly fatigued, I came back to my own identity holding the tepid tape. I waited. Nothing happened. Perplexed, wondering, I left Cecci's skull. At the table Izzy was smoking and writing rapidly. Absent-mindedly I perched on his skull, but he drove me away with an irritable slap of a hand. I alighted on the table edge to try to solve this strange problem.

The body of Cecci was still lying in the same position breathing rhythmically. The doom pronounced by what was evidently a doctor at a hospital deathbed, I now understood as if repeated by a disc, although at the time I had not grasped a word, for I had been "he." The memory of that experience, or rather the dream of a dream of another, as I believed it so to be, showed me distinctly in the light of the streetlamp in the pouring rain, the ravaged, paint-plastered face of the old prostitute on the bench who, herself, was obviously in the final stages of tuberculosis.[124] Occurred to me an idea that one

[124] The story is based upon an actual event. In *Artist Quarter* Beadle and Goldring relate a memory shared by the Argentinean diplomat, writer, and painter, Emilio Lascano Tegui: During a "stormy, rainy" evening in January 1920, while experiencing the delirium tremens,

dreamed, or had nightmares, which were apparently too feeble to penetrate, and register in, the conscious; to overcome taboos perhaps of a censor. Seething with curiosity, I winged back to Vee's room.

She was lying on her back breathing stertorously just as I had left her. My assault of her left nostril was so impetuous that she sneezed strongly, nearly expulsing me en route, and arousing a dread that I had awakened her, which I did not wish to do for the sake of the experiment. Fortunately she merely groaned; turned over on her side. By that time I was safely ensconced in her brain chamber once more. Feverishly I fumbled in the obscurity for the box of dreams of the subconscious as I deemed it to be.

* * *

Vee: I am gazing at a group of cows in a lush meadow. I like that one with the black and tan spots. She looks so contentedly wise, and regards me in such a friendly way as if she'd known me for a long time. Perhaps she has. Perhaps she's auntie Kate trying to tell me something about my lost boy? Oh, God, shall I never stop thinking of him? Why, he'd be – what? Twenty-five or six now. No, twenty-seven next month. I'm sure he would have been so handsome. Why, that cow might be he. I can't recall whether one keeps one's sex through the reincarnations? I must look it up. True, that steer there may more likely be

---

Modigliani refused to wear his coat and "insisted upon stopping on the seat alongside the railings of the Alésia church." While in the midst of this feverish delirium "a woman came and sat beside Modi, a street-walker [...] Babbling to her about a phantom boat, he finally collapsed. A taxi took him back to poor little [Jeanne] Hébuterne. A few days later came his end in the Hôpital de la Charité." See *Artist Quarter*, p. 294.

Bernard. I'm sure he'd have been very male. And Gerald? Ah, I've never been able to forget Gerald, my first love, and he was really my only love. Ah, Gerald, Gerald! it was all your fault. If you hadn't taught me the pleasures of physical love I should never have fallen so low. Bah! sex is evil, dirty! Now, the very thought disgusts me so that I can't bear to wash that filthy organ. I could tear it out. If I were a man, I'd cut it off. Oh, I can understand the Christian saints. The Catholics are right. There should be no sexual communion except for procreating. Sex leads to evil. Why, if I hadn't had a lover, my husband wouldn't have killed Bernard. Strange. I never saw it in that light before. But – O God – it's true. And I have been punished for my sin. I see it now. Yet I've never been able to forget Gerald. Queer that I should always think of him by association with Bernard? Yet it isn't, I suppose. He was there that tragic afternoon. He was the cause of it, God forgive him. Far away that seems now, and yet as if it were yesterday. Then the war took Gerald. Was that his punishment, I wonder? Would he have come back to me [in] the end, had he lived? … cursed him as a coward, yet it was his people who drove him away from me, although I told him he was breaking my heart. And so I lost both. A terrible punishment, but for my good in the summing up, perhaps. I didn't care anymore, and so I sank to the depths of ignominy, but my soul stood the test, remained pure, or I should never have had the courage to renounce and rise triumphantly to the heights of utter abnegation. Oh, I wonder whether Gerald would have risen too? But he was so earth-earthy, poor lad. No doubt it is harder for a man to develop his soul. He is so much more carnal than a woman. Who knows? – Gerald might be that bullock standing there looking at me so resentfully? I wonder why? No, Gerald, I'm afraid, would have been a bull, te he he! te he he!

Ah, I lapsed then in thought. That was that lamb chop I had yesterday. I told Mrs. Pinkworth that meat leads to evil thoughts. But she laughed and said she had nothing else to offer me. I should have refused, nevertheless. The proof is that I'm sure she still has evil thoughts even at her age. She has lots of photos about, and I'm certain that they were her lovers of whom she dreams. *That's* what comes of meat eating. She says that if she doesn't have her meat she feels poorly. Ah, she won't understand that that is merely a symptom of the stirring of the soul within her. She has not the moral strength to continue and so reach the heights. Yes, that must have been the lamb chop, for I noticed last night that my soul power had diminished. That was why I couldn't continue that astral picture. Oh, if people would only learn the truth, find the Light. If all people were vegetarians there would be no more wars. How right the Hindus are!

Oh, I'm so tired of France, but I haven't the courage to go back to England. They are all so material. And Paris is a horror, and I don't want to meet any of *them.* They have never developed as I have. The inner world is quite closed to every one of them. Yet a strange impulse has urged me for a long time to go to London to start that paper of which the world has such need. Yet has the moment come? I do not know. Tonight I'll try to find out what message that cow is attempting to communicate. Oh!

I had felt a male approaching from behind. I turned. Tallish, dark, with flecks of gray about a half-bald head. For a moment I don't recognize him. And I don't want to. But he insists:

"Why, Vee, who'd have dreamed of finding you here contemplating cows in a Normandy field? You always loathed the country."

"Why not?" I ask, sharply. I feel his eyes poring over my face, like a jeweler examining a watch. Why didn't I put on my veil? Oh, well, I know that my mouth is a network of wrinkles like a

withered apple, but still my figure isn't so bad. I haven't run to fat, and thick ankles.

"Well, well," he goes on, smiling in that way I always hated, "why, it's years since we met! I've often wondered what had become of you, Vee. What are you doing hiding in this hole?"

"What are you?" I retort.

"Oh, just motoring through. I saw your back silhouetted against the cows – I mean the sky, and thought that I recognized it. But I couldn't believe my eyes. 'Vee,' says I, 'in the country contemplating the beauties of rural nature and studying cows with enthusiasm – Oh, no, impossible!' But I couldn't resist finding out. Come, jump in my bus, and we'll go and have a drink for old times' sake?"

"No, thanks," I snap. "I never touch liquor."

"W – what?" the silly fool stutters. Then seeing that I am serious he adds, trying to stifle a laugh – Oh, I can see it! – "Well, let me run you back to the village anyhow. It's going to rain, as usual and – well, perhaps you'd like a cup of tea somewhere?"

"All right," I agree, sullenly, not seeing how I can well refuse.

We glide down the slope into the town, neither saying a word. I hate him glancing at me curiously like that, but I notice with pleasure that he's much balder and has quite a few white hairs. He isn't as well dressed as he used to be, either, and the car's a ramshackle old thing. He asks me where I want to go, but I don't know, as I scarcely ever go out anywhere.

"If you like," I reply, I don't know why, "you may have a cup of tea with me? I've some bread and butter."

"Topping!" he agrees, and I wonder if he means it. And then, pulling up before a pastry shop:

"I'll just get some tarts and things."

I rather like him for that, remembering that I always had a weakness for sweets.

"Where have you been all these years?" he inquires, as I direct him to my place.

"Oh – here."

"Years?" he repeats, annoyingly. "Why – what, still writing?"

"N-no," I say. "Not as I did, anyhow."

"Oh. Where did I last see you? Quite five years, isn't it?"

"More," I frown. I hate any reference to the past which reminds me too much of that life – I mean the life I want to forget. He doesn't say another word until I bring him into my rooms. He peers around impertinently at the divan-bed – Oh, I know the evil thought he's thinking! – the few books I've kept, and at pictures on the walls.

"Painting now?" he inquires.

"Yes," I admit, and go to the gas stove[125] to put on the kettle. He stands staring at the unframed canvasses, slowly passing

[125] On 30 October 1943, while suffering from gastroenteritis pain that she believed to be a symptom of cancer, Hastings killed herself by turning on the gas jets of her stove. According to Modigliani biographer Kenneth Wayne, she committed suicide in Worthing, Sussex, England on either October 30 or 31, 1943. Shortly afterward, Charles Beadle and Charles Goldring received a manuscript from Hastings' estate: an unpublished surrealist novella titled "Minnie Pinnikin," written by Hastings in French, which dramatizes her relationship with Modigliani. Wayne adds that the curator of the Museum of Modern Art, William S. Lieberman, was preparing for a 1951 exhibit of Modigliani's work "when he was put into contact with Goldring and Charles Beadle by the art historian Douglas Cooper" (the latter an intimate companion of art historian John Richardson). "Through them he obtained a copy of Minnie Pinnikin."

This is one of the last verifiable sightings that we have of Beadle before he disappears from the radar screen. (The information was transmitted by Lieberman to Wayne during a 2001 telephone conversation.) See Kenneth Wayne, *Modigliani and the Artists of Montparnasse*, New York: Harry S. Abrams, 2002, p. 205. Beadle's

from one to the other. Of course he doesn't understand a single one. I wonder what sarcastic remarks he will make. But he doesn't – not very.

"Curious," he says. "But I don't understand them."

"No, you wouldn't!" I retort.

"Have a cigarette?" he offers.

"I don't smoke," I inform him.

"Good Go – Sorry! Er – D'you mind if I do?"

"Oh, no, if you can't do without it," I tell him, contemptuously.

"Thanks," says he, and lights up. I turn crossly to prepare the tea. He sits in a carpet chair with his legs crossed, smoking placidly, but I'm certain he's laughing every time I turn my back. When I've put the tea tray on a small table besides him, he stubs his cigarette and says quietly:

"Now, Vee, don't be cross with me because I haven't changed, but tell me about yourself. I've often wondered what had become of you. What you've been doing and thinking all these years."

Years! Years! Why will the fool yap about years all the time? And as if I could tell him! He hasn't changed – as he says – just as material. Of course, it's different with a man.

"There's nothing to tell," I say, "I just live here."

"But haven't you any friends?" he asks, as if puzzled.

"Only a couple of old ladies who have scarcely enough to eat – you know, respectable poverty, poor dears – I go to tea with them sometimes and take them what I can to help."

"But what d'you do all the time?" he persists.

---

portrayal of Hastings as a figure who didn't exactly have her feet on the ground is echoed by Hastings' description of herself: "I was Minnie Pinnikin and thought everyone lived in a fairy land as I did." (Beatrice Hastings to Douglas Goldring, September 17, 1936, as quoted in Pierre Sichel, *Modigliani*, p. 265.

"Oh, just paint."

He glances up at a canvas.

"Explain what you are after, Vee."

I hesitate. I don't know how to explain because I fear he'll laugh. He was always so fond of laughing at people.

"You won't understand," I begin. "It's from the mind what you see there."

I know that that's an inadequate explanation, but his presence bothers me so that I can't think.

"Abstract? I see." He doesn't at all. "But d'you really see that – in your mind?"

"Yes."

"But what does it mean?"

"I don't know," I tell him. "How should I? That comes from the subconscious."

"Oh?" Yet he seems seriously interested. Perhaps he has had a change of heart after all. Who am I that I should scoff at another? In spite of my fears I begin to expound my art.

"You see – Well, I don't see that exactly myself – not consciously. When I paint, the guide takes control. I haven't the remotest *conscious* idea of what I'm going to paint. They're kind of replies to questions I ask the Infinite, you see. Oh, I can't understand myself," I tell him as I take down a canvas. "There, you see, that's a face, isn't it? a very handsome man with a beard of a rather Assyrian type, and here in the corner is another; and look at the curiously twisted lips without a face on the top of the strange column that resembles a Cleopatra's needle. Isn't that queer? And at the bottom there's the beginning of a word, an inscription in Latin, no doubt, but I can't make it out. The spirit is trying to tell me something in reply, but I'm not yet sufficiently advanced to comprehend. Can you see? That looks like a 'c' and then another 'c' after a space, and that's surely 'k,' isn't it?"

"What was the question you asked?" he inquires.

I look at him swiftly, but his face is quite serious. He really is interested.

"I asked the Infinite – which is the same thing as the subconscious – what it was that was most necessary for the good of my soul."

"Ah!" he says, and I don't like the tone. "But tell me, Vee, just how do you do it? Your way of working?"

"As I told you. It's simple enough – like all great things. You take a point on the canvas at random – or so it appears, for really it's guided, and then you surrender your hand and allow it to choose colors, and put them on where the guide indicates."

"Sort of automatic painting, instead of writing?" he suggests stupidly; but then of course, he *can't* understand.

"Yes – and no. Not such as those silly creatures who go in for planchettes,[126] table turning, spiritualism, and other benighted superstitions. You mustn't confound this with that ridiculous twaddle. I'm not yet an adept. One has to train for a long time – for years, and follow a diet strictly – no meat, nor farinaceous foods. Only a little fish, and vegetables."

"Sounds like a thinning cure," he says, glancing at my body.

There, I knew it was no use! I can see the shadow of his cynical smile just as he always had. If only he could see the light!

"How's your wife?" I ask him, sharply.

"Oh, topping, I believe, thanks."

"Is she with you now?"

"No jolly fear! She's up in Scotland with people. She's gone completely daffy on religion, and I've had to take legal

[126] "Planchette": A small triangular or heart-shaped board supported on casters at two points and a vertical pencil at a third and believed to produce automatic writing when lightly touched by the fingers.

proceedings to stop her from having my daughter's head stuffed with hellfire and chastity rot."[127]

"Perhaps you never understood her, Bill?" I reproach him.

"Oh, yes, I did, and do – too well! She was already inclined by nature that way – anemic and frigid. She always considered sex to be a sin after her fanatical people's teaching – and atavism, too, and now repressed sex has had its revenge – what she had of it – and has gone to her head. Very ordinary case, unfortunately. England's full of 'em. You never suffered from *that* in those days, Vee."

"I don't care to discuss the subject of sex," I tell him angrily, "and I never did."

"But Vee!" he exclaims, hypocritically.

I rise furiously. How dare he talk to me about sex! He's just like all men who think of nothing but *that!* I can feel by the way he looks at my body that he would if I gave him half a chance – if he still can. Oh, I know.

"Well," he says conciliatingly, "let me tell you about Paris. There's scarcely any of the old crowd left. Eddie – you remember Eddie and Belle? They're gone. Eddie died of consumption in Menton last year, and Belle – he divorced her four years ago, you know, and married a friend of hers, and just afterwards she took an overdose of morphine and died in her

[127] Beadle's wife Sylvia Hornsby died on 13 September 1915. Since this entire passage occurs at some point after Modigliani's death on 24 January 1920, the author is obviously fictionalizing the actual flow of events in his life. But since this is a tale replete with "time travel," such a blending and distortion of linear, chronological time is to be expected. Thus, *Dark Refuge* can be regarded as a fictionalized memoir, or as a confessionalist novel, but not as an actual memoir. Beadle's draft-registration card of 12 September 1918 notes that his "Nearest Relative" was his daughter Jane Beadle, then residing at 22 Gordon Road, Boscombe, a suburb of Bournemouth, England (while Beadle was living in San Francisco).

London flat. She'd gone back to the stage. Made an awful scandal as Eddie's name was dragged in. And Izzy's turned Catholic. Too funny for words. He met Jesus on the steps of the Butte after he had had an extra whack of hashish and cocaine. His Jesus was that drunken beggar who was always hanging around the Sacré-Coeur – don't you recollect him? By some real miracle Izzy had got hold of some quantity of cash, most of which he gave to his Jesus, who, of course, promptly got blind, but, by some drunken freak had himself shaved and bought a secondhand suit, so that Izzy didn't recognize him afterwards, and remained convinced that he really had met Jesus, arguing as proof that the beggar has disappeared as by a miracle."

Bill laughs vulgarly.

"I don't want to hear about any of them," I stop him.

"But, Cecci," he persists, "you've heard how he died of lung trouble and dope in the Charity Hospital? His portrait of you is in –"

"That doesn't interest me," I reply furiously – I don't quite know why. "He was just a sponging Italian Jew and had no talent whatever, nor – anything else. I – I never want to hear of him again – nor anyone else!"

Tears well in my eyes. I am conscious that something quickens in my veins and I loathe it. Bill is still virile, I can feel too, and – Oh, my face is a net of wrinkles! He has a few, too, but that doesn't matter with a man. Oh, damn him! Why did he come? Oh, how I wish he'd go. Oh, damn him, oh, God damn him! All this will upset my training and I shan't be able to concentrate for weeks. Oh, perhaps never again. I shall go away. I'll go back to England and start that paper. I've enough capital saved up now. I must find a refuge somewhere.

As I turn away to hide my eyes I catch a glimpse of him in a mirror. He is shaking his head with a whimsical smile. Oh,

curse him! Oh, I could kill him. Coming here to laugh at me! Why, why did I let him speak to me? But I turn and say icily:

"I'd rather you went, Bill, please."

"Well, Vee," says he, rising, "I'm awfully glad to have seen you again, but I'm just as sorry that my accidental visit seems to have annoyed you so."

I give him my hand, mechanically. I can't speak. He looks at me queerly and goes. I bang the door shut, and throw myself on the bed, sobbing, sobbing …

* * *

This experiment puzzled me more than ever. Had the dream been provoked by fears of losing her looks, old age, colored by her dabbling in Buddhism, Bahaism, and kindred isms? Yet myself entering on the scene was indeed most curious; not in the fact of my presence, as there was no valid reason why she should not dream about me as well as anybody else she had met; the uncanny quality lay in the statements myself had made to her regarding mutual friends who were still living; living in the world of my present ego. Prophetic? Such dismal fates might overtake the others – A trace of an atavistic superstition made me feel rather relieved that I was apparently still able to sit up and take nourishment; but I certainly could not see Vee metamorphosed as a nonsmoking, nondrinking vegetarian. Regarding my wife, yes, such a prophecy appeared to have a good chance of a lucky guess; for, in the present time plane, she was certainly heading for something of that sort. Then my musing stopped with a jerk. And that queer dream of Cecci and the deathbed scene, corroborated by what myself had reported in Vee's dream? Queer, I reflected, damn queer. Then the recollection of the crazy paintings and the Cleopatra's needle with what she imagined to be a Latin inscription, brought me a

laugh, and stirred the recovered hashish dream of the projection of the subconscious in the form of a naked black.[128] In a positive state of elation I darted back into the next room and attacked Izzy, who was still scribbling furiously as he smoked.

* * *

Izzy: I am on my knees, my eyes are closed. Mechanically my lips are muttering as I wonder how much that pig of a publisher has cheated me on my last volume of poems. Both the *Catholic World* and *The Truth* gave me a column apiece of praise – as they should do, considering that I paid them five hundred francs for each review. Vaguely I hear my own voice mumbling:

> "Agnus Dei, qui terns peccate mundi, misere!
> Nobis, Je-su!
> Jesu, audi nos!
> Jesu, exaudi nos! …"

But I never have trusted Father Antoine, my thoughts run on. He's Dufraine's friend and spiritual adviser, yes, and he is too worldly. How dare he, who is rotten with gluttony and lubricity, insinuate that I am guilty of avarice? He, who is always stuffing and guzzling in the houses of rich parishioners – Dufraine for example; – and yes, consoling their wives. O Jesus, forgive me for having evil thoughts! but all the world knows. And besides that, it was a mean trick to refer publicly to my life before I met Thee, Oh, Lord Redeemer.

> "Agnus Dei, audi nos!

[128] Unfortunately, the narrator is incapable of taking the next step: the realization that racism itself may have much to do with psychological projection.

Agnus Dei, exaucli nos!"

continue my lips to murmur.

Crossing myself devoutly as I rise I bow before the large crucifix upon the wall. Then I am startled by a halo of bright gold about the Divine brow. As I gaze upon those dolorous eyes I am drawn irresistibly towards Him. Humbly I kneel upon my hard cot. Simmering adoration boils into exultation, mounting like new wine to my head. Passionately I kiss the white, white feet. The very taste of blood from the cruel nails is on my lips. Reverently I take the crucifix in my arms to kiss each bloody hand, the suffering eyes, the thorn-pricked brow, that parched mouth from which fled words to save mankind. Would that I could cup my lips on every weal upon that knouted[129] back, the bruises on the shoulders martyred by the Holy Cross! The stained breast still reeks of the salty sweat of Thy agony. And Thy wound from the Roman spear is bittered by the vinegar. Thy beloved thighs are gritty yet with the dust of Gethsemane. Every member of my trembling body rises in adoration of this my Savior. With my body I Thee worship, O my invisible lover. A stifled cry is wrenched from my thirsty lips, "O sweet Jesus, I adore Thee!" as my libation spills.[130]

Sighing I sink down upon my cot exhausted. I can scarcely breathe. So strong has been the force of that puissant passion

[129] Knout: A flogging whip with a lash of leather thongs twisted with wire, used for punishing criminals.

[130] Given Jacob's sexual debauchery and homoerotic leanings, Beadle surely penned this phrase with tongue in cheek. In fact, this entire passage reeks of a barely veiled eroticism, especially as it climaxes with the phrase: "A stifled cry is wrenched from my thirsty lips, 'O sweet Jesus, I adore Thee!' as my libation spills" – reminiscent of the chronicles of certain medieval nuns whose "rapture" was clearly orgasmic in nature.

that all virtue has gone out of me, yet sweet content cradles me as my soul wanders mindless in the valley of heavenly solace. Then, as if from another world a sense of sin drifts upon me like a Paris fog.

"Mea culpa! but thou didst tempt me, O Lord!" I murmur reproachfully and, bending low my head, plunge into prayer. Calm now and sure of His all-compassionate understanding, I rise from the cot, cross myself, murmuring penitently:

> "Kyrie eleison![131]
> Christ eleison!"

and sit on the rush stool before my worktable. Idly I draw an album of press cuttings towards me and finger the pages. "Isidore Ginsberg – Isidore Ginsberg" leap at me like caresses. I cannot resist reading a blue-penciled cross heading:

ISIDORE GINSBERG: THE GENIUS OF THE MONK POET

Ah ah, they know who I am now! All those years of dark obscurity … Oh, what am I doing? Vanitas vanitatum. O Lord, forgive Thy servant. But oh, the fleshpots for which my wicked soul craves! Peccavi, O Lord, my Redeemer. Pardon Thy humble servitor, my Savior to whom I owe all. It is to Thee, O Lord Jesus, that I am indebted for these good things. Thou, who didst raise me from the ranks of the unknown to literary glory, teach me to spend Thy money in Thy good service – although brother François does exaggerate when he counsels me to double the percentage because my sales have gone up, little guessing how much I am robbed by these unbelieving philistines of publishers. Resolutely I thrust away the album.

[131] "Kyrie eleison": "Lord, have mercy."

Oh. I know that Father Antoine is right when he condemns, but – O Lord, I am so weak. Critically l reread my latest poem:

The priest who serves the Mass on Christmas Day,
You take him for the local curate? Nay!
He's one of God's own angels, that I say,
Who's not come here to beg, but praise and pray.

The Son of God has lost His Crown of Thorns.
He who finds it to Paradise shall go.
And for these words do not account them pawns.
Nor esteem them vain, as this tale will show:

Our Belayed Lord once did lose His Crown,
And a humble choir boy – if he was dense
He was as beautiful as Peter's pence –
Was led into the desert, and lay down

Of weariness, and lo! when he awoke
His pillow was the Crown. He did invoke
Psalms as he was drawn up into the skies.
But many faithful raised indignant cries
That such a brat should win such eulogies.

May all of those whom other fools begat,
Remember that God sometimes is like that.

That, I feel, is good and will certainly please the Superior as well as the devout readers of *The Tablet*. But again doubt arises regarding Dufraine. I cannot banish him from my thoughts. Is this a form of devil possession? I must ask Father Antoine. I

pick up Dufraine's letter with the check attached, and stare at it in anger. I am so sure he has cooked the accounts again.

There, I am sinning again. The Father Confessor will give me even more penitences – and I know he loves the excuse to do so. But I deserve them, Great Lord, I, a wicked sinner. Am I not always longing to eat more meat than is allowed – and tarts! I do so love tarts, although I am well aware that meat arouses the demon of lust. I must take more camphor so that I may sleep undisturbed by the Evil One's suggestions – but I do hate the taste of the rotten stuff, and the odor disgusts me. And quite lately I have been tortured with a hell-born desire for cocaine. That always happens after I have been out in the world on a lecture tour. Perhaps I should give that up for the love of our Savior? But then look at the money it brings in. Brother Francois would be furious should I be no longer able to give the same sacred oboli.

Devoutly I gaze at the Holy Face regarding me with such compassionate sympathy from the wall. Strange how the resemblance is more and more striking, indubitable, to Him whom I met on the steps of Montmartre, miserable infidel that I was. Surely indeed he was the Divine One. Yet why do doubts afflict me even as they did St Peter, wretched doubts that skulk in the side streets of my mind like a corner tradesman questing my passing? Yes, that is a good simile, for these doubts are of no more value than the wretched pennies I owe the grocer. Naturally those philistines mocked me. Was not Christ stoned? Yet why should they have scoffed, the unbelievers? Only a beggar he was, they jibed. But what matter that to the Son of God? Would He not rather manifest Himself in the guise of the humble and the meek than in that of a publican or a banker? No, no, I was not mistaken. Even Father Antoine is as convinced as I. A vision in a lifetime is vouchsafed to all who are worthy, said he. Never shall I forget that seraphic smile when He

proffered me His only coat, dirty and ragged though it was. No, no, I was not mistaken. What else but the spirit of Jesus could have moved him? And when, touched to the heart I, too, tended Him my overcoat, in truth in not much better a state than his, I was so stirred by the beauty of His face shining with righteousness that I kissed Him, and did He not instantly return that kiss upon my own lips? Ah, how divinely beautiful he was! I felt the sacred aura all about me, and so was I impelled to do as He had commanded – to give all that I had, reserving but a modicum for my own sustenance. Was not that money sent to tempt me to see whether I would make worthy use of it, whether I, the poor poet and despised Jew could, like Peter, deny Christ? Ah no! And was I not right? Have I not been paid a hundred-fold even as was written? No, no, my false friends that were, I pity you. I pray for you. But I cannot afford to love you any longer, stupid heads of calves! You laughed. Well, now it is for me to laugh. You shall be roasted in everlasting fires, and I shall compose verses in praise of God for all Eternity. But to work!

I slip my hand behind my neck under the hood and pull up the silk undervest which by special indulgence I am allowed to wear to avoid undue physical irritation when working for God. I begin to write:

> "Holy Virgin, only mother possible for our Lord,
> Honored both by marriage with, and maternity
> of God!
> Mother of Hope and Agony!
> Thy Divine Bowels which engendered the Son of
> God!
> Thy – "

I put down my pen dispiritedly. I have no inspiration this morning. That damned Dufraine haunts me. He must be an

emissary of the Devil. Oh, Great Lord, if only I had a sniff – just one. How I could write, chant Thy praises even better than ever I have! No, no, that is the Devil tempting me again. I had better go and meditate in the garden until the refectory bell …

* * *

Here again was a seeming confirmation of the story myself in Vee's dream had told her regarding the future of Izzy. Strange. Or was it nothing but an idea in my own mind popping up in various forms? Still, myself through Vee had also prophesied the death of Cecci which had been apparently corroborated by the deathbed scene. I began to doubt the dream hypothesis. Such coincidences might be possible, but highly improbable.[132] As I mused on this monk's curious experience the words of my naked nigger[133] of the subconscious floated: "sometimes we sublimate and sometimes we don't – we find other ways and means," and I smiled.

Here again I had found it as difficult to envisage Izzy as a monk as I had Vee as an ism fanatic. Vee had apparently, more or less successfully, sublimated into mysticism; but Izzy driven

[132] This entire passage is significant because now the protagonist / author steps beyond his usual Freudian interpretation of the unconscious to embrace a more transpersonal perspective of the psyche. The invocation of meaningful "coincidence" parallels Jung's thesis that the unconscious – when it's no longer able to integrate itself into consciousness through any other means – may trigger "synchronistic" phenomenon: acausal meaningful coincidence, which results in a transformative emotional experience. (Thus finding "other ways and means.") The theory of synchronicity was developed in the late 1920s or early 1930s, during Beadle's time in Paris.

[133] Since the "Bill" / Beadle protagonist is no longer speaking while in a state of anger, we may assume that he was accustomed to using this offensive term in a casual manner.

evidently by the flogging of the unsatisfied subconscious, had taken to "other ways and means," making the transfer from homosexuality to fetishism.[134] I wondered whether my flippant nigger was right in being sorry for those poor subs who were certainly out of luck. However, the poetical talent in both victims of life dodging had certainly deteriorated lamentably.

Speculating on what strange forebodings I should find among my friends, and quite humanly forgetting the existence of my omnipotent benefactor, I sped back to the studio and chose Francine:

* * *

Francine: I feel very tired and peevish. My back aches cruel, and my legs. The market bag is as heavy as a whole sack of potatoes as I climb wearily landing after landing.

"Cecile," I call sharply, pausing to get breath, to a gawky girl of fourteen following me, "I've forgotten the olive oil. You'd better go back and get some or your father will jaw me. Here's the money. Be quick, and don't loiter on the way. D'you hear?"

"Yes, Mama," she replies. She has the nasty squeaky voice of her father. She takes the two francs and the empty bottle from the bag. "And the tomatoes, Mama?"

"Oh, my God. I've forgotten those too! I don't know what's got into me this morning. Get half a pound, and see that they're not too ripe for salad, or he'll make a scene about that as well."

[134] Max Jacob was arrested by the Gestapo on 24 February 1944 and then held in the infamous Drancy internment camp, located in the northeast suburbs of Paris (where Jews were confined before being sent to extermination camps). On 5 March 1944, two days before being shipped to Auschwitz, Jacob died of pneumonia. His brother and sister were also arrested and deported to Auschwitz.

I drag my aching body up two more flights. As I fumble in the gloom of the landing at the door of the tiny flat, the quick step of a man sounds within, and a girl's voice cries: "There's Mama!"

The door is opened by a tall young fellow of eighteen, dark hair and big eyes, who greets me. He is well dressed, and looks like a bank clerk.

"Beel!" I exclaim joyfully and, forgetting my pains, take him in my arms and kiss him on both cheeks. I am a little hurt because he is cold, yet he has always been like that. He hates to show his feeling. He takes my bag and gives it to my youngest daughter of twelve, fair and blue eyed.

"Go into the kitchen, Madeleine," says Bill, "I want to talk to Mama."

Madeleine looks up at me questioningly, resenting the authoritative tone as always.

"Yes, yes," I tell her," do as Beel tells you. Have you got the hot water ready for the dishes? Well, hurry up and put it on."

We go into the living room. I am ashamed that it is in such disorder, but that morning my husband made such a scene about the coffee that didn't please him that I just had to lie down after he had gone. I wonder fearfully what makes my son look so serious, and a kind of panic takes me. He is so like his father, that short, sharp way of speaking when he is upset about anything.

"Sit down, Mama," he says. "he won't be back till noon, will he?"

I glance at him, startled. For years he has always referred to my husband as "he," a curious trick I thought, but now he seems to say it in such an alarming manner.

"No, but – What is it, Beel? You look –"

"I've news, Mama. Lots. First of all I've passed my matric."

"Oh, Beel dearest!" I exclaim delightedly, although I've never quite understood what that means exactly, but I know he has wanted to have it for a long time. As I take him in my arms again he accepts my kisses just as coldly.

"Yes, yes, Mama, but listen," he says. "There's more news than that. I'm not going into Maître Chenol's office –"

"What! But, my dearest," I protest, "you won't refuse such a wonderful offer so kindly made you to enter a notary's office, and –"

"You don't understand, Mama," he explains with that impatient way of his. "It isn't wonderful. There I can never rise higher than a chief clerk as I shall never have enough money to buy a practice. Besides, I don't wish to go. I'm going to write."

"Write!" I repeat in startled dismay. "But what?"

"There's no 'but what' Mama, I've already begun. There!" Triumphantly he flicks onto the table a folded newspaper. "There's my first article."

I stare at a column marked with a red pencil and at the bottom the name "Bill."

"What's it about?" I inquire, confusedly.

"Never mind, you wouldn't understand, Mama," he states.

That *is* a stab. Just [as] his father so often said.

"Oh," I murmur," but you've forgotten your surname, my son."

"No, I haven't. I don't like it," he says, rather hardly, and adds, more softly: "A writer may take any name he likes, Mama. And it's just that that I want to talk to you about." He looks at me queerly. My heart flutters. "I've known for a long time that 'he' isn't my father – thank God! Who is?"

"Who – who told you that?" I gasp, choking with shame and dismay.

"Oh, I've guessed that since I was a child. And once when you were having a scene, 'he' referred to me as 'that little bastard of

yours.' I never forgot. Besides, I've always felt that I was different. I hate him and he hates me, and always has. Don't cry, Mama. I'm a man now, and I can understand. I love you still, Mama, and always shall. That's why I hate him, for he beats you. Oh, I've seen it hundreds of times. But now, it's only just that I should know who my real father was – and where he is?"

"I don't know, my poor son," I reply, sobbing.

"But who was he?" he insists cruelly.

"A writer," I mumble.

"Ah!" The cry is of joy. "That's why! Tell me quickly, who was he?"

"Beel Far-daire," I tell him. I never could pronounce Beel's name.[135]

"Bill? That is why you called me that? I see. That means 'William' in English. I have studied much, Mama. Already I can read a lot of English, yes. The tongue of my father! And I did not know. That is funny all the same. Don't cry, Mama. I am very, very glad. You have seen him since?"

"N – no. He went back to England to his wife and daughter," I admit, reluctantly, I don't know why.

"Ah, so I have an English half-sister. What is she like?"

"I don't know," I confess. "I only saw the mother once – she was awful, oh, a fright with horse teeth and big feet and a mouth all twisted up like an old apple. She was a religious maniac and made poor Beel's – you father's life terrible. He always said so. Ah, he loved me my son."

"You've never heard from him since?" demands my son, scowling.

[135] Thus we learn that this Beel / Bill is the illegitimate son of the narrator Bill Farder. Since Beadle enjoyed playing with the phonetic rendering of words, one can easily imagine him coining this surname (Farder) based on its phonetic similarity to "father."

"Yes, he sent money – money for you – to go to school properly – and to college –"

"So that's why 'he' married you," exclaims young Bill savagely. "To get all the money out of you."

"He didn't!" I cry proudly, through my tears. "He wanted to, and that's why he hates you, and me too. We married under the 'separation of goods,'[136] and he had only a little to get him a good job. You had always enough for your education, my son, for Beel was always generous."

That is too much for me, and I burst into sobs again.

"Don't, Mama, don't cry!" pleads my son, as he tries to soothe me.

"Oh, great God, how I wish I had never married him, you can't understand, my little one. But what could I do with you alone in life? And if you hadn't a father in name what would the world say? Oh! Oh! Oh!"

My son jumps up and takes me in his arms, and kisses me on the forehead, the first time I have ever known him to do a thing like that.

"Don't, Mama," he whispers, "I love you always. But I've got to get on. I shall take my own father's name, and you'll see in a few years I'll be rich and famous, and take you and the children away. There, there! Does Maître Chenol know the truth?"

"Yes, your father sent the money through Maître Chenol."

"Ah! he has a good nature, Mama. That's why he has been interested in me. He understands that – that I'm different. He knows I can write, too. He's encouraged me a lot, and given me letters to people. I've got to go to lunch with him today to meet this editor of a paper who is a friend of his. I'll tell him that I

[136] In France, under the *séparation de biens* agreement, property owned at the time of the marriage as well as property acquired during the marriage (for example, through a gift or inheritance) remains owned by the person who purchased it or who acquired it.

know all. Mama dearest, I can never come here again while 'he's' here, you understand that? But you and the children will come to see me often. It's better that I know everything. I feel much stronger now, Mama."

I glance up through my tears. As my son bends down to kiss me he is the image of his father, even to the faintly mocking smile. I sob harder than ever. I hear the front door slam and his feet rapidly descending the stairs.

"Beel! O Beel!" I murmur, and wonder where he is, and what he is doing, and what he looks like now? Then I recollect my household duties that never cease. As I rise I catch a glimpse of my reflection in the mirror over the fireplace. Ah, my hair is graying! I have two chins and many wrinkles around my eyes. And the lithe figure that Beel so loved is swallowed by big drooping breasts and a bulging belly. Even my slender blue-veined hands which Beel raved about are red-jointed and swollen with washing and work to bring up five children. A-ah! he wouldn't love me now, Beel, who was so delicate and finicky. Oh my God! what a fool I've been. Yet it was Beel who paid for the operation to have my womb put right so that I could bear children. God, he never dreamed why I wanted that to be done, the fool. Oh, if I hadn't I shouldn't have had all these brats by – yet then I shouldn't either have become a respectable woman.

The flat door opens. Cecile comes in with the salad oil and tomatoes.

"What's the matter, Mama?" she asks, staring at me.

"Nothing," I tell her. "Go and help Madeleine. I'll come and get lunch ready in a minute."

Mechanically, I wipe my eyes and begin to arrange my hair. Then I let fall my hands. "What's the use now?" I mutter. I pick up the paper my son has left on the table with the red pencil mark over his first article. My pride spurts. My own son a writer

like Beel, *our* son! How Beel would laugh, and say something funny that he didn't really mean. I must hide the paper to read after "he" has gone back to the office. Then from the next page leaps at me a name. I gasp:

WILLIAM FARDER translated from the English by …

Beel! A story by Beel! His writing, which he would never be bothered to translate to me because he said I wouldn't understand, in the same paper as his own son! I forget everything. I begin to read the story. My daughters call and I reply vaguely: "In a moment, my darlings." I read on and on. "It's true, it's true," I mutter savagely. Beel always said that I wouldn't understand even if I could read his work. It's true. I cannot comprehend what he is talking about. Why – Oh, my God!

The flat door opens. In struts my husband. I stare at him, appalled that I have forgotten completely my duties. He glances at me with his silly blue eyes and at the unlaid table. His large belly seems to swell with anger as he snarls:

"Huh, that's all you've got to do, you lazy slut, read cheap serials? And when I come home there's nothing to eat. I slave all day and you can't even run the house. Oh, I know that that little bastard of a son of yours has been gossiping about me. The concierge tipped me off. I've forbidden you to see the little pig, and if I catch him here I'll wring his pretentious neck, the illegitimate son of a tramp, or God knows who."

"You, you little shrimp!" I scream at him. "Why, he'd pull down your pants and spank you like a child."

"That's enough, hold your jaw, you cow, or I'll –"

"You'll what? Sit down in that chair and shut up while I get something to fill your garbage can of a belly, or I'll slap you

myself with these hands that are worn out making food for you all these years, you little abortion!"

"That's what comes of marrying a cast-off whore," he sneers.

"You – you – what would you have been," I stutter, "but for me? Who gave you the money to procure a situation with the water and gas company? Go away!" I shriek at the two girls standing in the doorway of the kitchen watching, as usual, the scene.

I feel as if I were going mad as I glare at him. I could kill him as he sits there.

"You try to strike me," I tell him, trembling with rage, "and I'll lay you out with a chair, and that will be a job for M'sieu le Commissaire de police, I promise you ..."

* * *

I had never had the slightest inkling of Francine's matrimonial intentions. After I had left her and she had announced that she was enceinte, I had considered the fact due to carelessness. But here again was an incredible lapse of time – nigh twenty years. The boy couldn't actually be more than ten, since it was just a decade since we had separated. More than ever puzzled I opted to investigate Eddie's "future":

* * *

Eddie: I am lying in a chaise longue on a sunny terrace overlooking the sea. Every now and again I am racked by spasms of coughing, but they are much less since I left London. In a few months I shall be as right a trivet [137] again. Oh, damnation, that blasted cough shakes my whole body, and – Oh, there's blood on my handkerchief once more. I must hide

[137] "Trivet": A three-legged stand.

that, for if Dulcie sees it she gets so upset. The darling thinks it's my lungs. It isn't. It's just tiny blood vessels ruptured by the damned cough. That doctor in London frightened her, the idiot. I've always had a weak chest, I know very well. So had mater, but that doesn't necessarily mean that I'm a lunger. Good Lord, I could never have lived as long as I have done if I were. That filthy fog in London is enough to make anyone cough. I've a touch of bronchitis, that's all. The mater had too, frequently, but she didn't die until she was over seventy. Oh, hell again! It certainly does knock blazes out of one. Or are the night sweats the cause? Even Dulcie's hair gets sopped with it. Disgusting, but the darling never says a word. If the fools would only give me something that could soothe and stop it, I'd be quite all right. It's all jolly rubbish treating me as a lunger. Why, no lunger would have the virility that I have. Dulcie knows that, and any man who could satisfy her can't be a lunger, by God! I start to laugh and break into a cough. I swear furiously. I must have something to stop it. It's just a quarter to twelve, and Dulcie said she wouldn't be back from Nice until half past. I call for the maid.

She comes dancing like a nymph. She is really pretty, Milanese blond. I'm sure she must have a lovely body. She would make a wonderful party girl if she were trained, and Italian superstitions kissed out of her. Dulcie remarked that when she engaged her, but now she pretends that I'm too feeble. As soon as this weakness passes I'll break her in, by God! I'm certain she's got a lovely pussy, just like Belle's – a coral anemone within a golden chrysanthemum, as Bill once said. Clever chap, Bill. Wonder what's become of him? Somehow one loses all one's friends these days. Everybody's too lazy to write, I suppose, and you get out of touch. Ah, poor Belle, to think that all that beauty has rotted away long ago! God, death is horrible.

Tears well in my eyes. Quickly I wipe them away as the girl comes up.

"Pauline," I tell her, caressing a knee, "run swiftly before the mistress comes back, and get me that half decanter of brandy hidden in the buffet behind a pile of plates. I saw my wife put it there."

"Oh, but mossieu," she says, deliciously with her quaint Italian accent, laughing and showing her adorable teeth, "has had his allowance, and the mistress told me –"

"Don't be ridiculous, my beauty," I retort, slipping a few francs into her hand. "I'm feeling extra bad this morning, and I need it. It stops this horrible cough for a bit. When I'm better I'll kiss you until you faint. Run along!"

Pauline comes back laughing, not with the decanter but a glass half full of brandy. She has the cheek to tell me that I mustn't have any more now.

Impertinent little bitch! But you can't be really angry with Pauline, she's so damned lovely as she stands there laughing at me defiantly, her lips like ripe plums. I swig the lot. The liquor races through my veins, and immediately a threatening spasm of coughing passes. I feel perfectly splendid and sitting up, grab Pauline around the waist and kiss her. She turns her face away and struggles. She is too strong for me and wriggles away, giggling. She likes it, the wench. Oh, if I weren't so damned weak. I'd like to stroll around – fetch the rest of the decanter the little witch won't bring me. Ah! I'm not so strong as I thought I was. Cursing, I lie back.

Idly I watch Pauline dodging about the house. She's very lovely and lithe, and as healthy as a sand flea! A queer idea comes into my head. I should like to have a child by Pauline. If she had a child I could legally adopt it, I suppose. Don't see why Dulcie should object. When I married her she promised to have a baby as she knew that I simply must have one to con-

tinue the family, and she's never been able to do the trick – just like poor Belle. I've been jolly unlucky that way. So was Belle for that matter, and she tried so hard, poor darling. Even Bill couldn't, which proved that it was not my fault. Quaint, I shouldn't have minded if Bill had given her a baby. It would have been healthy anyhow, and might have had some brains, for Belle hadn't got any, and I haven't much, I know. After all, the child is the thing. One shouldn't be too selfish about it. Poor Belle, how I hated to divorce her. I still think that she wouldn't have been so crazy about the stage if I had told her the real reason about the child question. And now Dulcie can't, or won't, have one, damn it! The idea of everything going to that stinker of a brother of mine and his beastly flea-bitten wife makes me positively ill. I think she has always counted on my pegging out early because of my cough and what she calls a loose life, the uncivilized bitch with a troop of brats! That's all she married Bertie for, the silly ass, on the chance of his coming into the title some day. She'll be an old hag, even if she and Bertie do outlive me. And by God, I'll fool 'em! If Dulcie won't get herself vetted I'll take on Pauline whether she likes it or not, and not for party purposes, either. She's peasant stock, but that won't do any harm. In fact, fresh blood is needed in the family. Bertie's no bally[138] Hercules and the cubs he's thrown aren't too good. By God, that's a really topping idea. I'm sure Pauline would be only too jolly glad, and her parents wouldn't object if I fix them for life. Oh, what wouldn't I give to see a spunky little fellow running around, and know that he was mine. That desire's been gnawing for years. And then he'd go to Ludlow in his turn. Oh, Lord, that's true. The bastardy law![139] H'm. Well,

[138] "Bally" (British): Euphemism for "bloody."

[139] "Bastardy, as a legal term, designates the civil condition of a child born under illegitimate circumstances. Under English common law, children born out of lawful wedlock were classed as bastards. In the

Dulcie will have to pretend he's hers – and Pauline can be the wet nurse. Yes, that's the idea. Then they can't squeal about the illegitimate business. But I'd have to keep that low, for if Master Bertie got hold of the truth – Quaint, how I always used to be jealous of Bill that at any rate he had a daughter, even if his wife was a rotter.[140] I should like to meet Bill again. He was one of the few men I ever did really love. He had a beautiful body and I loved the smell and taste of him. His fluid tasted like salted almonds. What was that that he said? Oh yes, that people were like flowers. Some perfumes are agreeable, and not others. That's true. I adore violets, but the scent of lilies makes me sick. Quaint! I recollect wishing that I were a woman so that I could have a child by Bill. God, what a sire and a dam for a foal![141] That wasn't a bad idea of his either – One ought to be a perfect hermaphrodite, so's one could have a child by oneself. I laugh at the idea as I did then. Difficult operation, as I had pointed out. "Not at all," says Bill, "you could inject your own sperm into your own womb by means of a syringe." Wonderful lad was Bill. I miss him a lot. I've never read anything about him, so I suppose he never did succeed. Don't wonder. His bally books always bored me. And I remember once when I admitted it – oh, he said that he knew that they did, and replied that unlike Oliver Gold-somebody,[142] he wrote like a fool and talked like an angel. Damned witty, Bill, always inventing things. Oh, damn that cough! There's a ring at the gate on the other side of the

---

eyes of the law they had no parents, no kindred, and no ancestors." William S. Powell, ed., *Encyclopedia of North Carolina*, 2006.

[140] "Rotter" (chiefly British): A thoroughly objectionable person.

[141] A horse racing expression: A sire is the father of a racehorse; the dam is the mother.

[142] A reference to Oliver Goldsmith (1728 – 1774), an Anglo-Irish novelist, playwright, and poet.

villa. As I am wondering who it can be Pauline comes very demure, and presents a card on a platter:

Colonel Sir Brandon Thorpe Bart.

For a moment I can't think who – Why, Thorpe Primus, whom I haven't seen for fifteen years! Where was it? Oh, passing through Paris. As he strides across the terrace I scarcely recognize him. He's filled out dreadfully – prosperous flesh, beefy necked and a corporation like an alderman! And he was such a handsome lad in those days. He, too, stares as if puzzled.

"Hullo, Eddie," says he, "damned if I'd have recognized you, old boy! You look like hell – Oh, I barged into Soames Butt in Monte and he told me that you were here a – a bit under the weather, he said. Thought I'd drop in for a cocktail. But, I say, you do look run down, old boy. What's the matter? Too much booze and women, what?"

"Oh, no," I say, rather annoyed. "Beastly London weather and a touch of bronchitis. Sit down, my dear chap. The wife's out, but – Pauline!" I call, "Pauline!"

I tell her to bring me cocktails and a small table, a bit apprehensive that she may refuse as she's so damned cheeky. However, she obeys, and deftly mixes cocktails after the fashion Dulcie has taught her, roguishly watching my old pal.

"Well, where on earth have you been all these years?" I ask Thorpe Primus.

"Oh, India, China, and the Soudan after the war, but I sent in my papers as the wife got fed up with trotting around, and the kids were growing up, and after the governor's death we could afford to splash around a bit."

"Then you're married?" I exclaim, somehow astonished.

"Rather! Nearly fifteen years now, old boy. Why, yes, just after we met in Paris. But you are too, they tell me?"

"Oh, yes," I admit. "Twice. The first was a mistake. Charming child, but we couldn't get along together. She took to dope, you know, and that with a woman – and she always exaggerated. A little while afterwards she croaked that way. The papers got hold of it, of course, and tried to drag me in, but we'd been divorced years. Poor Belle!"

Again, at the recollection of her a sob rises in my throat. I snatch at my cocktail to drown it, but somehow the liquor goes the wrong way and starts a spasm of coughing which brings blood. I hide that skillfully from Thorpe, who is watching me with a rummy expression.

"You've got a hell of a nasty cough," he remarks, stupidly.

"Oh, that's nothing," I insist. "I'm heaps better since I've been down here in the sun. Another six months and I'll be as fit as anything. My Lord," I laugh, glancing at his rubicund face, "who ever dreamed of you turning into a country squire! You'll end your days reading the *Times* in a Club window."

"End *my* days!" says he, resentfully. Then he looks at me queerly again: "Funny, you always were a delicate lad Eddie, and you certainly were a beautiful boy. I hate to see you all tuckered up like this."

I think his remark is offensive. He's beginning to annoy me. He's utterly lost the athletic proportions that he once had. Looks the pompous army colonel, such as I loathe. I wonder how I could have loved this man.

"You must meet the missus," he says, after a pause, "when you're feeling chippier, and see the boy when he comes over for the summer holidays. Young Brandy's rising twelve, and he goes to Ludlow next term, and he'll be in Syme's, you bet. Lord, it makes a fellow young again."

Beastly bad taste. I wish the chap would go. Yet when he rises, I say, perfunctorily:

"What's the hurry, old boy? Stay to lunch. The wife will be back in a jiffy."

"Sorry I can't now," says he. "I've got the missus and a couple of kid daughters in the old bus, and we're due to lunch at Roquebrune. But I'll run over and have tiffin[143] in a day or so, and we'll have a chat over old times, what? I'll bring the missus too, if you like, and she can pal up with yours, eh?"

"If you like," I say, listlessly, but really I never want to see Thorpe Primus again. I feel dispirited and disappointed.

"Don't bother, old boy," he says, as I try to rise, loathing my weakness. "I'll find my way out. Cheerio!"

I positively hate him as he strides from the terrace and trips lightly down the steps into the garden. I seize the gin decanter and swig a glass to stop that beastly feeling of feebleness that's coming on again. Just then, of course, Dulcie appears in the open doors of the dining room, and comes flying to me.

"Oh, Eddie darling!" she exclaims, placing a hand on my head. "I told you you mustn't, and now you've got fever."

"Oh, I don't care," I say fretfully. "That's the only thing that makes me feel better."

The horrible sensation grows until my very life seems slithering out of my body.

"Dulcie," I plead, fondling her hand, "for God's sake give me another shot. Oh, if only I had a sniff."

She looks at me rummily, rather like Thorp Primus, and then bursts into tears, holding me tightly in her arms …

* * *

Poor Eddie! was my first reaction on emerging from this dismal experience. But of course, I corrected myself instantly; the emotion was nonsensical. Only a couple of years ago I had

143 "Tiffin" (British): A light midday meal.

stayed with Eddie and his new wife, Dulcie, in Austria with her people. That macabre touch was surely the nightmare quality of a dream. Yet – I did recall from personal knowledge that Eddie had had sweats at night which were indeed most unpleasant. Association naturally suggested the death scene of Cecci; and I remarked for the first time that that strange fungoid growth I had detected in Cecci's brain chamber I had also noticed in Eddie's. Was that a symptom of tuberculosis?

Also this experiment had corroborated once more the accidental death of Belle from an overdose of drug, which myself had reported to Vee, as well as Eddie's death at Mentone. Curious too, was the reapparition of Thorpe Primus whom personally I had never met; he who had been the principal figure in Eddie's dream of adolescence. Now surely, I mused, my subconscious, blackly clever as he was, couldn't have invented Thorpe so rationally, for subby was after all limited to my personal experience in life. Yet was he? Had he not proudly boasted that "he" was imagination?[144] Anyhow, the inference of my vision of Eddie was disturbing; seemed to be shattering to my dream hypothesis. Still, there was not yet enough data on which to construct a new theory. Wondering whether I should again find this seemingly supernatural prophetic quality in Belle, I hastened to mount into her brain box and seek the same mysterious contraption.

* * *

Belle: Eyes, thousands of eyes popping out of darkness; and rows of glimmers, and up in the sky pallid things like gray bats. I hear my own voice fluttering like a caged bird somewhere

[144] Once again, the narrator is wondering if the unconscious may possess a transpersonal quality.

above my head. A vast noise, resembling rain on a roof, seems to drown the orchestra. I stand smiling idiotically.

"Bow! Bow!" whispers a fierce voice from the prompt.

I bow and back away, bowing. The roof seems falling on my head. I want to run to save myself. As I reach the wings a hand pushes me forward again. Vaguely I comprehend what I'm expected to do. I know what it all means, but I can't think what. Mechanically, I walk in front and bow, grinning convulsively. The hail storm is louder than ever. A white front gleams before me. Huge baskets of flowers weave. Out of the row a word reaches me. "Encore! Encore!" I hear low whispers from the wings. I am still grinning and bowing like a marionette. People rush all about me. The orchestra seems to beat back the hail storm which dies away. A terrible nerve shock starts at the base of my neck and rushes down my spine. The flesh underneath the paint on my cheeks feels like cold chalk.

"Sing, you bloody idiot, sing!" whispers the prompt again.

By an effort I recognize the refrain and pick it up, automatically making the gesture I have been taught:

> "And when he said I love you
> I clean forgot the pain!
> Now that I have found him
> I know love was not in vain!"

Again the last note of my voice seems to jump about funnily over my head, as the thousands of eyes goggle at me, and the gray bat things flop vaguely. Dragging one of the baskets of flowers I stagger backwards. The roof begins to fall again. Dimly I recognize the curtain descending which shuts me off into another world. I clutch at a girl's shoulder as another shock shakes me, gripping my stomach, too.

"What's the matter, Belle?" she asks, holding me up by the waist.

"Quick, quick!" I murmur. "Get me to my room! I've waited too long."

The house is still roaring.

"Take another curtain!" a man's voice commands.

"I can't! I can't!" I moan. "Take me away!"

A vague crowd is congratulating me, but I don't care. I feel too bad. My legs collapse. I want to be sick. Someone picks me up and carries me bodily to my dressing room. There seem to be hundreds of people there.

"Go away! Oh, do go away!" I gasp as I am put on the couch. "Maggy, for God's sake make them go away!"

It seems hours before my dresser drives them out, for they all chatter and try to kiss me, and I can't stand it. And they want to give me brandy and champagne and put wet bandages on my head. But that's not what I need.

"Quick, Maggy," I whisper. "The needle! Oh, quick! I hadn't time for another in the entr'acte."

Again the shock comes on, starting on the back of my neck. My stomach contracts. I want to retch. Oh, God, I feel awful – as if I were dying. At last the door shuts.

Maggy loads a syringe skillfully. Pulling up my drawers I plunge the needle into my thigh, press home the piston, and lie back exhausted by the effort. Oh heavens, what relief, as the stuff goes through my body. I stretch happily.

"You silly child," says Maggy. "You've left the needle sticking in you. Why, you might have broken it inside your flesh, and then God knows what a mess to get it out."

"I don't care," I mutter blissfully, as she rubs the spot with iodine and pulls down my skirt. Oh, but I begin to feel good again.

"Would you like a drink, dearie?" Maggy asks, pouring out a brandy.

"I'll say I would," I exclaim, sitting up laughing. "My God, that gave me a turn, Maggy. I really thought I was passing out."

"What on earth did you do, dearie?" queries Maggy, handing me the glass of brandy.

"Oh, I was just silly. I –" I gulp down the brandy. I had forgotten for the moment thoughts that always upset me. "Oh, I'd got the jitters. Smythe Price got up stage and told me if I didn't put more pep into it I'd get the bird, so I took a double shot. But I couldn't get another in time, and the beastly muck ran out on me, I suppose. How did I go?"

"Go!" echoes Maggy. "You brought the house down, dearie. Smythe Price says he always knew you had it in you."

"Liar!" I say, smiling. "Funny, too. I scarcely remember anything about it. After the wheel song I went all blurry. What did I do?"

"Do, dearie? You danced like a mad Pavlova and sang like a Tetrazzini![145] I never knew you had such a voice. You drove the house crazy wild. You usually funk top notes, but this time you were a regular bloody nightingale, my word!"

"Funny," I remark, after finishing the brandy. "All I could see was hundreds of his eyes – looking at me –"

"Whose, dearie?"

"Eddie's. Oh, nothing. You don't know," I add, quickly. "Who's that?" as somebody bangs on the door.

"Oh, the crowd. Feel good enough to see 'em, dearie?"

"Rather!" I exclaim, jumping off the couch. "I'm sitting up and taking nourishment once more. Half a tick."

[145] Anna Pavlovna Pavlova (1881 – 1931): A Russian prima ballerina who performed with the Imperial Russian Ballet and the Ballets Russes of Sergei Diaghilev. Luisa Tetrazzini (1871 – 1940): A world renowned Italian coloratura soprano.

I fix my nose and lips and eyes before a glass.

"Now let 'em all come!" I laugh gaily.

Maggy opens the door. There's Smythe Price grinning his fat head off, and a bunch behind him.

"You're God's good lil girl," he announces, and snatching me in his arms sticks his scrubby moustaches against my face. "You've got 'em wild. Always knew you had it in you, my dear. Come, get dressed and we'll go to supper somewhere and talk cold turkey!"

"Belle! Belle!" shout voices behind him, excitedly. They crowd in, loading the room with flowers. A large woman gone fat, who sang a duet with me, barges through them and kisses me on the cheek.

"I knew you'd do it, darling," she pants.

"Thanks, dear," I say, knowing that she's a damned liar and would rather bite me.

A half-bald thin man grabs and kisses my hand.

"Congrats, ole thing. My night tonight, isn't it, sweetheart? We'll celebrate with bags of fizz, eh?"

"All right," I reply. "But you'll have to put up with Price. Biz. Twig?"[146]

"Oh, I suppose so, I've always got to put up with someone," he grumbles. "But he can't grouse now, what?"

"No," and I add seriously: "But, Ferdie, I am glad really that you'll get back yours. You were a brick to stand by me."

"Oh, don't talk bosh, childie. It wouldn't have mattered if you hadn't. You ought to know that."

"Don't be silly, Ferdie," I tell him, and kiss him on the nose. "Now be a good boy, and run away. I'll be ready in half an hour. Go away everybody!" I cry laughing, and shoo them from the room.

[146] "Twig": To understand the meaning of: comprehend.

I slump back on the couch, remembering other things. I know that at last I've made a howling success, but I don't care a damn unless –"

"What's the matter dearie?" inquires Maggy, who is undressing me.

"Nothing," I deny. "Just thinking. Isn't there a wire, or a letter?"

"No, dearie, only the ones you had."

"Give me another brandy."

She mixes me one and I lie back after drinking some, waiting for her to fix things. I recall the scene during those awful moments of success – those countless eyes – Eddie's eyes, they had seemed. Why? I hate thinking of him. I have been so busy trying to forget, and now this beastly success! I don't want success. Tomorrow my photos will be all over London. Price will offer me a thumping contract, the movie people will be after me, and – I don't care a damn about anything. Why, oh, why was I such a fool as to leave him? It was just the beastly smell of the theater that got into my silly head. And all those bloody fools who fill you up with fizz and flowers. Eddie hated them. Uncivilized, he used to say.

Funny too, how Eddie hated publicity. He was so cross that night in the Pigalle when I got tight and told a horrid old woman that after all I was a marquise. Bad form, I recollect, Eddie said. And I was so sick afterwards. "Oh all right, Maggy." I give her my face to go on taking off the grease paint. Funny, too, I *do* like the smell of it, and the feel as well. Still, I was a silly little fool to give up Eddie like that. Then when he fell for that blonde Australian or Aus – Austrian – I never knew which – I didn't care. I liked her too, in many ways. She had a wonderful body, and I loved her taste. We had so many wonderful parties together. Not like Betty, of course. I've never loved a woman as I adored Betty. Oh, Betty, where are you? Why don't you reply?

Even on this first night success you haven't even bothered to come to see my triumph. You are a rotter, Betty. After all these years the only one I've got is you, now.

Dulcie *was* a cat! I should have known what she was after – just his title and money, and she hoped he would not live long. That's where she was wrong. He wasn't strong and always had a cough, but Eddie wasn't a lunger. He couldn't have been so sexy had he been. She knew he didn't want me to leave him, but she pretended that she understood how I felt about it, and talked a lot of poppycock about the Glamour of the Footlights and how a real artist couldn't live without it. Christ, as if I really cared!

Still, it wasn't really and truly the stage that made me go. If it had only been that, Eddie would never have let me leave him, but I always knew that he wanted to have a child to carry on the title and things, and after the doctor examined me and said that I never should be able to have one, Eddie asked whether I couldn't have an operation; but again the doctor said No, and explained that I was underdeveloped – like a child. After that I could feel that Eddie changed, although he always tried to hide his disappointment. I think the only thing that always made him furious was the idea that things would go to his brother whom he hated – a mean, half-witted, uncivilized cub, he always called him, and said his sister-in-law was only fit to do the washing. I think Dulcie must have played up to that, too. I wonder if she's had a child by him now, the cat. Eddie might write sometimes all the same, but I'll bet it's Dulcie who stops him. I remember her saying something about it being better to break off for good, and finish with it. And yet I did like her, damn her!

Ah, at first I thought that it was Eddie's fault, but afterwards he insisted that it couldn't be, that it must be mine, for otherwise Bill would have done the trick, for I never took any

precautions. Funny, Eddie never, never got angry with me about anything. I do believe that if Bill had put me in the family way Eddie would have accepted the child as his. Oh yes, it's my fault, because you couldn't imagine that Bill was incapable of giving any woman a child. And Eddie was very, very fond of Bill, that's true. Once when he was caressing him while Bill was having me, he said laughing that he was jealous, not of Bill but of me, that he wished that he was a woman so that Bill could give him a baby; and I remember we started to talk about what kind of a child it would be. And then Francine got mad because she couldn't understand what we were talking about, and when Eddie translated – Oh, how she glared at him as if she could kill him! Queer, too, when Bill had me, I often did really wish the doctor was wrong, and that Bill would put me up, just to prove to Eddie that it was his fault; and besides, I would rather have had a baby by Bill, as I should have felt more certain that it would be a boy. Funny, I never thought of that before, but I do believe now that I loved Eddie more as I did a woman – Betty, for instance. It doesn't seem the same as loving a man, more tender and – and closer to you somehow. He seemed to kiss and caress more like a woman. Ah, if only I had been able to have a baby by either one I shouldn't have thought such nonsense about the stage, and – and then *this* wouldn't have happened, for Eddie was always so frightfully particular about who we invited to a party like that.

And that swine, whoever he was! But really it was an awful party. We were all so mixed up, and I was so tight and full of dope that I couldn't recall next day who was there. Just the date, too, so it must have been then, and since there's been nobody except Tony and Reggie, and they both swear they haven't, and offer to have a medical exam. Oh, God! I may have given it to them both. I'm glad I told, though, because now they can take something to stop it in time, if I have. That's the worst of it – as

the doctor said, I ought to have come to him before to be treated, but then how was I to know anything about it as it was right deep inside me, and nothing hurt, or itched, until I began to wonder, what those queer spots were. Oh, that damned, bloody, delicious muck that makes you feel so good and happy that you don't know, and don't care, where you are, or who it is.

"All right, Maggy," I murmur, and obediently get up and go through the motions mechanically as she dresses me.

Then as she goes away to fetch something I draw down my undies and glance at the stains on one side of my belly. Yes, they're much paler and the swellings in my groin have already gone down. But that's what the doctor said – it goes away almost instantly with iodide of potassium, and the mercury really cures you after two years. I drop my underskirt hurriedly as Maggy comes back. What would she say if she had seen? She'd probably refuse to touch me and scream all over the place. Two years! But all doctors kid you along. That girl whatshername told me the mercury made her lose all her teeth and hair as well. My gums are sore already, and I know that years afterwards the microbe thing attacks your brain and you go mad. No, I'm done. That's why I really don't care anymore what happens. I could never go back to Eddie – nor anybody else. And Ferdie is just crazy about me, as he thinks I'm virtuous. But Christ! I couldn't be such a rotter as to let him when I was like that. Funny, if I had though he wouldn't have put up a penny to back me! He'd have put me down as a little whore. He's that kind of fool who thinks about women like that.

O-oh! I'm beginning to feel flabby again. I don't want to go to that damned supper and talk biz with Smythe Price, and look at Ferdie's longing eyes. If only Betty would reply I shouldn't feel so bad. I'd sense I had someone here with me. Oh, I've got the blues. Even mother turned against me again when I was no

longer a marquise, said I was a little fool, and that she didn't blame Eddie for not wanting a wife who sold her body to the public gaze. Just the same old stuff as before I ran away from home. But all forgiven when I married a marquis. Christ, what would she say now? My success would mean nothing to her. Her daughter on the stage and going straight to hell, and so on. Oh, she makes me sick. She *is* a rotter. All she thinks of is her silly social position, what the neighbors will say. After all, she was only a clerk's daughter, and father was the son of a boot maker until he started a factory. Oh, they make me tired, these snobs. How mother used to make me laugh yapping about her daughter who was a marquise. And now she wouldn't help me if I were starving.

Funny, the effect is just trickling out of me, but that shot ought to last a couple of hours! Oh, if I'd never given up hashish and taken to this beastly heroin. Hashish does not knock hell out of you as this muck does, but then you can't *act* under hashish – you need complete quiet and no noise. I wonder if Maggy's been playing any funny tricks. She's a dear old idiot, but she doesn't quite understand.

"All right, Maggy," I say, as a hammering comes on the door. "Let 'em wait!" and I add sharply: "Did you monkey with that last shot?"

"No, ma'am," she says, and then I know she's lying when she says "ma'am" instead of "dearie."

"All right. But I need another."

"Oh, Miss Belle!" she squawks.

"Oh, Miss Nothing," I exclaim. "Give me the syringe, and I'll do it myself. I can't go in this state and talk contracts with that Price swine. I feel like a dead cat."

"But ma'am, there – there ain't any more. You never take more than two at night, and this evening you've had three."

"I know I did," I retort, furiously, "and if I hadn't I shouldn't have had a success. There! Why on earth didn't you have the gumption to put a tablet to dissolve? How much did you give me in the last shot? Tell the truth now!"

"Half," she replies sulkily. "You're taking far too much, Miss Belle."

"What's that got to do with you?" I demand, angrily. That's why I'm going to pieces already. I should have just collapsed in the restaurant. You're an old fool, Maggy," I add, affectionately, for she is fond of me, I know. "Without *that* I shouldn't have any of the charm, the gaiety, the idiots talk about. Don't you know that? Why, look, tonight I was doped to the eyes, and didn't know what I was doing, and I've never had such a success. Lots of *us* are that way."

"None as ever I knew," replies Maggy, sourly. "Drink maybe, but never that stuff."

"Oh, hell, I haven't got time now so I'll have to take it raw, and that always upsets my stomach. Damn you, Maggy!"

"But I only meant it for your good, dearie," retorts Maggy softening.

"You silly old fool," I reply. "I know you did, but you don't understand what you're monkeying with." I peck her on the, snatching up my bag, take out a box of tablets. "Water, please, Maggy," I cry. "No, brandy. I need a kick to carry me over."

Maggy hastily fills a glass with brandy and water. I gulp a tabloid.

"You look lovelier than ever tonight, dearie," says Maggy, trying to butter me.

"Oh, go to hell!" I exclaim, suddenly irritable. I shall have to wait, as the effect of the damned stuff isn't as quick by the mouth as by the needle. The brandy helps a little, though. A knock comes on the door. Maggy opens. The porter hands a

letter, saying something about the boy having forgotten to bring it up.

"Oh!"

I recognize Betty's handwriting. She hasn't forgotten, bless her. Already I feel better, joyful. I put down the box of tablets to tear open the envelope.

Darling,

So sorry, but I can't. It's such a long time since we met, isn't it? and life's so jolly swift, and such lots of people in it, aren't there? It's difficult to remember everybody, isn't it? Besides, I'm frightfully gone on a new couple I met lately, so I'm sure you'll understand. You tell me you've gone back on the stage again. Splendid! I'm certain you'll have a ripping success! although I can't quite recollect which one you are, but I'm sure you'll understand.

Cheerio! Betty.

"Oh, the cat! Oh, the swine!" I gasp.

"What's the matter, dearie?" queries Maggy.

"Oh, nothing. Shut up!"

Betty turns me down! That's the last straw. I sink down on a chair, my eyes welling with tears. Oh, it's unbelievable. "I can't quite recollect which one you are." Betty! Oh, God, Betty! I can't stand that. But I mustn't cry. I'll ruin my makeup. I don't care – nothing, anymore. Hell!

"Maggy, give me another brandy, and a stiff one, and don't argue. Quick, oh quick!"

"O, don't take on like that, dearie," says Maggy, pouring out the brandy. "No one ain't worth it. And you do look tragic, my word."

I am staring straight ahead of me. I don't see anything, and my head seems simply whirling without any meaning. "Nothing, nothing," it keeps on saying. The tears well again to my eyes. But I mustn't.

"Christ!" I mutter. "Betty!"

I take the glass of brandy. Then why not? Nothing means anything anymore. No Eddie – no Betty. And I'm done, anyway. Why go on?

I grab the open box of heroin tablets on the table and empty the three that remain into the glass, and drink the lot. I glance at Maggy as I do so. She hasn't noticed, for her back is turned. I jump to my feet, laughing. Maggy turns.

"Feelin' better, dearie?" she inquires, tenderly.

"Rather!" I say, joyously. "Just top-hole.[147] Night-nightie. I'm off."

I rush from the dressing room down the dismal corridors to the stage door. Smythe Price and Ferdie are both waiting for me with more flowers, the fools. I feel madly gay. Laughing, I dance on the pavement before the car, and sing my successful refrain:

> And when he said I love you
> I clean forget the pain!
> Now that I have found him
> I know love was not in vain!

"Oh, you darling," bleats Ferdie.

"She's in great form," exclaims Price.

[147] "Top-hole" (chiefly British): Excellent, first-class.

A fit of laughter takes me. I laugh, laugh, laugh! The funny faces, the chauffeur, the cheering idiots on the curb, Ferdie, with his silly moustaches, Smythe Price and his long, bulby nose! Oh, ha! ha! ha! ha!

My legs crumple … Eddie! … Betty! …

* * *

Here was overwhelming evidence apparently of the other indirect reports of Belle's death, slightly different in substance, as reports usually are to facts, for Belle had undoubtedly committed suicide. Such interlocking of coincidences, I reflected, really couldn't have been invented by the most ingenious and mischievous subconsciousness.[148] There must be some prophetic verity about this infernal contrivance. Pros and cons seething in my own mind, I attacked that of Volodia who was lying inert with his head upon Georgette's bosom.

* * *

Volodia: My nerves are tingling as if each one had a separate end. My hands and feet quiver and jump. My stomach is contracted, and the muscles sore from trying to retch. The flesh beneath the skin feels as if it were frozen. My nostrils are quivering, around my mouth is a tense prickling, my eyelids and the nerves below the temples feel like knotted strings. My toes are sore, and the socks blood-soaked from the continual spasmodic twitching. Another spasm starts at the base of my neck, runs down my spine, and shoots out through my limbs as if about to tear my body to pieces.

[148] On page 294 of *Witch-Doctors*, the protagonist muses about a type of "coincidence" that "sometimes seems to have a telepathic basis as explanation."

I moan as I watch a big man with shoulders like a gorilla. He has a bald head and a round unshaven face as greeny gray as his huge belly, partially sticking through his open, filthy dressing gown. In one shaking hand he is holding an opium pipe, and with the other is raking irritatedly with a piece of wire. Then he drops the wire on the bed, and violently taps the mouth of the pipe on the palm of the other hand. Some dark stuff rolls out, which he claps to his lips as a famished ape a nut. Again he agitates the pipe, and beats it furiously. A little more dross rolls out:

"Hermann," I plead, in German, "for the love of Christ, give me a little!"

He grimaces derisively, and pops the remnants of the dross +into his mouth. Then picking up the wire, he starts again feverishly to rake.

Groaning with pain, and aching for relief, I turn my head on the greasy pillows without slips to avoid seeing him. In the light of a stub of a candle on a table is a jumble of things; an opium-cooking lamp, needles, a broken hypodermic syringe, cigarette stubs, dead matches, a mess of ashes. On the dirty blankets of the bed are two open books, a check book, and a filthy sock, full of holes. Another truckle divan is covered with piles of books, and others are scattered on the floor littered with papers and empty beer bottles. On a large table are dirty plates, stacked scraps of bread, and a soiled shirt. On another smaller table is a single-ring gas stove, which is boiling a kettle of water. A belching sound makes me look around. Hermann is sucking noisily at the pipe.

"Hermann," I implore, "for the Holy Virgin, give me just one suck! I'm dying."

But he squeals with rage as he plucks the pipe from his mouth, and stamps on the floor.

"There isn't any more," he snarls, "and what I had isn't enough to nourish a baby." He laughs shrilly, as if that were a great joke.

"The tea," I whimper. "The water's boiling. Try that!"

"Pink Jesus!"[149] he swears, "I'd forgotten that."

He gallops like a clumsy elephant across to the gas stove, bends down to get the tea out of the cupboard, and puts the pipe on the floor. I watch him anxiously, fearful that he will upset the hot water. He grunts and blasphemes to himself as he looks for the teapot. Then he slips the packet of tea into the pocket of his dressing gown, and goes on his knees, accidentally kicking away the pipe. He finds the pot, gets up, and stares stupidly at the boiling kettle.

"Where's the Goddamned tea?" he bawls like a child. "Oh, I can't find the tea."

"In your pocket," I shout as loudly as I can.

He fumbles for it, empties some into the pot, spills some, and drops the bag. Then he tilts the kettle and pours boiling water on his wrist. With a howl he lets go the pot which crashes. Instantly he forgets the pain and, going on his knees, frantically tries to pick up the pieces.

"Help! Help! Volodia" he squalls, half crying.

Clinging to the bed I drag myself along and then, on all fours, crawl towards him. I collect the spilt tea and the bag, somehow hoist myself onto my feet, and throw it into a handy coffeepot full of dregs – but that doesn't matter. Then holding one wrist with the other hand I contrive to pour in the boiling water. But another spasm seizes me, and centers in the pit of the stomach. Moaning, I just manage to reach the bed, and collapse.

Hermann is still stupidly trying to collect the bits of crockery ware, mumbling and swearing as he drops each one to pick up another.

[149] British slang for heroin.

"The tea! On the table!" I scream at him as soon as I can. "For love of the Holy Virgin, rinse the pipe! I'm dying!"

He hears, abandons his silly efforts, and clambers up, looking about as if he were blind.

"Where's the pipe?" he whimpers. "What have I done with the blasted pipe? You've stolen it, you lousy thief! Where's my pipe?"

"On the floor where you put it, you brute," I tell him. "There! No – at your feet!"

The spasm passes. I try to stretch and sit up. The sweat of agony on my face and body feels icy. Ah, he sees it, the fool! As he bends to get it, he bangs his head against the table. But he doesn't seem to feel, and grabs the pipe. Ah! the dross he stole is taking effect. His hands are nearly steady, and his face less green. "Quick! Quick!" I whisper. The vent of the pipe is plugged with a cork. He pours in the hot tea without slopping much and, covering the mouthpiece with a hand, shakes violently. Then raising the pipe to his lips he begins to gulp the lot.

"Give me some, Hermann, please! Holy Virgin, give me some," I plead. But he takes no notice, and again fills the pipe. Although I am still shaking with jitters, I drag myself from the bed as he once more raises the pipe to his lips.

"Hermann!" I scream. "Hermann, leave me some, leave me some!"

But he goes on noisily gulping. I shriek with anxiety, and clutch at an arm. With the other hand he gives me a push that sends me onto my back on a heap of dirty clothes and books in a corner. I lie cursing as I watch him drain and suck every drop. I.

He chucks the pipe onto the table, straightens up, and sighs heavily with relief. Then he sits on the bed, takes out a crumpled cigarette from the pocket of his dressing-gown, and

begins to giggle as he lights it. I peer at him through my fingers as I cry, wishing that somehow I could kill the great brute.

Oh, to think what a fool I was to believe that swine when he promised to get my violin out of pawn. And that's eight months ago. And I thought that he had money. Why, even then he was starting to pawn his watch and things to pay me for the dope, and he was always going to get cash, but never has done. Says he can't get money out of Austria, but what's he going to do then? The electricity is cut off, they won't give any more credit for food, and he can't even pay the charwoman to clean up the place. But he doesn't care as long as he can get another shot. Just look at the giggling fool. All he wants to do is to sniff, or stick dope into him, and lie and smoke opium and read. Rotten muck. And I've got to slave to cook pills for him. Oh, the swine hound! Convulsively, my hands twitch. There's a broken knife under the table. I wonder if I could steal up to him and plunge it into his elephant back? That would teach him to giggle when I'm suffering.

But still what could I have done? It seemed better to stay with him than to go on peddling dope. They'd got me marked and would have pinched me sooner or later, just as Georgette said. She'll get nabbed too, if she doesn't look out. Still, it's easier for a girl to get by, fat as she is, there's some of them that like 'em that way. Oh, the swine, if he'd only pay me the five hundred he owes me for dope. And they won't trust me now for a single gram if I were dying. And the beast, he didn't even appreciate my beautiful body. He's as good as dead that one, no use to a boy or a girl.

Oh, Jesus Mary, why did I take her diamonds? It's no use, I can't resist, but then they don't understand that I merely want to play to them. Not even Theodosia. Oh, but how I wish now that I had taken the other jewels as well. I could have sold them, and kept the earrings to play to instead of having them stolen,

and they wouldn't have done anything more to me than they did. Oh, oh, to think of aristocratic and wealthy people, and nice baths, and silk underclothes. Oh, but they're all alike, the dirty bourgeois. If you touch anything that is theirs they scream for the police. Materialists! True, Theodosia wasn't as bad as those rotten Vienna women. She didn't have me locked up. Just refused to allow me to enter the house again. But it wasn't that that wounded me; she broke my heart because she so utterly failed to understand that I must have jewels to inspire me, to play to. That was what hurt me the most. And that rotter Max. When I met him in the street he just smiled and told me I was a guttersnipe, and to consider that I was lucky that Madame was a great lady and had been very chic to me. Oh, Jesus Mary, there is Hermann giggling again. Oh, if I had the strength to kill him! Oh God, what's that? I start convulsively in fright. I hear heavy footsteps in the corridor. The police? Hermann's giggle turns into a grunt. He rolls off the bed and, picking up the tray with the opium lamp and needles and things, throws all of them into the middle of the blanket, bundles it up and shoves it under the bed – as if the dicks would never think of looking there, the great fool! Then he snatches a book and flings himself on the bed, and pretends to be reading. He's mad.

"Did you hear that, Volodia?" he whispers, with goggling eyes.

The footsteps are still advancing up the corridor. But I remember that it is a long one, and that lots of people live in the line of studios. Yet I am still trembling with fright. Then Hermann, his thick lips grimacing, gets up and waddles in his bare, dirty feet across to the door to listen. Suddenly he makes a ponderous jump for the table, snatches up a meat hatchet lying among the debris, and then tries to shrink his huge body into the corner behind the door. His small eyes glare like a madman. I can see his fat knees wobbling. The footsteps advance. He

utters a choking cry, drops the hatchet, runs back to the bed, and seizes a book.

"If you give me away," he growls, "I'll kill you."

Oh, curse him, he's a rotten coward, and he isn't suffering as I am after drinking every drop of the dross. I want to rush to the door to open it for the police, but I dare not move. He'd kill me before I could reach them. Then I hear a key rattling in a lock. Oh, of course, it's our next-door neighbor. Still, I sigh with relief, and that great poltroon he grins, and begins to giggle happily again. Another spasm comes on. I cry out with the pain of it. The nerves beside my eyes feel like two E strings about to snap; there is something in my head, too, that is about to burst. I shall go mad if it continues. I hope I shall, and kill him, the giggling idiot.

"Now, cry baby," he jeers, "get up and go and get a couple of grams, and then we'll be all right!"

"Give me some money, then?" I whisper.

"Money, hell," he growls. "Just tell your pimp that I'll have a check at the bank on Monday and then I'll pay him double. Now get a move on, you snipe."

"He won't," I reply. "You've said that fifty times. It's no good, because I let him down promising the five hundred you said you would give me!"

"Oh, you lousy little bastard, you've got no courage," he snarls, "get a move on! That stuff won't last another hour, and I've got to have another. Go and see your girlfriend who gave you the diamonds."

"I daren't, and she won't see me," I say. "And what's that got to do with you, anyhow?"

"You will," he insists. "Go and telephone. Tell her you're dying, and if she won't, just let her know that you'll inform the police. She'd look pretty during a raid on one of her Friday-to-

Tuesday parties. She'll cough up for fear of a newspaper scandal. Now get!"

"She's too rich and – and well known – a great lady," I retort. "You can't get that sort. The police would just pinch me."

"Well, that don't matter as long as you get some cash to get the stuff with. I tell you, you little snipe, that I've got to have it. Anyway, if you are pinched, I'll get you out as soon as my money comes."

"Your money!" I scream at him. "I could get what we need now if you hadn't let me down every time, and –"

"Are you going or not?"

Hermann heaves his great body off the bed. His small eyes are like a mad pig's. Ponderously he goes to the door, picks up the hatchet, and comes over to me. I shrink back among the clothes and books. I know he's going to kill me.

"Go on, you great big cur, murder me!" I shriek at him, "but give me the money you owe me."

He stands above me goggling. His dressing gown is open, and I can see his dirty, hairy thighs, and around his lips is smeared the dross extract he had been sucking from the pipe, curse him! Even, there's a blob on his fat nose.

"Go on! Go on!" he repeats, stupidly, waving the hatchet.

"You touch me!" I scream, pretending to pull a knife from under me, "and I'll kill you!"

"Ooooh!" he roars, and the great coward jumps backwards. Then suddenly he lets out a howl like a big baby and, throwing the hatchet across the room staggers to the table, snatches up the pipe, pours some of the cooling tea, and sucks again. But I know that there isn't anything worth having, so I don't care. Then he chucks the pipe on the floor, smearing more dregs upon his mouth with the back of his hand, and crashes heavily on the bed.

Now the icy feeling begins to crawl all over me. My nerves make my limbs start convulsively, which I cannot stop. As I shake and moan in agony, I notice that the stub of candle is burning out. There isn't another. I shall suffer and die in the dark. Hard edges of books I am lying on, and as I move to try to make my twitching body less uncomfortable, I drag something for my head. It is a waistcoat. A wild hope rushes. Hermann always loses everything, forgets everything. Perhaps? I peep through my fingers. No, he isn't watching me. He is lying down smoking another cigarette, fumbling with a book close to the candle. He seems to have forgotten again. He's always like that. Mad. So much the better. Cautiously I pull down the waistcoat, and go through the pockets. Nothing. But as I grope in the last one I feel something that crackles. Then I recall that Hermann has a pocket made inside the vest to carry money in. My trembling fingers plunge in, and draw out a packet. Wrapped in a fifty franc note are two packets of cocaine! Oh, Beloved Mary! I glance up swiftly. He still seems to be reading. Stealthily I slip the note and one packet into a pocket. Crouching, I open the other. But my hands are too shaky to tilt some of the powder into the crook of my thumb and forefinger, and I can't wait. I push my nose down and sniff, once with each nostril.

A-ah! What a relief! Instantly the effect commences. I am so taken with the heavenly solace from suffering that I forget everything. As I sigh, a roar like a bull sounds. Hermann has seen. In his bare feet he thunders towards me. I recoil. He snatches the packet from my hand. The powder spills. With a growl like a wild beast he seizes me by an arm and hurls me across the room. I lie where I have fallen, stupefied with the pleasure of the soothing effect of the drug, watching him on all fours with his face to the floor, snuffing and snorting like a pig. But I don't care. I don't care [about] anything. Life is flowing

back into my veins, my nerves are relaxing, and I have fifty francs and a packet of cocaine. I am free!

His white swine face all covered with cocaine on top of the opium smears, Hermann clambers up heavily onto his feet, licking his fingers, and giggling with content. I will wait, I think cunningly, until he lies down, and then slip out into the street. Free!

God! I start convulsively at a loud hammering on the door. I hear the voice of the police shouting to open. As I start to my feet Hermann utters an oath, runs for the bed, and pitches right onto his head. Again comes the impatient banging, and an angry voice. I hesitate, trembling with fright as I stare at the motionless form of Hermann who, in his pig greed, has taken too much. I can't think what I should do. A heavy boot kicks the door. At the second blow the cheap lock gives. Three dicks in plain clothes rush into the studio. One seizes me, and another stands over Hermann.

"Search him," says a third man.

I know that I am lost. Instantly he finds the packet of cocaine and the note for fifty francs – pieces of conviction for having sold the dope to Hermann.

"Come on," says my captor, brutally dragging me by an arm, "we've been looking for you these months."

"Get an ambulance and take the carcass off to the hospital," I hear the chief order …

* * *

Although I came out of this strange trance feeling positively ill and jittery after the sufferings I had experienced in the form of

Volodia,[150] I was relieved that he had not ended as tragically as poor Eddie and Belle! Indeed such painful periods must have been for him fairly frequent; logical and inevitable to his mode of living. The indirect reference to Theodosia, the "girlfriend" in Herman's vocabulary, stirred a curiosity to know how he had parted from her; presumably a victim of his passion for "borrowing" jewels. I then tapped the last member of the group, Georgette:

* * *

Georgette: "I didn't order the supper," I am exclaiming, furiously. "It's not my fault that my friend decamped."

"Who is your friend?" demands the manager, standing between two indignant waiters. "I met him in the Café de Paris[151] and he invited me to supper, said he had a private income, and offered me a flat and told a long yarn about having lost all the money he had on him [at] the Casino, and if I'd pay he'd cash a check as soon as the bank opened, and when I said I couldn't as I hadn't had any luck lately, he made faces, pretended that he was taken short, and borrowed five francs for the lavatory, and I sat here like a pumpkin waiting for him to come back."

"It's a put-up job," says a waiter, excitedly. "She's done the same trick in Cannes."

"She's a dope peddler, too," adds the other. "I saw her slip him a packet."

[150] The narrator not only witnesses events and shares the thoughts of his subjects; he also feels their emotions as he merges with their identity.

[151] "Café de Paris": A chic Belle Époque-style restaurant located in Monte Carlo, founded in 1868.

"It wasn't!" I deny angrily." That was the five francs I handed him, the thief, the last I've got, name of God! Besides, if I'd sold him stuff I'd have money, wouldn't I?"

"That's enough," says the manager, gruffly. "You can tell that to M'sieu le Commissaire de police. Tonio, fetch a policeman."

"The boy has already gone," replies a waiter, vindictively.

"Oh, don't please!" I exclaim, terrified, thinking of the morphine and syringe in my bag, and if they find that I'm lost, even if it is only for my own use. I look around the restaurant wildly, still hoping sillily that the blackguard may come back. Then I see walking alone towards the exit a tallish, slightly bald man with big eyes.

"Beel! Beel!" I cry, starting up.

He turns.

"That's a gentleman I know," I tell the manager, almost choking as I watch anxiously whether he will recognize me. Men are like that sometimes, but thanks to God he has no woman with him. "He's an old friend! Beel!"

"Great God, I'm saved!" I mutter piously, as he smiles and comes towards me. A policeman in a cocked hat appears. The manager begins to speak with him.

"Beel!" I call, desperately. "I'm in an awful mess. Save me!"

"What's the matter?" he inquires in that queer, cold English way he always had, glancing at the manager, the policeman and the waiters. But he understands everything instantly. He was always chic, Beel!

"That's all right," he tells the manager in his grand way. "This lady is a friend of mine. Give us another bottle of Veuve Clicquot."[152]

[152] "Veuve Clicquot": A quality champagne produced by the House of Veuve Clicquot Ponsardin. (In 1775 they invented rosé champagne; the company also created the first riddling rack.)

The manager bows and smirks, and the policeman turns away disappointedly.

"Well, Georgette," says Beel, proffering a cigarette as he sits beside me, "what are you doing at Monte?"

"Oh, I don't know," I say, embarrassedly. "I – just for the season –"

"And Volodia?" he inquires.

"Oh, Volodia – you don't know? He's dead, poor soul!"

"Ah?" says Beel, calmly. "The needle, I suppose?"

"Yes. He – we separated – just after you left the studio," I explain. "He got too bad to play anymore. Couldn't, as he had sold his fiddle. He took to peddling, and then somehow he got

---

In a footnote on page 53 of Jeanne Modigliani's *Amedeo Modigliani: une biographie*, Paris: Olbia, 1998 (authored by Modi's daughter), Beadle is described as "an impecunious and battered Englishman who had lived in Montmartre for a great many years." (And *Artist Quarter* is characterized as being based upon unfounded "gossip" that was "assembled" by Beadle and then "collated" by Douglas Goldring.) However, in this passage of *Dark Refuge*, Beadle is presented as a well-heeled gentleman.

At this point in his life the money may have been coming, at least in part, from Beadle's wife, Sylvia Hornsby, who is portrayed here as being still alive. When she died in Cannes on 13 September 1915 at the age of twenty-four, she left behind a substantial estate of £8355, willed to both Beadle and the English artist Walter Edward Penn (Penn died in WWI). The following year, on 30 October 1916, Beadle embarked from Cadiz, Spain, arriving in New York on 14 November. He remained in the States till the end of 1919, successfully pursuing his pulp fiction career. But his funds may have eventually run out, or have been reduced, as a result of post-WWI inflation and the Great Depression. In another passage in *Dark Refuge*, when the protagonist encounters Vee toward the end of her life, she takes delight in describing his shabby car and down-at-heel persona: "He isn't as well dressed as he used to be, either, and the car's a ramshackle old thing."

hold of a boyfriend who looked after him for a year or more, but the police raided them and found the stuff on Volodia, and somehow the boyfriend – an Austrian, he told me – got away. Bought himself off, I heard, but they pinched Volodia and passed him by the tobacco[153] – tortured him, you know – and wouldn't give him a shot, to make him blab all he knew, and he denounced me. Then the dope squad picked me up. Thank the good God, I had time to rush into the water closet and throw away the syringe and stuff, but they dragged me off to confront Volodia in prison, poor little devil. He'd gone all yellowish and looked like a dead monkey, and he was so jittery that he could scarcely stand up, and couldn't do anything but cry and cry and shake all over, and he was so awful that I forgave him everything, although I was wetting myself with fright, thinking that they'd never let me out. But Volodia didn't recognize me – he couldn't, poor darling, recognize anybody, although I never knew whether he did, or pretended that he didn't to help me. But that saved me, for they hadn't any pieces of conviction which, as you know, Beel, they must have; but they were swine, for they tried to get me on another count that I wasn't registered, but I never really did the streets, you know that, Beel, although one must live, and anyhow I was flush at the time having just got rid of a good packet, and anyhow the dick took a fancy to me, and came home instead, and so that was all right. But, oh, I had an awful scare, and that's why I cleared out of Paris and have been down here ever since, for they're much easier on the coast."

"All these years?" inquires Beel. "How long ago is that? Nearly five, isn't it, Georgette?"

"I suppose so," I say, hating him for talking about years, for I know too well I'm not as young as I was, and neither is he, but

[153] *Passage à tabac*: The torturing of detainees, by beating them savagely. A tactic often used by police and military forces.

still – "Oh, I've been back several times, and I was in Algeria for nearly two years with – with friends, and after –"

"Where did you first meet Volodia?" he interrupts, sharply.

"Oh, a long time ago in a cafe in Montmartre," I tell him, and I laugh and drink some more champagne, glad that he is so interested in me. "You know, Beel, I took him for a sucker. Wasn't that droll? He was so chic – Oh, swagger clothes and well fed, he looked as if he was stinking with money. I'd only got started – I mean, I'd just come to Paris from Dijon, you know I'm a Burgundian, Beel. My father was in the post office and mother died when I was a child, and he married again, and my step-mother was a cow, and –"

"Yes, yes," says Beel, impatiently, just as he always was, "but go on with the story."

"Oh, but Beel, you'd have liked me then for I was slender, and just the kind you like, and if only I'd met you – instead of Francine –"

"Never mind Francine," says Beel rudely, pouring out more champagne.

"Don't be cross, Beel," I tell him, pouting, for I want to please him, because you never know. "Well, Volodia was at a table by himself in dress clothes and he looked so chic, and I could see by his eyes that he was like that, and that he wanted some, so I gave a sign and he replied and had me over to his table. Immediately he asked if I had any on me; I told him a packet was a hundred and slipped him one, thinking that it was all right, and he went straight off to the lavatory to take a sniff. But while he was gone I asked the waiter who he was and got an awful shock, for he said that he was only the violinist who played for his meal and twenty francs. Oh, I was angry, but when he came back he was so charming and handsome that I just couldn't be mad any longer – I liked 'em young in those days! – and he played so beautifully that I was quite gone on

him, and didn't even ask him for the hundred francs. Well, we got chummy and afterwards he told me that he hadn't a penny except what he earned in the café, and had been crazy for some coke. He said he had been working for some very rich people who had suddenly kicked him out into the street with no money and only his violin and what he stood up in, because a lover of hers was jealous of him, and that because he had played in lots of important concerts he had got this job at starvation wages. But, of course, I didn't believe the story about the jealous lover, and when I asked him why they really had shown him the door he didn't reply, saying only that they were a lot of cows, and women were always like that. When he had left he had had only twenty francs, and you can't buy dope with that and he asked if he could sleep in my place; so I said 'Yes,' as I had a lovely flat then, Beel, – you should have seen it –"

"Yes, yes," says Beel, irritatedly. "Shall we have another bottle? Go on."

"Well, he was droll, that one, I thought, and I took him up to my flat, and we had some stuff together, and then suddenly he said that he'd play for me alone, and pulled out two great diamond earrings and put them on the chimney piece, and started to play staring at them as if he were dotty. I hadn't seen so many daft ones then, and I was scared, as I thought that he was really crazy. But when he'd finished playing and I asked him where he had got the jewels from, he said that they were presents from the woman who had employed him, which of course I didn't believe, but I said 'My God, they're worth lots of money! Why don't you sell them and buy clothes and everything you need? Look at the dope you could buy. I know someone –' But he laughed at me and said I was a fool and didn't understand, that he'd rather die than sell them, that they were his art, and a lot of daffy stuff like that."

"He'd stolen them, then?" interrupts Beel.

"Of course he had. Rich ladies don't give diamonds like that away, what do you think, and then chuck the man out in the street."

"H'm," says Beel, "so that's where Belle's diamond ring and Francine's, and Eddie's fancy cigarette case went. We never suspected Volodia. We'd always put it down to the concierge's daughter."

"Well, after that I started thinking, and he went to bed, but he was no good. Just like a great baby that only wanted to be kissed, you know, but somehow he got over me. I felt as if he were a child who needed a mother's protection, but in the morning when I started at him about the diamonds he was just more crazy than ever, and wouldn't hear of selling them, but all the same he calmly proposed to go on living with me. I said he could, but the next time he was asleep I lifted his precious stones and sold them for three thousand francs. Oh, he nearly went mad, and cried and howled and sobbed when he found out that they were gone. I had to nurse him and kiss him for hours before he would stop, whining that he couldn't play anymore, and that he wanted to die. But I never let him know that I had taken them, and made him believe that somebody must have come into the flat when I was away and he was under the stuff. Oh, I was honest, Beel. I never took a penny for myself. He lived for months with me and had everything he wanted – even he wouldn't go out and play anymore because he hadn't his silly diamonds. Then I had an offer to go away to the Côte d'Azur and I had to leave Volodia in the flat alone, and do you know what he did? Why, he sold every stick to get dope, and when I got back he wasn't there, and I never saw him again until just before you found him, and he'd pawned his violin and was starving. I was pretty broke myself then, but I couldn't let him down, could I, to sleep in the street, so then I told Francine

about him and she told you and you got his fiddle, d'you remember?"

"Yes," says Beel, smiling, "and it was a pity I ever gave him back his violin, seemingly. Do you recollect how I always went with him to a concert and took it away when he had finished his number? Poor Volodia! And the others? Cecci? Have you seen him since? I've been abroad."[154]

"Oh, yes, he left that English poetess a long time ago. I loathed her, didn't you?" I tell him. "And then he married an American girl – or a German, I don't know which – because he thought she had a lot of money, but she hadn't much and he blued it[155] on dope and booze, she got a baby, and they're still in Paris – or they were when I left; and that English friend of yours – you know, the one whose wife you and Francine were crazy about – I saw him in Cannes a few weeks ago, but he didn't want to know me, but that was because of his new wife, a blonde, and she's awful stuck-up, and he looked terrible bad as if he were passing out."

"Oh?" he says, as if he were thinking of something else, and so [I] try hard to invent something that will warm him up and, suddenly I remember that he was a writer.

"And your books, Beel?" I inquire smiling. "Do they sell well now?"

[154] As mentioned above, Beadle departed from Europe in October 1916 and traveled to the U.S., where he frequently published stories in *Adventure* magazine. His novel *Witch-Doctors* appeared as a four-part serial in the 18 March through 3 May 1919 issues of *Adventure* (later published in book form in 1922). He returned to Paris by November 1919 and settled at 7, place du Tertre, in Montmartre. This scene in *Dark Refuge* may correspond to his return to France, shortly before the death of "Cecci" / Modigliani on 24 January 1920.

[155] "Blued it": Beadle seems to be portraying Georgette's imperfect use of English, thus substituting "blued it" for "blew it."

"Oh," he replies with a funny smile. "I've given up writing a long time ago," and he draws the saucer with the folded bill towards him.

Again I try to think what I can do to get him interested again, but dismally I recall that he never did like plump women, and although I've done my best I've put on flesh. He glances at the bill and raises his eyebrows slightly. I must do something.

"Would you like an old brandy?" I suggest wildly. "They're good here."

"No thanks," he says, absently, pulling several notes out of a well-stuffed pocketbook. Oh, if only I could get him home with me! He'd never miss a few, he's so rich.

"And your wife, Beel?" I go on. "Is she with you?"

"No," he says, coldly, sliding notes between the folded bill. I feel cold all over as I notice that he shuts his pocketbook and puts it away. "It's no use," I groan to myself, and recall poor Volodia screaming at me because I couldn't get Beel *then.* After all I'm an old friend –

"You're all alone tonight, Beel?" I say, desperately.

"Alone," he repeats, brutally, "and alone I stay," and rises.

No, there's nothing doing. I'm certain now by his eyes that he does take that filthy hashish stuff he was so fond of, and once a man gets deep in that he has no more use for a woman than I have for a man. Volodia was like that, too, but then I loved him like a mother. Still, fifty francs … Then he holds out his hand. Ah, great Lord! I feel the crackle of notes. He was always chic, Beel!

"For old times' sake," says he, smiling, "in case you're out of luck. Now I must be going …"

* * *

There was no manner of doubt now that this strange apparatus was in some miraculous way an index, not of dreams, but of the future. That very scene in every detail had actually passed at Monte Carlo a year or more ago. That date that was the past to me, had been the future to myself-that-was at the moment of the investigation.

That was the only rational explanation. And those prophetic dreams, as I had considered them, of Cecci and Eddie, whom I knew, or it seemed that I did, to be alive, were therefore still in the future. But indeed, I was so dizzy from jiggling to and fro in concepts of the past, present, and the future, that I could no longer comprehend clearly in what time state my thinking ego was functioning. Vaguely I apprehended that these phenomena must be a kind of contracting and expanding of Time like a concertina.

Seething with curiosity I streaked back to my own cozy skull. Patiently squatted my phosphorescent Cook. Unthinkingly in my excitement I attempted to ask him a question. But I had no voice. I had never noticed somehow that he had never actually spoken; nor had I. Angrily I willed him to instruct me by telepathy, or in whatever way he had done so before, how to choose the particular magic tape that should televise, as it were, my own dying moments. Nothing was manifested. The middle eye I then remarked had no longer that friendly twinkle; was occupied with other matters. See, or prelive, my own future I would! Exasperatedly I began to fumble in the apparatus expecting it to open …

An icy wind swept me into space. The tail of a passing comet plucked my hair. My arms dropped off. Trying to run after them my legs decamped. In impotent dismay I watched them, continuing the same motions, disappear until they were specks of soot. An angry oath blew my tongue and teeth out of my mouth; they fell as plummets do. I endeavored anxiously to see

where they had gone, but my eye sprang after them; began sporting like butterflies. Through the empty sockets cascaded jewels which were, I knew, my virtues and my vices; and much I wondered that each gem was more beautiful than the other.

Then my genitals sloughed; my penis chased an amorous star with the ardor of a stag after a rutting doe; my testicles became the moons of a lonely planet. My belly split; my guts convolving their length, resembled a sea serpent frolicking in an indigo sea. In order departed the rest of my entrails; heart and liver, kidneys and lungs, each tearing a strip of flesh to fashion wings which with my backbone, ribs, and skull, formed a constellation on their own. Remained the husk of my identity fluffing about like a moth in a moonbeam.

I drifted towards the Milky Way which suggested the window of a Board Room, frosted to prevent the staff and the public from seeing what the directors were doing. Through the Black Hole in the sky I blundered into apparently another solar system. A star, which winked friendlywise, drew me. Eddying slowly down like a dandelion seed on the warm air of a sullen dawn I was drawn towards a world that looked like ours, but the city on a river that I saw seemed strange; the houses were old, and the folk were queerly dressed – such as only I had seen in pictures. But when I was come to a broad street, wherein was a crowd, I recognized Whitehall.[156] Before a first-story window upon a platform knelt a handsome man with disordered, curly locks and gay, but ruffled, clothes; and his head was on a block. Beside him stood another man holding high an axe.

Ready was I to shudder; but the axe did not fall. I perceived that nothing moved. The lips of a parson nearby remained open; the sound of a vowel droned like a bumblebee. The crowd

[156] "Whitehall": A thoroughfare in London, where the chief offices of the British government are located.

stared avidly; rigid. I remarked a bird seemingly petrified in midair.

Thus I apprehended that I had indeed overtaken centuries; but that now I was travelling at exactly the same pace as Time; hence there was no movement. Only the present existed. Had the bird continued to fly, the axe to fall, then, inevitably, those acts would have been swallowed by the insatiable maw of the Past.

Marveling, I fluttered on through what I took to be other systems until caught in the attraction of another cordial stellar wink. This star had likeness to the other, and so to what we call "earth." Gradually approached a panorama of a vast desert with a few villages and a flat-roofed town beneath a brassy sky, and on a wine-dark sea moved tiny objects which I took for seagulls. As I zigzagged down I perceived that they were ships with many banks of rowers; furnished with queer sails of divers colors. Each galley was attached to another. Men appeared to be fighting, uttering loud cries; others were swimming. The scene so resembled the making of Ben-Hur[157] that I sought the camera boat where maybe I should find some friends; but that I could not do, which I thought was very odd. As I admired how well they acted, for the warriors looked as if they were really fighting and killing each other, the blood to be genuine, and the corpses on the decks and in the water, quite dead, I noticed, standing on the high poop, a tall, tough man who was bawling more lustily than the others; waving a funny kind of cutlass. The face struck

[157] "Ben-Hur": General Lew Wallace's novel *Ben-Hur* was published in 1880. Between 1899 and 1920 over twenty million people saw it performed on stage. An authorized film version, *Ben-Hur: A Tale of the Christ*, was released by Louis B. Mayer's MGM in 1925. Featuring a cast of one hundred thousand actors, it was the most expensive silent film of its time. One of the big action scenes in Mayer's *Ben-Hur* portrays the collision of two warships.

me as familiar. A draught of air as he made a pass with his weapon sucked me in close. I could see distinctly that he was not made-up; hence he could not possibly be the famous Hollywood star whom I imagined I had recognized. As I pondered aggrievedly upon this deception I distinguished the war cries of the sailors. Indubitably they are shouting "Antony!" and others "Egypt!" [158] Then only did I realize that I was witnessing the Battle of Actium. So bemused had I remained from shuttling from one time period to another, that I had mistaken the reality of an actuality, for such was the Battle of Actium in its proper time frame, merely because the appearances were not familiar to my accustomed modern vision, for the unreality of the cinema world; and moreover, I had clean forgotten that I was but the husk of my own identity willy-nilly overtaking the centuries at a vertiginous speed.

Inexorably I was borne along up this staircase of Time as an express lift passes floors, glimpsing worlds where the highest form of life was apes chattering futilely in leagues of simian nations of their own; where vast beasts resembling tanks plunged through swamp and over prairie; where the sky was of steam and gas, and volcanoes burst like firecrackers on a Chinese New Year amid a seething sea; and on and on until there were no more worlds and naught seemingly but incandescent void. After aeons that incandescence settled into blobs like electric globes in a daylit room. Through these gaseous cosmogonies was I dusted until once more I skirted familiar-looking worlds where horned tanks surged through slime, and more monkeys jibbered in more leagues of nations.[159]

[158] Most likely a reference to the 1934 production of Cecil B. DeMille's *Cleopatra*, starring Claudette Colbert and Henry Wilcoxon.
[159] A cynical reference to the League of Nations (10 January 1920 – 20 April 1946), which was in many ways a predecessor of the United Nations.

And I wondered where I was and what it was all about. Then dawned as slowly as a star cools the hope that in some miraculous manner I had turned; was on the age-long back trail to my own cozy skull. Hovering like thistledown above a flat-roofed town in a barren and rocky countryside, I espied three crosses set upon a hill. On each cross was a man. At the feet of the middle one were women weeping in the dusk, and as I floated nigh I heard that one of the dolorous eyes murmur:

"Oh, God my father, how many more times must I suffer thus, for Thou Knowest well that it never does any good."

Pondering upon this mystic utterance I was wafted on past many other worlds until by hazard the husk of my own identity was fluttered like a papyrus seed along a river on a warm night breeze, and into a low-ceilinged room where upon a bed of ivory and gold I recognized Antony coupled with Cleopatra; and much amazed was I that passion was in their acts but none was in their eyes. Dolefully Antony explained to me:

"You see, ole stick, Time has brought knowledge, but no wisdom; for now we are aware that, by the bloody idiotic law of mathematical recurrence, just as inevitable as the repetition of a sequence of numbers on a roulette table, we have performed this act X number of times in the past, and are doomed to do so for Y number of times in the future – a kind of cinema, if you get what I mean, where the hero marries the same heroine every morning, afternoon, and evening, for all eternity. We've lost our delusions and our illusions as well, and that – is hell!"

"But, Tony darling," murmured Cleopatra reprovingly, as she swatted a fly on his shoulder, "you're spoiling the rhythm."

"Yes, yes, lovely, I'm coming," answered Antony, dutifully, and went on with his tiresome job.

Rather peeved at this typical feminine tactless interruption, for I had found Antony quite a good sort and I should have liked to have continued the conversation, I was bustled along the

interminable curve of Time until on a day, as it appeared, I descried a well-known silhouette seated on a half-cooled mountainside of a newly divorced moon fishing for Rhizopoda.[160] After his own fashion my hashish god welcomed me. But indeed I was still offended at the manner in which, so to speak, I had been given the bum's rush from my own skull, and I said so with as much dignity, I trust, as a disembodied gentleman may. Then did he make me to understand that in seeking to prelive I had transgressed the Greatest of All Taboos; for should Man be permitted so to do he would realize his Own Insignificance, and thus deprive the Gods of much Hilarity in contemplating his Antics.

"Are there then gods?" I inquired, naively.

"Indeed to goodness!" he replied, soundlessly. "Every epoch has its own fashion in gods manufactured by man until Time leads him to the Only God, which," he added modestly, "is myself, the Last Delusion, The Unique One, whose name is YT-IL-IT-UF[161] which, like Time must be read backwards to be understood."

"I don't quite understand," I whimpered, frightened. "Do I just keep on going?"

"No," I was informed, "for if you did you would overtake your own manner of death, which is taboo. You must go back in Time."

"But," I protested, "every world I've passed lately has been becoming more and more like my own whereas, when I started, they were exactly in the reverse order until I struck nothing, or whatever it was?"

"Quite so," he intimated, "for you were traveling in Time which is like Light, a curve; ergo, a circle –"

"That's what Einstein maintains!" I asserted joyfully.

[160] "Rhizopoda": Creeping protozoans: amoebas and foraminifers.
[161] "YT-IL-IT-UF": "Futility," spelled backwards.

"Quite so. I told him," he replied complacently. "You were travelling faster than Time, therefore overtaking the Past, until you came to what you call the Beginning, which is merely the Inevitable Catastrophe. Then you entered into the Future, just as flying North on your silly earth after you pass the Pole you will find that you're going South."

"I see," said I, brightly. "Then in due course of time – ha ha! – you will arrive at the point you started from, the Present?"

"No, not the same Present; for there is no Beginning and no End, but only Eternal Recurrence; for on every trip knowledge is gained, but no wisdom – as your boyfriend Antony told you, and you'll remember what he said, no doubt?"

Then the god caused me to see a vision: I stood in an arbitrary Present before a vast merry-go-round; instead of a circus lion or giraffe, was passing an airplane; on one side was the tail of a horse disappearing; on the other the shadow of a bolide[162] approaching. I understood.

"Round and round and round like that," I bleated, terror stricken. "But what then is the use of anything?"

"Why, nuffink!" he giggled merrily, as he exhibited ironic sets of cathedrals.

"Oh, I've got such a headache," I moaned, "an' I wanna go home!"

"Without a head?" he tittered. Then compassionately he shot out one telescopic hand; grasped a luminous circle which I knew was Time; and with the other hand knocked a dent –

* * *

– and I was blinking at the middle eye of the alabaster idol, Ganesha, in the flickering light of the guttering candle stub.[163]

[162] "Bolide": A large meteor or fireball, especially one that explodes.

[163] At the beginning of the novel the narrator depicts Ganesha's "frog's mouth expanded in a laugh exposing rotting teeth which were

cathedrals," the "cathedrals" referring to the deity's rows of teeth. As noted earlier, the symbolic image of a sardonic god exposing his decaying molars and laughing at his own creation is anticipated in Beadle's 1931 letter to his niece: "I feel like a chewed star spat out by God's yellow teeth on the tattered carpet of the infinite." (This is later incorporated into *Dark Refuge*, with only minor modifications.) But Beadle's notion of the Sacred Absolute as a realm composed of hostile forces that will disgorge one into the void must be viewed from a broader historical perspective. Picasso spoke of a "wicked god" as early as 1933; and the encroachment of evil upon the world's political scene throughout that decade led him to envision the *axis mundi* and its traditional "sacred center" as being a fulcrum point of destruction. Lydia Gasman refers to this as the artist's "'cosmophobic' vision of the universe," an "anticosmic view" that runs through Picasso's "verbo-visual texts from the mid-1930s." Indeed, Fascism was often regarded by contemporaneous philosophers as the earthly embodiment of a more universal, transpersonal evil. While Beadle was portraying his own dismemberment upon "the dusty carpet of the Infinite" (1931-38), Georges Bataille was writing about his "confrontation with the evil 'left-hand' side of the 'sacred'" (1938) and the "'heavenly' hostility and the 'meanness of the sky'" (1939-43). Although cosmic dental imagery does occasionally appear in Picasso's writing (most notably, when he imagines the "teeth of the sun's jaw" are "planted in his flesh"; 1938), for Picasso the deadly arrogant god is a celestial bull (1936). During this horrific period of terrorizing aerial bombardment ("the fire of the sky"; 1935) he describes these demonic military air squadrons as bestial, "horned angels" diving down from the "center of the infinite void" (1939). Such malign divinities are merely assuming their latest incarnation when they appear as the "winged bulls" (1937) of Hitler's Luftwaffe, careening "from the 'roof' of the world" and raining death and mayhem upon the innocents, who flee in horror until, in Picasso's words, "everything [is] bruised and pulverized [to] cinders" (1936), with "death that could fall from heaven on so many right in the midst of rushed life'" (1967). For Bataille, the void itself "resembles a bull" (1935-36). See Lydia Gasman, *War and the Cosmos in Picasso's Texts,*

Afterword:

The Dark Refuge of Charles Beadle

Although various sources have stated that Beadle's first known publication was an essay titled "A Talk with the New Sultan of Morocco" (*Pall Mall Magazine,* October 1908), I was able to unearth an earlier travel piece, "Our Trip Down the Zambezi," which appeared in the May 1907 *Wide World Magazine: An Illustrated Monthly of True Narrative, Adventure, Travel, Customs and Sport.*[164] Under the byline "C. Beadle" an editor notes: "The narrative of an exciting and interesting canoe-voyage down the mighty Zambezi and its tributaries. Ranging from fights with pugnacious hippopotami to interviews with a king and his unconventional sister, the whole trip was packed full of incident and adventure." Which indeed it is.

The article chronicles a trip to Chikoti, Zambia, that occurred in early August 1904 (three years before the publication date), when Beadle was twenty-two years old. He relates that, along with a traveling companion and a crew of native helpers, he's returning from a "prospecting and hunting trip along the upper

---

1936-1940, New York: iUniverse, 2007, pp. xi, 2, 8-9, 261, 290-291, 351, 363; and passim. While Beadle is creating a "just-so" portrait of man's cosmic dilemma, Picasso is attempting a visceral exorcism, via word and image, aimed at life-threatening, hostile spirits.

Beadle's fascination with dental imagery is also displayed in a short story, "Magic Head," which features a buried-treasure map that is secretly etched on a gold dental plate. It was published four months after *Dark Refuge* in the 25 October 1938 issue of *Short Stories*.

[164] Still accessible at Google Books. See pp. 276-283.

reaches of the Zambezi and its tributaries, the Kabompo and Mombeji." (The spelling of these proper nouns is often based upon phonetic renderings of local dialect, making some of the actual locations now difficult to determine.)[165] On the return trip described in the piece, they embark "a little above the junction of the latter two rivers."

As promised by the editorial byline, the story is filled with rampaging hippopotami that seem to enjoy nothing more than overturning fragile canoes and killing as many men as they can in the process. The natives regard one of these beasts as a real "devil" since it's destroyed so many men; and they warn Beadle to be wary when he crosses an upcoming bend in the river. When his crew approaches this dangerous passage, their canoe is upended by the amphibious "devil," and one of the crew members is killed.

Continuing downriver to Lealui, they pay a visit to King Lewanika, a native ruler whose capacious hut contains a mahogany dining table and whose "wardrobe is very extensive, and all made by a London tailor."

After a genial visit with the king, Beadle travels to Nalolo to meet the king's sister, the queen. There he learns that, until recently, a queen had the right to either divorce or strangle her husband if she decided she was growing bored; and that this particular queen possessed the "reputation of having been

[165] A text published in the December 1908 issue of the *Geographical Journal* comments upon the "many variations" in orthography from one map to another and cites as examples: "the Dongue has previously appeared as 'Zongwe,' the Mombese as 'Mumbeshe,' or 'Mombeji,' the Lifupa as 'Lufupa,' and so forth. In such cases it is, of course, quite impossible for those unacquainted with the country to pronounce which is the more correct form." See "Map of Part of Northwest Rhodesia," *The Geographical Journal*, London: The Royal Geographical Society, 1908, p. 598.

rather a bloodthirsty young woman in the past." A few years earlier she had demanded the execution of one of her councilors; but when the executioner balked she picked up a battle-ax and completed the task herself.

Upon bidding the bloodthirsty queen farewell, Beadle heads toward the junction of the Leugauli and Zambezi River. Two days before their expected arrival at Sheheke, one morning while he's dozing in his canoe, he's almost tossed overboard by a rambunctious hippo that rises out of the depths and attempts to capsize the boat.

> A huge, speckled black mass – a monster hippo – seemed to be rising underneath the boat; all the paddlers had jumped and were swimming for dear life [...] I leant forward to pick up my gun, and at the same instant the hippo raised the bow of the boat out of the water, throwing me backward – luckily, on the top of the canopy and not in the river. Recovering, I tried to fire at the disappearing form of the hippo, but, alas! the safety catch was on. Murmuring sweet words of joy, I rectified the error and awaited events.
>
> Presently the brute rose again about ten feet away and came at me open-mouthed. Firing point-blank into his gaping jaws, I leaped for the bank, now only a few feet away, hearing a crash and a snort as I scrambled through the reeds and up the bank. I looked about for his lordship, and soon I caught a glimpse of him, making upstream under water. He disappeared round the bend, and I was about to follow along the bank when successive Martini shots, followed by yells, came from his direction.

Thus, it's finished off with some additional rifle fire from someone in a hunting party located further upstream.

Thanks to this cantankerous beast we now possess one of the only extant photos of Charles Beadle. Most of the other images that accompany the piece feature unpopulated landscapes or are taken from such a distance that the features of the crew are indiscernible. But one close-up photo depicts full-length portraits of several figures, and it's accompanied by the caption: "Inspecting the dead hippopotamus – nine bullets were found in his body, and he had been responsible for the destruction of several canoes."

The photo portrays a slender young white man, wearing a pith helmet and a striped short-sleeved shirt, standing in shallow water near the edge of the shore and gazing down at the animal's hulking mass. His hands are resting on his hips, and his trousers are rolled up to his knees. But unfortunately his head is turned away from the camera, and we can barely make out any facial features. Two Black men stand behind him, beside several canoes floating in the river. On the left-hand side of the image another white man with a stockier build is standing a few feet away and is also donning a helmet and a dripping pair of shorts. His face is enshrouded in shadows as he turns in profile to regard the dead hippo, its stiff legs jutting up in the air.

It would certainly make sense that the author of this piece would include at least one portrait of himself for such a photo essay – and one in which he's posed near the center of the picture. And indeed, a careful look at the narrative confirms that Charles Beadle is captured in this image. First, the author describes the arrival of a hunter who was almost killed by the beast:

> A man in an iron boat presently put in an appearance. Apologizing for the inconvenience he had caused us, he explained that he had wounded the brute the previous evening and had been looking for him ever since. He told us that he had also been upset. The pugnacious hippo had charged him after leaving me and upset his boat, although he could not lift it. While we were chatting the boys had recovered my boat and dragged it into the reeds. Master Hippo had managed to put his teeth clean through the bottom and bite a lump three feet long and a foot deep out of the side.
>
> We then inspected the carcass of our late friend the enemy, as shown in the next photograph. The boys had dived, fastened a rope round the tusks, and dragged him into a sand-bank. Nine bullets were discovered in his head and mouth. We learned later on that he was responsible for the destruction of two other canoes, belonging to a party which had preceded us.

We know from information provided on Beadle's WWI draft-registration card that he was of medium height and slender. This mirrors the build of the man in the center of the photo but not the one on the left-hand side. Therefore, it's safe to conclude that the two figures wearing helmets are Beadle and the man from the iron boat. Everything else in the picture is precisely as he describes it: the rope trailing from the hippo; the helpers who retrieved the boat (which is visible in the reeds); and Beadle and the other hunter inspecting a bullet-ridden carcass.

***

Four years later, in May 1908, Beadle led an expedition into Morocco. That October it was published in *Pall Mall Magazine* under the heading:

> A Talk with the New Sultan of Morocco. An Englishman entertained at the Court of Mulai-El-Hafid. The new ruler's prospects and relations with the powers, with some remarks from the sultan on his high opinion of the English, and his arrangements with regard to his deposed predecessor. By Charles Beadle, F.R.G.S. Illustrated with the author's photographs."

The FRGS acronym indicates that he's a Fellow of the Royal Geographical Society. Subsequent research revealed that Beadle was elected in 1906, when he was twenty-five years old. In February 1907 he was also elected to the Royal Colonial Institute.[166]

Beadle embarked from the Port of London aboard the SS *Agadir* on 23 April 1908, heading for the Moroccan coast. On the ship's passenger list, which I retrieved online, his name is the first to appear, in the First Class section.

At the opening of the tale, the author notes that upon his arrival at Mazagan[167] on 4 May he secured the service of William Redman – a European well-versed in the local customs who is fluent in Arabic – and together they traveled to the nearby town of Azzimour.

[166] Source: *Journal of the Royal Colonial Institute*, London: Royal Commonwealth Society, February 1907, p. 138.

[167] El Jadida, originally known as Mazighen; a Moroccan port city on the Atlantic coast.

There they are received by the governor, who provides Beadle "with a letter of introduction to his brother, the Grand Vizier to Mulai-El-Hafid."[168] After a fortnight in the Mazagan region, on 19 May they embark on the *Gibel Kebir*, a steamer headed to Tangier. But upon their arrival they are prevented from traveling any further, and their progress is halted. Beadle reports they are "held up for many weary days" and are warned that, due to the "present state of anarchy and civil war," their trip can only lead to "capture or massacre at least."

Undeterred, he follows the advice of a local and decides to proceed from another direction. At midday on 8 June he boards a steamer, the *Quetzil*, and arrives at 6 a.m. in Larache where his companions, William Redman and Captain Andrew Belton, are awaiting him, having arrived a bit earlier on another vessel.

The three men wend their way through a swarming mob near the Custom House ("I had but my camera and revolver"), check into their prearranged accommodations, and then dine "with the other European visitors" at the Hotel Lucas. The following morning, under a "fierce" sun, they prepare for the trip to Alcazar and are provided with "some sorry looking pack animals" that are "peeping from under their cumbrous straw pack saddles."

It proves to be a "wretched journey" in "intolerable heat"; but the worst part is the "thousand unprincipled ways in which every attendant imposes on the credulity or good nature of the traveler." It's for this reason that, on their way to Fez, Beadle is "effectually disguised in the native garb." And he catalogs some of the pitfalls that would await them minus such a disguise: "Otherwise, in the disturbed state of the country, with one sultan superseding another, and the army in a state of utter division, we should have stood a chance of decorating the

[168] Abdelhafid of Morocco; aka Moulay Abdelhafid (1875 – 1937), the sultan of Morocco from 1908 to 1912.

country roadside with a heap of our devoted bodies." This fancy turn of phrase – infinitely preferable to "we might have been killed" – highlights the young author's nascent literary bent.

The inherent dangers of traveling as Europeans on the road to Fez or Mequinèz are such, he continues, that his team is "required to procure the necessary escort from the British vice consul." Even so, after several troublesome encounters along the way, he concludes: "I might have had reason to view some of these encounters with even more miscellaneous feelings, had I known that my guide accounted for my complete disguise by confiding to our assistants that I was a dancing girl bound for the household of a distinguished native official. At other times I was, it seemed, a holy man, a *shereef*;[169] and so on." He adds: "There is plenty of humor, and lying, in Morocco." And apparently, some transvestite theater in the best British tradition. But it's also a place where one learns the value – and artistry – of a story well told. In any case, thus camouflaged, the author is transported through the suburban olive groves, arriving at Mequinèz (most likely Meknes, a city in north-central Morocco) on 14 June.

And then we're treated to an authenticated photo of Beadle, which is captioned: "The author in Moorish costume."[170] The image is reminiscent of a similar photo of a robed European in Africa – that of Arthur Rimbaud. The slender figure – one that would have to be petite to pass as a young dancing girl – conforms in shape to the one featured in Beadle's previous article.[171] But once again his facial features – veiled and hidden in shadows – are difficult to make out.

[169] "Shereef": Variant spelling of *sharif*: a descendant of the prophet Muhammad, through his daughter Fatima.
[170] The article is featured on pages 473-479.
[171] In his autobiography, *The Frog Prince*, Maurice Girodias tells us

Following a series of interactions with various intermediaries (including the grand vizier and the minister of foreign affairs), Beadle is finally received by Sultan Mulai-El-Hafid. After exchanging formalities they embark on a mule-back ride to the Government House, where the sultan seats himself "cross-legged on a gilt Louis XV sofa" while Beadle is positioned in a chair beside the couch. From this ringside seat the author notes

> in appearance the sultan was undoubtedly a handsome man, with large black humorous eyes alight with vivacity, a black well-groomed beard, and olive skin, high forehead and rather prominent cheekbones – the lower part of his face, if anything, was the weaker. Particularly I noticed his really beautiful hands and feet, tapering fingers, and filbert nails. He was of medium height, slim, and well formed. He immediately took stock of us, and smiled as if pleased, whispering something to his grand vizier, which I heard later was to the effect that he liked these Englishmen.

---

that shortly after his father Jack Kahane died, Maurice was sitting in the Obelisk Press office and staring a wall of authors' photos: "Pinned to the gray burlap that covers the wall are the actors of the past, each one looking into the dim, dusty room from his or her place in space and time. The mysterious eyes of Anaïs [Nin]; a photo of [James] Joyce, the sour-faced magister; [Lawrence] Durrell's profile, chubby and pugnacious; the satanic face of Charles Beadle, the author of *Dark Refuge* – who knows, perhaps one of the true prophets of the future?" See Maurice Girodias, *The Frog Prince*, New York: Crown Publishers, 1980, augmented English translation, p. 350.

Beadle adds: "In conversation he proved to have a very broad mind, and showed a keen insight into foreign politics." At one point the sultan asks "Why was it that France was allowed to carry such a high hand in Moroccan affairs?" He also poses "many questions regarding the occupation of Egypt, and of the French operations in Algeria." The sultan's main preoccupation is with maintaining autonomy and independence for his country, while at the same time pursuing an amicable relationship with England.

The interview lasts for a good two hours, after which the sultan "thanked us for having been the first Europeans to visit him in Fez as sultan, as also the first to enter since all Europeans left at the outbreak of revolution in August of 1907. We were to go anywhere we liked, to see the sights of Fez; its ministers had orders to see that we were provided with an escort and anything else we might require, and he bade us make our stay as long as possible."

Rather heady stuff for our young aspiring author. Not many twenty-six-year olds get to experience something like this, and fewer still are capable of rendering such an experience in so artful a manner.

Reading between the lines of this account, one begins to wonder if Beadle was serving as an unofficial government agent. And indeed, the story takes an additional (and more clandestine) turn while growing curiouser and curiouser. For, according to a confidential government memo penned in the British Foreign Office, Beadle and his pals were raising some nervous eyebrows back home – as well as placing their lives in jeopardy. An index of confidential reports from the Foreign Office summarizes a 21 June 1908 memo as follows: "Englishmen at Fez. Refers to [memo] No. 105. Informs of their names. They are being treated as if on mission from His Majesty's Government. Steps taken to counteract this impres-

sion. Encloses copy of letter from Lord Mountmorres relative to Mr. Beadle, one of the Englishmen in question." Memo No. 105 reads in full:

Mr. White to Sir Edward Grey. – (*Received June 29th.*)

(No. 118.)

Tangier, June 21, 1908.

Sir,

I HAVE the honor to transmit herewith translation of a letter received by Mr. Consul Macleod from his Arabic Interpreter reporting the arrival of two Englishmen, alleged to the Emissaries from His Majesty's Government.

On the 11th instant [11 June] the Consular Agent at Alcazar wrote to inform me that two Englishmen, accompanied by Mr. Redman, a British merchant at Mazagan, had arrived from Gibraltar via Larache and were proceeding to Fez. Mr. Carleton did not mention their names, nor the object of their intended visit to Fez. Upon receipt of Mr. Carleton's letter, I at once instructed him to call the special attention of these gentlemen to the warning issued in April last, but I have heard nothing further from Mr. Carleton on the subject.

It is difficult to say whether these travelers have alleged that they are Emissaries of His Majesty's Government to give themselves importance and ensure a good reception, or whether the report originated with Mulai Hafid and his officials, and is intended to lead the people to believe that His Majesty's Government have recognized him, or at any rate are in negotiation with him.

I have, &c.
(Signed)

HERBERT E. WHITE.

Enclosure in No. 106.

Lord Mountmorres to Mr. White.

5, Central *Chambers, South Castle Street, Liverpool,*
June 4th, 1908.

Sir,

I HAVE the honor to enclose herewith a letter address to Mr. Charles Beadle, who has been staying in Tangier. He is leaving today, and is likely to be absent from Tangier for about a fortnight. On his return, about the 17th of this month, his address will be Hotel Cavilla, Tangier.

As I have reason to fear that if the letter lies there it may be tampered with by persons into whose hands I am particularly anxious it should not fall, I should esteem it a very great favor if your Excellency would see that this letter safely reaches Mr. Beadle.

Your Excellency will probably have received from the Foreign Office, prior to the receipt of this letter, information which will indicate to you my reason for being anxious as to the safety of the accompanying letter.

I have, &c.
(Signed)

MOUNTMORRES.[172]

Beadle's trip also received prominent attention in the mainstream British press. On 25 August 1908, the *Dundee Evening Telegraph* published an article on page three titled: "Under Which Sultan? Powers and Positions in Morocco. The Pretender's Claim." It begins: "Confirmation of the defeat of Abdul aziz, Sultan of Morocco, and of the proclamation of his brother Mulai Hafid, as Sultan, has been received at the Foreign Office in a dispatch from Mr. White, Chargé d'affaires at Tangier." Under a second subheading titled "The Men Behind Hafid," the article continues:

> How much of Mulai Hafid's success is due to the six enterprising young Englishman who arrived in Fez in the middle of last month has yet to come out.
>
> The story of how three English Sultan-makers arrived in Fez is a most interesting one.
>
> The principal of the contingent is Mr. Ellis Ashmead-Bartlett, [173] who was convinced that much benefit would result from the success of Mulai Hafid, and determined that, with the aid of

[172] Foreign Office: Confidential, Part 37, Further Correspondence Respecting the Affairs of Morocco. April to June 1908, pp. ix, 75-76. The National Archives (Kew, UK), accessed at archive.org. Thanks to my colleague Christopher Sawyer-Lauçanno for unearthing this Foreign Office memo on 20 July 2022.

[173] Ellis Ashmead-Bartlett served as a lieutenant in the Second Boer War and was later a war correspondent during WWI.

certain friends, he would furnish that aid on various conditions.

Hafid offered in return for English (unofficial) assistance to give concessions for the building of railways, mining, the reorganization of the finances of the country, various important political posts, and a partial control of at least the Customs.

Three Englishmen named Charles Beadle, Redman, and Belton left for Fez, and their reports made it imperative that Mr. Ashmead-Bartlett himself should sail for Morocco, leaving affairs in England in the hands of Mr. Arkell Hardwick.[174]

On arriving at Tangier he found that his three friends, unable to wait for him, had started up country.

He therefore decided on the very risky plan of making his way direct to Fez, where the Moorish Pretender had by this time taken up his headquarters.

Luckily for him, his plucky attempt succeeded. Disguised as a native of the country, he reached the Moorish capital, recruiting on the way two more Englishman from a town near the coast.

On 30th July Mr. Arkell Hardwick left London for Tangier, and the last that was heard of him was that he was on his way to Fez across the desert.

[174] Alfred Arkell Hardwick, a native of Dalston, in northeast London, who served in the British South African Police. He was later killed in an airplane crash in north London in 1912.

In an article titled "Tasting Adventure and Revolution," historian Geoffrey Pocock[175] describes a decisive battle that occurred between the opposing sultans and how the victorious forces of Mulay Hafid defeated the army of Abd El Aziz (the Battle of Marrakesh; 19 August 1908). In the same piece Geoffrey reports that Beadle, Redman, Belton, and Hardwick were in Morocco during this conflict and that they were members of the Legion of Frontiersmen. This was a civilian group created in 1905 by Roger Pocock, a veteran of the Boer War. The organization served as an unofficial intelligence gathering group, whose purpose was to prepare its members for war and to maintain peacetime vigilance. Geoffrey says that the Foreign Office wasn't exactly thrilled with the Legion or with its presence in Morocco (which is certainly apparent in the memo cited above). And he adds that Beadle's novel, *The City of Shadows* (1911), offers the "best account" of the conflict and that the hero is partially modeled upon Andrew Belton.[176]

In an email that I received from Geoffrey on 1 July 2022 he informed me that, according to Roger Pocock's *Chorus to Adventurers*, "Belton was not very pleased" by the way he was portrayed as a fictional character. Geoffrey added that "Roger Pocock and Beadle seem to have been friends rather than just acquaintances, but there are only brief mentions of Beadle in Pocock's pocket diaries." And he kindly included these snippets

[175] Published at frontiersmenhistorian.info on 1 June 2016. Pocock is also the author of *One Hundred Years of the Legion of Frontiersmen*, Phillimore, UK, 2004.

[176] In a letter that Beadle sent to his niece Isabel in the late 1920s or early Thirties he writes: "You mention having had only 2 books of mine. Esquimau and City of Shadows? Latter isn't a book it's drivel – or journalism which is prostitution." For more on Beadle's letters to Isabel see the Appendix in this edition.

from the diary, which is housed at the Bruce Peel Collection, University of Alberta:

> [6 March 1908] Dismissed Stevens from S. Africa agency and took on Beadle, just back from Borneo.
>
> [17 November 1908] Beadle to camp.
>
> [12 July 1909] Beadle to dinner.

A 9 December 1909 diary entry notes that Beadle was one of several friends who "visited Pocock the day after an operation on his foot." (But their whereabouts are not recorded.) Regarding the men of the Legion, Geoffrey said that "an accurate version of their life and adventures" was "difficult to find":

> We usually describe them as men who got together round a fire winter evenings smoking their pipes and telling 'camp-fire yarns' of their adventures, which they often embellished. Their fiction books can be useful because they often based them on their own escapades and were able to put words into the mouths of fictional characters, which they could not use in their factual accounts for fear of the laws of libel, etc.

Beadle's journeys across Africa and Asia allowed him to gather the rich imagery that, in the years ahead, would pepper, inspire, and fuel his adventure stories and novels. He was already paying attention to the important little details that crystallize into the filaments of an engaging story (e.g., "Particularly I noticed his really beautiful hands and feet,

tapering fingers, and filbert nails"); thus, in these early efforts, the reader is witness to the promise of a gifted raconteur. His travel essays also provide us with something rather precious: an extensive discourse, in Beadle's natural voice, chronicling events from his actual life. (And with *Dark Refuge* in mind, one cannot help but wonder if it was in hashish-festooned Fez that he first dabbled with the toxins that produce an "artificial paradise.") The same ability is displayed in "My Narrow Escape From a Lioness," a tragic account in which a teenage boy is devoured by a lion and in which the author himself narrowly escapes such a fate. Published in the 7 August 1910 *Brooklyn Daily Eagle,* the story chronicles a hunting party in Mashonaland, South Africa, that was organized on Beadle's behalf in the fall of 1900.

In the spring of 1911 Beadle published his first novel, *The City of Shadows: A Romance of Morocco*. The book is dedicated to Olive Grimaldi, a well-known fashion artist whose work appeared in numerous periodicals of the time, including *Pall Mall* magazine (which had featured Beadle's "A Talk with the New Sultan of Morocco"). The reviews were positive and appeared in at least half a dozen mainstream British papers. The *Times* called it "A keen, closely knit, strenuous narrative of adventure." The *Manchester Courier* lauded Beadle for his "wide knowledge of Morocco and its people" as did the *Westminster Gazette,* which complimented him on his "vivid presentation of Mohammedan life." The *Croydon Chronicle and East Surrey* picked up on Beadle's ability to spin a riveting yarn: "Lovers of exciting and strenuous adventure will find their tastes admirably catered for." The widely circulating *Daily Mirror* offered vigorous praise and a colorful set of details:

> There is a strong thread of narrative, strung pretty thickly with the beads of stirring event; there is

> effective character-drawing, and there is a perfume of the hot southeast in which its scenes are laid, in *The City of Shadows.* It is a story of the sort of thing which is still possible and might at any moment happen in the fierce and fluid politics of North Africa – reversals of fortune as sudden and complete as any in the Arabian Nights, upsetting of dynasties, amazing coups of diplomacy and arms. Mr. Beadle obviously knows the country, and has the gift of imparting the spirit and savor of the queer things he has seen and the yet queerer people he has met.

The twenty-nine-year-old author must have been pleased. All this set the ball rolling, and from that point on he steadily published novels and short stories.

In July 1912, during his thirtieth year, *Windsor Magazine* featured what may be Beadle's first published short story, "The Triumph of Tony": an irony-laden tale of Victorian courtship, which occurs aboard an ocean liner. That same year he published his second pulp novel, *A White Man's Burden.* Although it doesn't appear to have garnered as much attention as *The City of Shadows,* I did locate a review published in Midlothian, Scotland, in *The Scotsman*:

> Life in an unhealthy region of Africa, where British representatives carry on their work amid dangers and difficulties, is interestingly described by Charles Beadle in a *White Man's Burden.* Going out as an administrator, "to wait, in heavy harness, on fluttered folks and wild," Herbert Fedden soon finds that the most difficult problems that confront him are not those created by the

> natives. He is accompanied by his wife, to whom the dull life is by no means agreeable, and this and other circumstances render possible the complications and misunderstandings that follow the arrival of an old lover whom she had jilted. Many people of widely different characters assist in the development of the somewhat slender plot, and all are convincingly portrayed.

The portrayal of "many people of widely different characters" that are all "convincingly portrayed" is a keynote of Beadle's novels, which are often filled with numerous protagonists. (As we shall see, this is especially so in the case in *Dark Refuge*.)

In 1913 Beadle's stories appeared in *London Magazine* ("The Better Man") and *Cassell's Magazine of Fiction* ("Romance for Sylvia"). These were well-known periodicals that featured the sort of *divertissement* that was deemed appropriate for the Victorian readership of the time. (For example, "The Better Man" portrays a love triangle featuring two brutes whose friendship is broken by the appearance of a vulgar yet irresistible washerwoman.)

If we examine the writing that he exhibits in these early tales, there's no doubt that the author possessed a highly polished style, but the storyline and plotting of most of his work is anchored to the genre of commercial fiction. Clearly, he was trying to make money. His nonfiction pieces also exhibit a skillful, imaginative use of language; but since they describe actual events they ascend to a higher literary level because they aren't constricted by potboiler scenarios.

Unfortunately, Beadle didn't publish much nonfiction after the success of his first novel, but I did locate several other essays, including one that appeared in the December 1914 *Badminton Magazine of Sports and Pastimes*, titled "A Decade of

Christmas Dinners." For our purposes, the primary value of this piece is that it fills in many of the missing details of his elusive biography. The article is structured around various locations where the author spent his Christmas holiday over the span of a decade, while wandering from one otherworldly locale to the next. The opening paragraph places him in Rhodesia:

> Some 7,000 feet above the sea level on the sweep of a bare hillside lies Inyanga Fort: eight round and three rectangular huts, all thatched and built of stone, every piece of which had been carried and mortised with *darga* (mud) by our own bare hands, troopers of the Rhodesian police …

For reasons that I'll explain below, we can probably date this first holiday to either 1899 or 1900.

Next he appears in Beira, in central Mozambique, where the Pungwe River spills into the Indian Ocean. As usual, the author is attentive not only to the crowning events of the chronicle but also to the finer points that help to "paint" a scene: "With the gorgeous pageant of the sunset in crimson and purple the high note of the mosquito was heard; and in the distance the throbbing chorus of the frogs began as the short twilight deepened into violet shadows."

The next year he's camped near Klerksdorp, South Africa: "On a gentle slope at the base of a large boulder-crowned kopje was a wilderness of tents; the camp of ten thousand men, a group of the many columns organized into the big 'drives' of the western Transvaal." This is probably the period of the Second Boer War. The following Christmas he's in Johannesburg, where "Now and again swirling dust devils swooped along through the warm clear air, blinding, smothering dapper officers on well-groomed chargers, khaki colonials and regulars, straw-headed

civilians, muslin-garbed women and girls in rikshas and carriages, and natives swaggering in European garb."

There's also a Christmas celebrated after a prolonged excursion in Zambia: "For nine months we had been wandering in the heart of Africa." His party camps near the Kabompo and Mombeji Rivers, having "run short of provisions" and now appearing "lean and as hard as nails," with the porters growing "thin and needy" as well. But suddenly he gets lucky and bags some edible game: a "Christmas dinner of suckling pigs – roasted in hot embers – and mealie *kabobs,* the most enjoyable and best-appreciated dinner I have ever had." While describing this particular holiday he also mentions having kept a diary: a precious document now lost to history.

The following Christmas Beadle returned to England via a ship that passed through Dungeness, Kent. After long "awful delays" on the way to Gravesend, the "prodigal arrived in time to join the family circle – who had long since given him up as usual – with the advent of the flaming Christmas pudding." The passage is notable for featuring a rare commentary about his family.

The seventh Christmas episode begins with the phrase "An outpost of Empire: a thatched bungalow, offices and store-houses" and appears to be the description of a Government House. He then portrays the surrounding countryside: "the bamboo-clad foothills of the giant Gamballagalla" (the Ugandan name for the Rwenzori Mountains), "a little to the south of which a two-thousand-foot escarpment to the Semliki River and Lake Albert Edward level."

All this places Beadle at the border of Uganda and what is now known as Democratic Republic of the Congo. And we know that he was there in December 1905, because he says so at the opening of another travelogue, titled "Two Close Calls – A Huntsman's Tale of the Red Rubber Country": a nonfiction

piece published in the June 1910 issue of *The Captain* magazine: "I left Toro (Fort Portal), my diary tells me, on the early morning of the fifth day of the New Year, 1906. I had been held up at this Government station for some three weeks, engaged in recruiting and registering fresh porters before crossing the border into the Congo." Fort Portal, also known as Kabarole, is located in western Uganda and was the seat of the Toro Kingdom. In his piece in *Badminton* Beadle portrays a view from a veranda on Christmas morning, where he observed the "snow-capped peaks of the Gamballagalla glisten in the sun before being enveloped in their perennial mists." Now watch how he transports this experience into his novel *Witch-Doctors*, published decades later: "From the compound, looking towards the northwest where the snow-capped Gamballagalla rose violet against the horizon, another brown cone peeped above the green fronds, the late residence, and now the tomb of King MKoffo ..."[177]

The following year he celebrates the holiday in a harbor town somewhere in the "Far East," where

> Through the trees of the *maidan*[178] was a vista of the lights of steamers and junks in the harbor beginning to twinkle, eddy and surge. Outside in the broad road was a motley throng: women and men in rikshas, gharries, and open landaus with silver-mounted harness and woodwork in which sat the bland figures of Chinese merchants; a few odd coolies on foot, a turbaned policeman, a solitary motor car, Malay girls in brilliant scarlet

[177] Beadle also published a fiction story, "A Pinch of Fever," in the June 1915 issue of *Badminton*, and several passages in this story closely mirror certain scenes in *Witch-Doctors*.

[178] "Maidan": An Asiatic or African parade ground or esplanade.

> and yellow headcloths and sarongs, sedate Japanese, and a trio of British tars. [Sailors whose clothing was often stained by the ship's pine tar, which becomes sticky at a relatively low temperature.]

And then, the ninth Christmas is spent in the colorful city of "New Fez":

> In the evening we toasted each other and the old folks at home in Spanish wine over the customary Moorish dish, pretending that the weird, albeit tasty, mess of stewed mutton smothered in *cous-cous* and flavored with raisins was turkey. Moorish pastry and sweet mint tea proved in the intense heat a fair substitute for the national pudding. Afterwards the few other European residents, French, Spanish, Italian, arrived, heralded by a prodigious knocking at the outer nail- and tin-encrusted gates, a flashing of lanterns, and scuffle of retainers suggesting medieval days.

The tenth and final episode chronicles another return to England, where the wanderer appears to be a stranger in a strange land:

> The verdant decorations, the diminutive trees burdened with chromatic toys, and the toasts flying on every side, brought back a sense of reality with a jerk. A momentary feeling of strangeness as an alien passed. One looked across at a fellow wanderer; so different to the other well-groomed men on either hand, brown of face, with

> the "watching the skyline" expression in the eyes. We both smiled in sympathy; he understood, the others could not. Yet these were our fellows whom we had toasted so often in the solitudes.

This valuable document seems to have eluded previous Beadle biographers, and it provides some new and juicy details from his prodigious wanderings. The ten-year period would roughly correspond to his 1899 service with the Rhodesian Police (described in the first episode); his December 1905 stay in Fort Portal, Uganda (the seventh episode); and his sojourn to England in 1908 (the final episode). We also know that he traveled through Morocco from 1908 to about 1910-11; but by 1911 he relocated to Hampstead, England and published *The City of Shadows.*

The dating of the "Christmas dinner" travelogue remains ambiguous, however, because if we use the seventh, Ugandan episode to anchor the chronology, this would date his Christmas in Fez to 1907; but in his earlier account of first entering Fez (while disguised as a dancing girl), he says that he didn't travel there until May 1908. Maybe he was using artistic license to condense these Christmas events, and it's perhaps for this reason that the essay doesn't include specific dates. We should also note that Fez el Jedid or "New Fez," where Beadle consumed his ninth Christmas dinner, was a separate entity from the historic Fez el Bali. New Fez was constructed later, in 1276, and served as the symbolic seat of government. (The decision to separate the cities by about 2.2 kilometers was part of a defense strategy.)

The years 1914-16 would prove to be eventful ones. This was the period during which Modigliani composed an elegant pencil drawing of Beadle, which was stolen from the author

(although it later surfaced in the Perls Galleries in New York, in 1951). A journalist named Vera D. Edwards mentions it briefly in a review she published in the *Sioux City Journal* on 18 May 1930. Writing about Beadle's novel *Expatriates at Large,* she opens her article ("Paris Quartier Latin Sans Romantic Gloss") with the sentence: "A portrait of Charles Beadle has just come to light, by Modigliani, the artist who died practically unknown and has now become a sensation in the world of art." (Most intriguing of all, the review features a photo of Beadle standing in profile and provides an unobstructed view of his facade. See the Illustrations section, below.)

***

About four months before the outbreak of WWI, Beadle entered into an ill-fated marriage with Sylvia Grace Ellen Hornsby, which was officiated at the British Consulate General in Paris on 14 March 1914. They were living at 4, rue de la Grande Chaumière, a few doors away from the famous Académie de la Grande Chaumière (located at #14) where Modigliani, Gauguin, and many other artists drew from the nude model. (As noted in *Artist Quarter,* Modi would later live at #8.) On the marriage certificate Sylvia is registered as "artist"; Charles as "novelist." The witnesses to this star-crossed event were Ruby Hamilton Williams and Joe Z. Askin.

By the following summer Charles and Sylvia were living in the Villa Robinson in St. Tropez, in the Var department of Southern France. On 8 July 1915 Sylvia gave birth to Jane Owen Beadle, in nearby Cannes.

An unusual document has surfaced that attests to Beadle's sunny location and to his occasional bursts of glowing self-confidence. On 20 August 1915 Theodore Roosevelt (1858 – 1919), the twenty-sixth president of the United States, posted

the following missive: "My dear Mr. Beadle: Thank you very much for sending me your book. I am sure I shall enjoy reading it. With all good wishes, Sincerely yours, Theodore Roosevelt."[179] It's addressed to Charles Beadle, Esq., "Robinson" Saint Tropez, Var, France.

Although "Teddy" Roosevelt might have enjoyed the rough and tumble adventures of *The City of Shadows*,[180] perhaps the author sent him an advance copy of his forthcoming novel (see below). In any case, they shared an African connection. After his presidency (1901 – 1909) Roosevelt embarked upon an extended safari, traveling to Mombasa, Kenya, to the Belgian Congo, and then, following the Nile, to Khartoum in the Sudan. This year-long expedition (funded by Andrew Carnegie, to collect animal specimens for the Smithsonian Institution) lasted from 21 April 1909 to 14 March 1910 and is chronicled in Roosevelt's *African Game Trails* (1910). The former president was also known to be an ardent consumer of pulp fiction, and since *Adventure* was his favorite pulp magazine he may have read some of Beadle's adventure stories when they appeared there a few years later, in 1918.

Two months after she gave birth to Jane, on 13 September 1915 Sylvia died in Cannes, where she's buried. Her probate records

[179] "Image 76 of Theodore Roosevelt Papers: Series 2: Letterpress Copybooks, 1897-1916; Vol. 103, 1915, Aug. 20-1916, Jan. 19," Library of Congress, crowd.loc.gov.

[180] Roosevelt served as a mediator between France, Germany, and Great Britain during the First Moroccan Crisis (1905 – 1906) by arranging a peace conference that determined the "status" (or control) of Morocco. Since *The City of Shadows* is a fictionalized account of the 1908 Battle of Marrakesh (the decisive conflict fought between opposing Moroccan sultans), Roosevelt might have been drawn to the subject of Beadle's book. It's also possible that Roosevelt was familiar with Beadle's 1908 interview with the sultan of Morocco, published in *Pall Mall* magazine.

indicate that just before her death Charles was still residing at the Villa Robinson in St. Tropez. Thanks to the efforts of my colleague Céline Cardon, we were able to retrieve her death certificate (a tricky task, since it's indexed under a misspelled surname). The document indicates that Sylvia died at the Hotel Beau Rivage (now known as the Hotel Majestic) during a period when the villas and hotels of the Côte d'Azur were used as hospitals, especially for the soldiers of WWI. Thus, it's probable that she died "in hospital."

Sylvia, Jane, and Igor Bely (Jane's husband) are all interned in the same plot, at Cannes' Cimetière du Grand Jas. A girl named Elizabeth Owen Bely is also buried there.[181] Céline's further research revealed that Elizabeth was the daughter of Jane and Igor. Born in Bournemouth, England three and a half years before her parents were married, Elizabeth was only sixteen years old when she died (7 August 1946 – 23 August 1962). Her remains were placed in this grave after she was first interned in another cemetery.

In the fall of 1915 Beadle published his third novel, *A Passionate Pilgrimage*. I found only a single review of this work, published in the 2 October *Freeman's Journal* in Dublin. And the reviewer is not kind:

> The pilgrim in this novel is an individual who missed the engineering profession through a love quarrel, and thenceforth figures dramatically in a series of love adventures. Scenes are laid in England, and shift to Cape Colony, and even to darkest Africa. The central character's facility for falling in love is as great as his knack of moralizing and philosophizing, and his intensity in one direction is equaled by his shallowness in the

[181] *Carré* 20, number 49. Information retrieved on 18 July 2020.

> other. The reader always feels his education was cut short, and that to physical courage of a sort he adds moral obtuseness. As to the female characters, their merits, where they have any, and their failings are alike in an exaggerated strain. The narrative contains some interesting descriptive passages, especially in that portion treating of scenes in the jungle.

The dearth of reviews might have something to do with the manner in which the passions of this particular pilgrimage are rendered. On 13 October, Beadle's publisher launched a pair of identically worded ads in two British papers, *The Daily Telegraph* and the *Evening Standard*. Under the heading *A Passionate Pilgrimage,* we read: "Some of the Circulating Libraries do not consider this book 'thoroughly wholesome literature,' whereas one of the oldest established of such libraries has it in circulation. In view of the conflicting attitudes assumed by the Libraries, the Author and Publishers would be interested to know the opinions of Readers of the Book." Quite an ingenious publicity ploy in attempting to turn a negative into a positive!

One more mention of the novel appears about a month later, in the *Liverpool Echo.* A feature column, "Echoes from Everywhere," ran a piece titled "What Men and Women are Talking of." Composed of a list of quotations culled from various books, it includes three quotes from *A Passionate Pilgrimage,* one of which reads: "Never try to tell a girl why you love her – she doesn't want to know, and you don't know yourself."

After inheriting a substantial amount of money from Sylvia, Beadle set sail for New York on 30 October 1916, departing from Cadiz, Spain. On the ship's manifest he lists Beatrice Hastings under the heading "Closest friend living in country of departure," noting her address as 13, rue Norvins, Paris. Thanks to

this manifest we also know that he was residing at Place du Tertre, in Montmartre. (Max Jacob lived nearby, at 17, rue Gabrielle.)

A year after his arrival in the States, Beadle's stories began to appear in the *International,* an arts and culture magazine. The occultist (and consummate fakir) Aleister Crowley had assumed editorship of this periodical in July 1917; and it was under his leadership that four of Beadle's pieces were featured between October 1917 and December 1918. The first is a poem, "An African Love Song," which appears to be either a translation or an imitation of a traditional African song. It represents the author's fledgling attempt to work in a more literary mode. Although he was imbued with many of the racial biases promulgated by the British Empire during this period, at least Beadle was able to recognize the artistry contained within African verse.

Next, his short story "NQO" appeared in the December issue: a tale that portrays a British colonial soldier who falls under the spell of a witch doctor. The style is similar to that of his *Adventure* stories, which would soon follow. (The theme of magicians would be fully fleshed out in Beadle's *Witch-Doctors,* which was featured in serial form in *Adventure* in March 1919 and then published as a novel in June 1922.)

Another Beadle story, "The Palm Tree and the Window," appeared in the March 1918 *International.* In the previous, February issue, under the heading "Jugging the March Hare," Crowley refers to this forthcoming piece as an "Eastern comedy." In April the periodical featured Beadle's "A Doctor of Men" ("a delightful sketch of life in the Latin Quarter of Paris with its curious mixture of religious fervor and debauchery"). In the November issue, in a column titled "The Editor Boosts the Next Number," Crowley describes Beadle's forthcoming work in the December issue: "A story of African magic by Charles

Beadle is really better than any of Kipling's African tales. That's going some, but it is true." Unfortunately we don't even know the title of this piece, and there aren't any available copies of the Beadle stories that followed "NQO" in the *International*.

We also don't know how he first became acquainted with the notorious Crowley, but as Beadle wasn't shy about approaching magazine editors (nor was he shy about anything else), it's likely that he first contacted him shortly before arriving in Manhattan. Afterward, it would have been easy to arrange a meeting, since the magazine's offices were located at 1123 Broadway. We also know that the two men renewed their acquaintance in Paris in the 1920s. (Nina Hamnett, a Montparno expatriate and friend of Modigliani during this same period, writes about Crowley's Paris days in her memoir, *Laughing Torso*.) And when Beadle returned to England just before the outbreak of World War II, he visited Crowley in Chiswick to solicit his memories of Modigliani and Montparnasse, in preparation for his *Artist Quarter* book.

Hoping to gain some insight into Beadle's relationship with Crowley, I contacted Tobias Churton, author of a multivolume Crowley biography. Churton was about to publish his latest tome: *Aleister Crowley in Paris: Sex, Art, and Magick in the City of Light*. After he confirmed that "Crowley knew Beadle in New York during WWI," he kindly provided me with a sneak preview of some of the bits that he'd uncovered:

> New Year's Day 1920 ... Leaving Victoria for Paris at 10:00 a.m. he [Crowley] … quickly fell in with Walter Duranty[182] and well-traveled pulp fiction writer Charles Beadle.

[182] Walter Duranty: Moscow bureau chief of *The New York Times* (1922-36) and recipient of the Pulitzer Prize in 1932.

> [8 January:] [Crowley encounters] "Willy" [Duranty] with Beadle at Lapérouse [Parisian restaurant].
>
> [10 February:] Renting a pleasant house at 11 bis, rue de Neuville, Fontainebleau … Willy and Beadle came to lunch on the 10th.

Since Crowley had assumed the persona of a diabolical magus, he was probably drawn to Beadle's renditions of native folklore, magic, and mystery, which included characters that were sorcerers. One can only speculate about how Beadle regarded Crowley's antics, but perhaps a passage in *Witch-Doctors* offers a clue:

> There are two types of magicians: those who are partially conscious hypocrites, and those who are gulled by their own fakes; for he who makes magic must be ever ready with an explanation of failure and very ingenious in the making. The fool, believing in his own medicine, is as much astounded at failure as the victim is angry.[183]

***

There exists one other document that contains a mother lode of pithily rendered biographical detail, and it remains the most widely cited source of information on the author's background:

Beadle's first *Adventure* story, "The Christ-Man," appeared in the 18 May 1918 issue. The magazine routinely provided a special forum, "The Camp-Fire," that featured letters from their contributors that supplied additional information about the

[183] See *Witch-Doctors*, p. 189.

authors or about how they composed their tales. Beadle's first and most informative contribution to the "Camp-Fire" column was published in the 3 July issue, which also featured his second *Adventure* story.

> My native heath is somewhere in mid-Atlantic. I was born rolling and have been ever since. No moss. My infancy was spent around Siam and the farther East: early memories, fire-flies mosquitoes and ayahs. ["Ayah": a nurse or maid native to India.] Educated at boarding schools in England; hence no home life and consequent atrophy of the sentimentalities. Parental Government required me to become a consulting marine engineer; but a congenital dislike of work and a gaudy poster persuaded me to learn poker, to starve in Cape Town where I held down a waiter's job for four hours and to join the British South African Police.
>
> Too late for big rebellion but kindly chief got up a small one to console me; saw Boer War in B. S. A. P. [British South African Police], Morley's Scouts (unpaid Looting Corps) (if any of the Scouts should read this should be glad to hear from them) and Stock Recovery Dept. After Peace held various jobs from three days to a week – in a news office, a bar, hawker, insurance agent – and peddled cheap jewelry for three months (and made money!); served in Transvaal Customs and became Asst. Compound Manager to the Witwatersrand Native Labor Association.
>
> Then I raised a syndicate to support me for an exploring-trip on the headwaters of the Zambezi. Returned to London to promote a company; failed

> – of course. A head on a coin sent me to British East Africa and Uganda; native trading, running transport from Victoria Nyanza to the Kilo Mines, Congo; shooting and various ventures. England again, company promoting; and failed again.
>
> Went to Dutch Borneo, rubber planting. Afterward returned to go to Morocco; penetrated into interior in disguise during rebellion; met Pretender Sultan, Mulai Hafid; instead of cutting my throat or crucifying me as predicted he gave me a palace and an escort and treated me as an ambassador; eventually I failed and Hafid lost his throne. We both had a royal time, anyway.
>
> Until I came to America last year I have lived in France.

When Beadle says "My native heath is somewhere in mid-Atlantic. I was born rolling and have been ever since," he isn't speaking in merely a metaphoric manner. On 26 or 27 October 1881 he was born at sea while aboard the SS *Cilurnum* (a Merchant Marine vessel). His parents were Isabella Kay and Henry Beadle; the latter was the ship's captain. According to their marriage certificate, both Henry Beadle and Isabella's father, Peter Kay, were "master mariners"; so it's likely that the men were previously acquainted as colleagues. The certificate states that Henry's father, William, was a "gentleman." Other genealogical sources confirm that Henry descended from sea captains.

Charles' life was soon disrupted by a tragedy: the death of his mother from consumption when he was only two years old. Isabella perished while sailing aboard the *Cilurnum*, the same ship upon which she gave birth to her son.

Readers of *Adventure* may have wondered how much of this autobiographical sketch was merely a tall tale, but the more we unearth about Beadle the more his account proves to be accurate. Genealogical research conducted by Beadle's descendents revealed that Charles "Marmaduke" Beadle enlisted in the British South African Police, Matabeleland Division, Regimental Number 1019, on 26 November 1898 and was discharged (along with his brother Henry) on 18 July 1901. Upon discharge he had a different regimental number, one that indicates he had transferred to a division in Mashonaland. For his service in the Anglo Boer War Beadle was awarded the Queen's South Africa Medal. His great-niece has speculated that Charles may have fictionalized his middle name ("Marmaduke") in order to enlist a second time. We also find a reference to this imaginary moniker in *Dark Refuge,* when the Beadle protagonist "William" cringes upon hearing his wife and mother-in-law pronounce his first name: "How I hate that name (why hadn't I been called Marmaduke, or Clarence, or Montmorency St Clair de Plushbottom?) on their lips!"

With the constant expansion of digital resources, new tidbits continue to surface that help to complete the biographical puzzle. For example, I recently unearthed an article published in the 30 September 1922 *Deseret News* in which he reiterates many of these same details but adds an interesting twist at the end:

Beadle Tells Something about Himself

> Houghton Mifflin Company like other publishers have the habit of sending out to their new authors brief questionnaires which sometimes when filled in and returned prove really exciting reading. Charles Beadle, whose tale of darkest Africa "The

> Witch Doctors" was just published, began his interesting career by being born in mid-Atlantic, he was educated in England, served in the Boer War. For his services there he received the Boer War medal "for never having seen a shot fired." His politics are "tribal" and "his professional record" as follows: "Bum, waiter, mounted policeman, member of unpaid Looting Corps (Boer War), Transvaal Customs Service, traveler in cheap jewelry, asst. compound manager, explorer, company promoter, asst. manager rubber plantation, transport running, asst. king maker and concessionaire hunter, writer." In answer to the question of chief inspiration of "Witch Doctors" he says: "Residence among savages in Africa for some ten years and similar residence in England, France, and America."[184]

The last line is intriguing. The use of the term "savages" to describe African tribes was, unfortunately, rather commonplace back then. The British publisher of *Witch-Doctors*, Jonathan Cape, even ran an ad in the 7 July edition of the *Times* with the tagline: "A picture of life among the Savages of the African Jungle." But not so common was the notion (which Beadle seems to be putting forth here) of living among the white savages of England, France, and America.

In any case, his work for *Adventure* now goes into high gear; between May 1918 and December 1926 a total of twenty-six of his tales will be published there, including serialized novels and novellas. For an author of adventure fiction, this was certainly the place to be. The magazine first hit the newsstands in October 1910 and featured British novelists such as Rider

[184] *Deseret News* (Salt Lake City); section 5, p. 3.

Haggard, Rafael Sabatini (*Captain Blood*), and Baroness Orczy (*The Scarlet Pimpernel*) as well as American writers such as Talbot Mundy, Arthur Friel, J. Allan Dunn, Harold Lamb, and Gordon Young. It steadily rose in circulation, and on 21 October 1935 *Time* magazine ran a piece about *Adventure* titled "The No. 1 Pulp."

John Locke, a connoisseur of adventure fiction who has republished Beadle's stories under his Off-Trail Publications imprint, has recently remarked upon Beadle's unique talent as an *Adventure* author. When I asked for his personal reaction to reading Beadle's work, he said:

> I'm always looking for authenticity, because I feel that feeds into the fiction in a special way. And I'm convinced he had that. He got out of South Africa in 1900 or 1901. Then he shows up in Morocco around 1908 and is there for four years. And wrote a lot of fiction set there as well. But that seven or eight years in there, he must have been working his way around Africa. And hearing things and experiencing things. But there's no autobiography of it. He didn't recycle it into true stories of Africa. It's all in his fiction. So in a sense, you can get at his life in that period through the fiction. And the fiction did seem authentic to me. You read it and you go: "OK, there's no way that he made all of this up." He'd obviously been there.
>
> So, I like the fiction with some authenticity built in. And with Beadle, it's also his authenticity of location. In *Adventure* you did get the case of, say, someone went to the library and read up on the Sahara Desert as much as they could and then just

> invented a story. That would fool most people if you did it well. But it would probably not have those magical quirks that you get if you had actually been there and seen the unique elements of life that would never have found their way into print otherwise. And for me, Beadle was one of those: the authenticity. To find someone who'd actually been places and seen things, that to me is kind of the holy grail. The fiction spoke for itself, and the content.[185]

Other periodicals that featured Beadle's work during this period include (roughly in order of first publication): *Everybody's, Ainslee's, Argosy, Romance, Top-Notch Magazine, Short Stories, The Frontier* (all in the U.S); and, in the U.K., *The Blue Magazine, Tip Top Stories of Adventure and Mystery, The Regent Magazine,* and *The 20-Story Magazine*. (*Short Stories* was also reprinted in the UK.) Most of his contributions are written in the style of his *Adventure* stories; but there are some notable exceptions that hint at his ability – and perhaps his long-term goal – to pen something bearing a more literary stamp.

In 1920 the highly respected journal *Coterie* republished Beadle's "African Love Song." A quarterly of art, prose, and poetry, *Coterie* boasted an impressive editorial board, including Conrad Aiken, T. S. Eliot, Richard Aldington, and Aldous Huxley. In this particular issue we also find a poem by Douglas Goldring, who would later coauthor *Artist Quarter* with Beadle. It also hosts work by several of the journal's renowned editors; poetry by Amy Lowell; and drawings by Ossip Zadkine and André Derain.

It may have been through personal contacts made in Paris or London that Beadle's work found its way into *Coterie*. Known

[185] Telephone interview with John Locke, 22 July 2022.

primarily for publishing modernist poetry, six issues of the journal appeared between 1919 and 1921, and it featured artwork by Montparnos such as Modigliani, Nina Hamnett, and Moïse Kisling.

By this time Beadle had completed his American adventure, which included an August 1918 visit to Grand Isle, Louisiana; residence at the King George Hotel in Sausalito and, beginning in September, at 334 Mason Street in San Francisco. (This information is derived from announcements placed in *Adventure* for readers who were seeking travel guide consultations.) He was back in Manhattan by October, as evidenced by a letter penned to the author Theodore Dreiser. (See Illustrations.) By November 1918 he had returned to Montmartre, residing at 7, place de Tertre – the setting of a dope-fueled orgy portrayed in *Dark Refuge*.[186] But according to a notice in *Adventure*'s 3 August 1920 issue, the wayfaring author could now be reached via the "Society of Authors and Composers, Central Buildings, Tothill St., Westminster, London." This message is also reprinted in the 18 October and 16 March 1920 issues. A letter written by Beadle and reproduced in the 3 May 1921 *Adventure* announces his return to Paris.

By July 1922 – the summer of Beadle's fortieth year – reviews of his most commercially successful novel, *Witch-Doctors*, began to appear in the British and American press. (It was published by Houghton Mifflin in the States and by Jonathan Cape in England.) At least twenty-six periodicals feature reviews of the novel, most of them filled with praise, including such notable and widely-circulating papers as the London *Times*, the *New York Herald*, the *New York Tribune*, and the *New York Times Book Review and Magazine*. One of the more intelligent articles

[186] This address appears in two separate issues of *Adventure*: on 3 December 1919 and on 18 March 1920.

appeared in the 15 October edition of the *Oakland Tribune*, and it offers a cogent summary of the action and adventure:

> A villain who might have come out of the movies, a knowledge of native life in Africa, the superstitions and voodoo practices and a melodramatic tale in unusual setting, make of *Witch Doctors* a story packed with elements to hold attention.
>
> Charles Beadle has written something "different." The results, apparently, of an interested study into the savagery of the jungles, he has put into a story a strange, mystic and almost too exciting story. There is no question Beadle could write an interesting book on his theme of witch doctors without the aid of the narrative. The reader will thank him for the inclusion of this knowledge and will find it not the least enjoyable part of the book.
>
> An American scholar is betrayed by a brutal officer in Africa, sent to the jungles with a party of natives instructed to see that he does not return. Bernier knows enough of the native customs and fears to play upon them. He makes himself a god in the village and outdoes the witch doctors in magic. In the end he saves himself and his betrayer, but not until there have been some close calls and some terrifying adventures.
>
> The incidents are sharply drawn and dramatic. They hold together pictures of African tribal life, pictures in which native characters are introduced faithfully by a man who has made their study an occupation. It is easy to imagine these African scenes are all important. They are what will

> remain in the reader's mind when the book is closed and what make of a good and thrilling story a distinctive one.

The *Times* of London was one of the few publications that picked up on a deeper, underlining thread contained in the plot. Speaking of the conflicting protagonists (the German, Zu Pfeiffer, and the American, Bernier), the reviewer notes: "On the contest between them is based the drama of a story which reflects in different terms and on a smaller scale the emotions of the Great War." And a review in Rochester's *Democrat and Chronicle* highlights another salient point: the tale juxtaposes the fetish-worshipping African tribes with the Anglo-Saxon's fetishizing of religious icons and the "goddess" embodied in rites of romantic love.

But what's particularly striking about *Witch-Doctors* is the way in which the author evokes the reader's sympathy for so many characters (both major and minor), largely through the use of dialogue and interior monologue. One often senses Beadle's affection for his protagonists, which in turn serves to trigger the reader's own fondness for them.

***

In the spring of 1927 Beatle's fifth novel, *The Blue Rib: A Romance of the Riviera*, was published in London by Philip Allan. A publicity notice proclaimed: "Here is that rare event, an original book, impressionistic, elusive, and highly amusing. The hectic kaleidoscope provided by the Riviera of these days has never before been depicted with such aloof intimacy. There is a delicate little plot, but the spell of the book lies in its characterization. Mr. Beadle, though his African studies are well known in this country and America, has never had his fantastic

novels of Western life published in the English language. On account of the intimate picture which is given of life on the Riviera it is a book that will be much discussed." (*The Publishers' Circular and Bestsellers' Record,* 20 August 20 1917, p. 248.) But the reviews were mixed. A journalist for the *Aberdeen Press and Journal* writes: "Monte Carlo again suggests gaming and gamesters, high stakes and confused intrigue, and these are supplied in plenty in Charles Beadle's *Blue Rib,* and elusive title that barely justifies itself in the story." But the *Montrose Standard* in Angus, Scotland was more enthusiastic:

> The author in his new book gives his readers a new, original and impressionist picture of the lure of the Riviera and portrays in clever style the many sides of life among the cosmopolitan crowds of all nationalities that gather at these gay resorts. Mr. Beadle's African studies are already well known in this country and in America, and now the reading public will welcome the new novel on account of the intimacy with which he handles his subject. A delicate plot runs through the book but its strong point is the clever way he depicts the various characters in the novel and the intimate picture he draws of the gay life on the Riviera. A book that will no doubt be appreciated by many, and at the same time one that will likely be subjected to considerable discussion.

The *Birmingham Post* regarded *The Blue Rib* as a "jazz novel … delightfully vulgar." And a reviewer for the *Sheffield Daily Telegraph* in Yorkshire writes: "*The Blue Rib* tells a story of intrigue, blackmail, gambling, and love (of various descriptions) on the Riviera. It is lively and amusing though to what extent it

represents actuality we should not like to say. One hopes that even the Riviera is not quite like that."

What none of these journalists mention is that Beadle may have had a personal reason for wandering along the Riviera in search of a story. His daughter, Jane, who was born in Cannes, returned to the Côte d'Azur at some point after the First World War. She lived there in the 1920s, was married there in January 1950, and died there in 2002. After Neil Pearson published his Jack Kahane biography, he was contacted by Beadle's great-niece Patricia (a descendant of Charles' brother, William, via William's daughter Barbara), and he later had the pleasure of meeting her. Thanks to this contact we know that the roving, nomadic author frequented the Côte d'Azur during this period. In a letter that Pearson sent to a colleague of the publisher John Locke, he writes:

> I went to Patricia's home and spent a hugely enjoyable day with her, piecing together the story as best we could. She was good enough to allow me to take photocopies of Beadle's letters to her great aunt. The letters, dating from the late 20s and early 30s, are written from Paris, Saint-Malo, Antibes, Nice … he seems to have led a chaotic existence, moving from one flea-ridden hotel to the next, trying to keep one step ahead of his creditors. One letter gives his address as c/o a branch of Barclays Bank, another as "Hotel Esquimau." The letters, apparently all written to the only member of the family who would have any contact with him [William's daughter Isabel, the aunt of Patricia], are extremely difficult to decipher …[187]

[187] Thanks to Neil Pearson for sharing this with me.

As with many of Beadle's novels, copies of *The Blue Rib* are extremely rare. According to the WorldCat index, only a half dozen institutional libraries include one in their collection. The same number applies to *The City of Shadows* and *Dark Refuge*. But these novels fared better than *A Passionate Pilgrimage*, of which only two copies are currently shelved (one in the British Library, the other in the National Library of Wales).

***

In November 1928 reviews for Beadle's *The Esquimau of Montparnasse* began to appear in the British press. In Yorkshire the *Sheffield Independent* called it "a clever satire on the ways of strangers who go to Paris in search of wild Bohemianism. They come with greedy eyes, hoping to shocked by vice and perversion, and end up by themselves shocking the Parisians. The Americans suffer chiefly as subjects for satire." That same month a reviewer for the *Birmingham Daily Gazette* in Warwickshire wrote: "Mr. Charles Beadle evidently knows the real artistic life of Paris from within, otherwise he could not have satirized the sham, largely created by wealthy vulgarians, as he has done with so much gusto in *The Esquimau of Montparnasse*. This is a novel of unusual kind; it has not only Gallic wit but also a close understanding of the Gallic attitude."

The motivation for writing the novel seems clear: by now Beadle was disgusted by the circuslike atmosphere that adhered to Montparnasse, much of it created by the posthumous legend of Modigliani and his so-called bohemian life. ("Bohemian isn't a manner of living," instructs the Esquimau, "it's an attitude of mind.") Now, the quarter was attracting the kind of vulgarian Anglo-Saxon that Beadle abhorred. When it was republished in America two years later under the title *Expatriates at Large*, some

of the reviewers – especially those working for small-town newspapers – were horrified by Beadle's rendering of lowlife debauchery. Others were intrigued and fascinated, as exemplified by this sympathetic piece from the *Buffalo Evening News*:

> Paris always has been the paradise for the seekers after the colorful joys of life. But of the old gay life there, it appears, there is little left but the husks; and these are being trampled on by swine. The City of Light is being infested by expatriates who have, to a large extent, made it more like a lunatic asylum than anything else. This, at any rate, is the burden of *Expatriates at Large* by Charles Beadle.
>
> *Expatriates at Large* shows a greater madness of the amateurs of delirium then *The Sun Also Rises*, but a gayer futility than *Sleeveless Errand*. The author has assembled a queer collection of people from various countries, who are fatuously pursuing the bubble joy. There is no very definite plot, except and so far as the mere impact of persons casually come together may constitute plot.
>
> The chief character, called Eskimo, seems to be a strange compound of Sancho Panza and Don Quixote, Socrates, Plato, Anatole France with a liberal dash of a poet of the French decadence and a member of the group of Aubrey Beardsley. He is a poet, philosopher, prophet and buffoon. Altogether, a singular and amusing character. It is he who explodes the lamentable excuse that fake artists, decadence, and the hungerers after thrills offer for coming to Paris to be free to do the things

> they have been brought up to believe they shouldn't do.
>
> This is a mad book, but very interesting and not a little enlightening.

The most amusing anecdote to emerge about this divide of opinion over the novel's value concerns that of a critic who initially doubted the veracity of Beadle's portraits. The *Argus-Leader,* a newspaper published in Sioux Falls, South Dakota, featured an article in March 1930 that contains the following information:

> When his novel "Expatriates at Large" was published in England under the title, "The Eskimo of Montparnasse," some of the critics, although they praised the book declared that Charles Beadle the author, had invented some of the places and situations dealt with in the book. They could not believe that even Paris could contain the dives described there. Mr. Beadle, who has been living in Paris for many years and was an intimate companion of the noted artist, Modigliani, who died recently, immediately issued a challenge. He offered to take any of his critics on a personally conducted tour to prove that nothing in "Expatriates at Large" was exaggerated. The critic, Wilfred Whitcomb, who happened to be in Paris accepted; and after two nights declared himself thoroughly satisfied that Mr. Beadle was right and went into a small country town outside of Paris to recuperate.

The following August the *Detroit Free Press* chimed in: "The publishers [of *The Esquimau of Montparnasse*] quote a passage from a letter from the author to a friend in which he says that he had offered to push a peanut the length of the Champs-Élysées with his nose if he could not prove on a personally conducted tour that he was not over drawing the picture. Wilfred Whitcomb took up the challenge, he writes, and a couple of nights finished him."

A comparison between *The Esquimau of Montparnasse* and *Dark Refuge* yields a strange contrast, despite the fact that each novel portrays the same geographical landscape. While *Dark Refuge* features a deeply introverted, visionary dive into the psyche of the author and that of his closest friends, *The Esquimau of Montparnasse* portrays a collection of mostly puerile figures whose characterization is drawn via their thrill-seeking actions and (intentionally) insipid dialogue. The narrational point of view is completely extroverted as it chronicles the superficial transit of these frivolous protagonists. As a satirical novel, its purpose is to slyly and cynically comment upon how the beatific landscape of Paris is now befouled by tourists who remain blind to the sacred stuff of art and to the charm of the ancient city that engendered such priceless creations.

As with *Dark Refuge,* the novel contains thinly disguised portraits of Beatrice Hastings and Modigliani, but I have yet to find a reviewer who seems to have noticed this. Unlike *Dark Refuge,* these particular characters make only brief, fleeting appearances, yet their cameos are instantly recognizable. Hastings is described as a woman named Chicken, "clad in a flamingo robe with a toque garnished with lace like a ham, and with a cunning little veil falling discreetly over the eyes." Beadle also re-creates an infamous scene of aggression from Modigliani's biography: when Hastings caught her friend Simone Thiroux getting cozy with Modigliani at the Café Rotonde, she threw a

wine glass at Simone, leaving her with a permanent scar above her eye.

Beadle sets the scene by first describing the artist and his mistress seated inside the café: "The corduroy-clad man, with the face of an unwashed Roman senator, caressed the inner forearm of a girl with the face of a Raphael angel [Simone] while, with glittering gypsy eyes, he discoursed in voweled French upon the relation between the Italian Renaissance and African sculpture." Meanwhile, the locals grumble about how the quarter is being overrun by Anglo-Saxons, who care only about cocktail parties and "le dancing" and whose presence serves to jack up the rents. In the midst of this hubbub, the Hastings character enters the café:

> "Hullo, Chicken," says the Esquimau, "what're you doing here?"
>
> But the Chicken was occupied in staring malevolently beneath the brim of her veiled hat at the man in corduroy who, with the Raphael angel in one arm, gesticulated eloquently with the other.
>
> "Ow!" squealed the Chicken as if someone had stuck a pen into her, and snatched up the Esquimau's glass:
>
> "Saligaud!" she squealed and, turning, ran out of the café.
>
> The glass, missing the man's head by an inch, smashed against the wall and a flying splinter left a bleeding weal on the angel girl's cheek.[188]

***

[188] See *The Esquimau of Montparnasse*, pp. 65, 186, 191-192.

In 1931 a far more literary footprint appears in the form of verse, when Beadle published three poems ("Hashish," "Voyage," and "Small Body") in Bob Brown's avant-garde anthology, *Readies for Bob Brown's Machine.*[189] The author's fellow contributors include Kay Boyle, Paul Bowles, James T. Farrell, Gertrude Stein, Ezra Pound, and William Carlos Williams. Although Beadle's attempt at poetry isn't really successful, the poems provide further evidence that he may have been hoping to shift gears and to pursue a more sophisticated genre of writing.

The additional evidence that we have for this assertion appears in the form of a literary short story, "Black Velvet," published in March 1932. Once again, an author known primarily for his fast-paced, danger-ridden commercial fiction manages to break into a prestigious literary journal. *This Quarter* was one of the leading expat magazines in Paris; and this particular issue includes first appearance work by such distinguished guests as E. E. Cummings, Rupert Croft-Cooke, August Derleth, A. L. Rowse, and Paul Valery.

Running just three and a half pages, "Black Velvet" contains some remarkably vivid imagery that captures the brightly painted African landscape. It also features what may be considered an "open ending." A colonialist selects a beautiful young Black woman to be his erotic playmate; and, at the end of the tale, when he prepares to return to his proper British household, he simply passes her on to his incoming colonialist counterpart:

[189] Bob Brown's biographer, Professor Craig Saper, has informed me that, like Beadle, Brown also published stories in *Argosy* and *Top-Notch* magazine. Brown arrived in Paris on 6 April 1928, and both writers spent time in Cagnes-sur-Mer. See Craig Saper, *The Amazing Adventures of Bob Brown: A Real-Life Zelig Who Wrote His Way Through the 20th Century*, NY: Fordham University Press, 2016.

like a gift to be shared among men. The story is open ended in the sense that we don't know if the narrator approves or disapproves of this action. Instead, it remains a "just so" chronicle. But of equal importance to the plot is the author's mastery of the English language. Some of the more poetic passages achieve a richness and sophistication that calls the reader back, to linger over the melody and imagery. The story opens:

> Lusts steamed as multicolored as the hot stenches of the tropical forest. From greeny filigrees apes chattered exotic obscenities to screaming parrots. Scarlet, cobalt and yellow birds glimmered in vernal twilight like a dreamer's sensual desires. Flies droned of fetid couplings. Earth oozed fecundity.

Then, a couple of paragraphs later:

> Dawned the odors of smoke and yeasty beer. Banana fronds were laced in vivid green. The jazz of the jungle muted to the yapping of curs, cries of children, bleating of goats, lowing of cattle; and ululating in staccato, shrill notes, round and yellow, velvety, erethismic as a woman's caress.

Thus, "Black Velvet" hints at a talent that will later emerge in *Dark Refuge,* just six years later. In an author's development – no matter what his age – much can happen in just a half dozen years.

***

Sometime in the late 1920s or early 1930s, Beadle engaged in a correspondence with his niece Isabel (daughter of his brother William), which continued until at least 1938. Isabel's sister Barbara later inherited the letters (twelve of which were penned by Beadle) and then passed them along to her daughter, Patricia. As I mentioned earlier, after Neil Pearson's *Obelisk* was published in 2007, Patricia contacted Neil and they spent a pleasant afternoon together reading through these missives. When I spoke with Neil in July 2022, he described some of their salient points:

"The correspondence started with a letter from Isabel," he said, "who would have been very young, while Beadle would have been almost fifty."

Isabel begins by expressing her surprise upon hearing that she has a female cousin living in France, adding that she'd like to meet her, although at present she's unable to travel there. She also conveys her wishes for her cousin's happy marriage. Later she refers to Beadle as the father.

Apparently Beadle had asked Isabel to come to France to serve as a member of his daughter's *Conseil de Famille* (a council formed to look after her interests). But this is a responsibility that Isabel feels incapable of pursuing, since she isn't privy to the unique circumstances of the situation. She adds that she feels that only he, as the father, can properly determine whether the groom can bring his daughter happiness.

From this we may surmise that the "bride to be" is Beadle's daughter Jane, who was born in July 1915 and whose mother died two months later. The institution of the *Conseil de Famille* was formed for the protection of the interests of orphans and minors. In practice it's composed of three members selected from the maternal side of the family and three from the paternal side. A final member, a presiding officer, is the local justice of

the peace. Besides making decisions about a minor's estate, the council has the power to approve or oppose a marriage.

Therefore, it's likely that Beadle was hoping to appoint two other members to the council that would support his interests in his daughter's affairs. It's also likely that his archenemy – his mother-in-law, Teresa Isabel Ashwell (1866 – 1940) sat in opposition to his every wish on this same *Conseil*.

The Napoleonic Code of 1804 set the marriageable age in France at fifteen years of age for females and eighteen for males. (In 2006 this was changed to eighteen years old for both sexes.) If Jane had wanted to marry as a minor between the ages of fifteen and twenty, the marriage would have occurred sometime between 1930 and 1935.

Although we were unable to find evidence of a marriage conducted during this period, subsequent research by Céline Cardon revealed that on 3 January 1950 Jane married Igor Bely (a Russian, born in Odessa on 29 May 1916), in Nice. A chemical engineer and a translator, Igor was the son of Michel Bely and Olga Vonine; he died in Nice on 1 May 1978. As mentioned earlier, Elizabeth Bely, the daughter of Jane and Igor, was born on 7 August 1946 in Bournemouth, England.

Beadle also alludes to the *Conseil* in a letter dated 19 February 1931, composed on a letterhead from Le Normandy Café-Bar located at 1, Place Grimaldi, Nice. The handwriting in this missive is particularly difficult to decipher, but thanks to Neil Pearson's dogged persistence several key phrases are now legible. After referring to "le juge de paix" (the justice of the peace), Beadle complains about wasting his time "waiting on these half-witted idiots." He also mentions that he "gave the damned property" to his daughter, which might explain why she remained in Nice for most of her life. (At the time of her death she was residing at 8, avenue Georges Clemenceau.) And Beadle adds: "My kid is crazy to meet you." Thanks to this letter

we know for certain that he maintained some sort of relationship with Jane.

Neil continues:

> At this time he was on the Côte d'Azur. Obviously, he seems to have come into Nice and Cannes, but he was working fitfully in Grasse. The correspondence started, I think, as a result of the family getting wind of a postal address for Charles sometime in the late Twenties. [This could have been one of the many notices that appeared in *Adventure* magazine.] And the first extant letter is from Isabel to Beadle …
>
> They mostly speak to the dissolute life he led. They ramble. They're constantly talking about how impossible it is to find either a job, or money, or a commission. I think he was teaching English as a second language in Grasse and eking out a living there. [Located on the hills overlooking the Riviera, just north of Cannes.]
>
> There tend not to be addresses on the letters. Letter four is from Barclays Bank, Nice, on the Promenade des Anglais. Letter seven he heads: "Chateau Esquimaux, Cagnes-sur-Mer." As you know, Cagnes-sur-Mer was a big watering hole where bohemian Paris went to summer. I think Chateau Esquimaux is a made-up name; it's just the house where he's staying. Letter eight isn't dated but is written from the Hôtel des Capucines, in Paris. [Addressed 13, rue des Feuillantines, in Montparnasse.] Then there's one from Palais-Royal, which was on the rue de Beaujolais in Paris. Palais-Royal Press published *White Gambit*.

> Then there's the Maison Jeunnes, Antibes. He moved around; he moved around a *lot*. And you get the feeling he was usually sleeping on someone's floor. Saint-Malo ... Then there's one written on the note paper of the Normandy, a café-bar, at number 1, place Grimaldi, Nice. That was clearly his stomping ground. But it sounds as if he was geographically and psychologically all over the place. He's often asking for money, but not in so many words. I mean, he's saying: *Could you use your family connections to see if such-and-such publisher needs* ... You know, it's that sort of stuff.
>
> I get the feeling that they're barely out of their teens, these girls.[190] And they've found this old soak of an uncle they never knew that they had, who now thinks that they've got more clout in the world of letters than he does. But there's a lot of self-pitying going on. There's a lot of: I have no money; I don't know what I'm going to do. He talks to them in a way that you think: *Really* ... that is actually deniable. He keeps *just* the right side of propriety.[191]

Neil points to one letter in particular, written from Nice, that gives us a "flavor of their tone." Beadle begins by complaining that he doesn't care for relatives and never did, adding that he's managed to avoid any contact with the extended family for twenty years – and now these nieces suddenly appear! He doesn't even know how old they are, but admits that math is not his strong point – as he's always had trouble calculating

[190] In 1931 Barbara was only twenty-four; her sister Isabel, twenty seven.

[191] Interview with Pearson conducted by telephone on 24 July 2022.

bills – not to mention paying for them. Upon learning that one of the nieces has decided to become an art teacher, he responds by asking why not enter into some alternate form of slavery – such as marriage? Or better yet, relocate to America, where a woman can divorce after only six months and then collect a nice pension!

Besides helping us to reconstruct his whereabouts, the correspondence affords us an intimate glimpse into Beadle's psyche – one that reveals a more sardonic side of his character. But there's also a playfully provocative tone that runs throughout these letters. He refuses to self-censor; and rather than adopting the role of a traditional respectable uncle, he takes it upon himself to be as outlandish as possible as he "educates" his nieces by sharing his unorthodox worldview. Perhaps he wants to see just how far he can push them into his jaded perspective. At the same time, he makes it clear that he's granting them a certain access to his life that he's unwilling to share with anyone else in the family. For example, in a letter from Nice he writes: "As for news as I told you I don't know any relatives respected (none have any money as far as I know) or otherwise … I'm a savage. Savages may not look at their mother-in-laws[,] and the Esquimaux bury alive their old people when they become a nuisance. Excellent. That's why I won't recognize you as relatives. Send me your sketches and tell me all about yourselves." In a letter composed at the Hôtel des Capucines in the fifth arrondissement in Paris, he says: "Oh by the way I've had another novel published in Paris. Of course it doesn't sell but I'm sending you a copy." In a postscript he adds: "I send book on condition that the fambly" [purposely misspelled] – (I have a fambly complex – any fambly!) neither see nor hear of it. (Barbara if you like.)" Since Beadle has severed himself from his relatives, we may read this as a high

compliment, regardless of the sarcastic tenor of his communiqués.

Unfortunately his handwriting is so atrocious that much of the communication remains indecipherable, and all too often we're left with mere fragments of transcription.

Beadle's seventh novel, an adventure story titled *The White Gambit,* was published by Palais-Royal Press in Paris in May 1933. (Most likely, this was the novel alluded to in the letter above.) While his precarious state of affairs was largely due to his dissolute lifestyle, the catastrophe of the Great Depression would have made things even more difficult. It was one of the worse years of the economic crisis; and so, one wonders how the timing may have affected the fate of this novel, which attracted scant attention. In addition, Palais-Royal was a small publishing house, one that lacked the resources of Beadle's British and American publishers. Nonetheless, a copy of *White Gambit* made its way to the *Daily Times-News* of Burlington, North Carolina, which featured a review in its 10 June edition. It reads, in part:

> One of the most unusual and most unconventional books which has come to our attention in several months is Charles Beadle's *The White Gambit* [...]
>
> It is not the plot of this story – strange as it is – however, which most forcibly strikes the reader: it is rather the exotic beauty of the language in which the book is written. Mr. Beadle concerns himself saliently with style. He does not, as so many of the younger writers have done, attempt to create a new language; instead he molds today's language into new combinations, refreshing it and giving it something of new life.

> This is the story of the downfall of a savage tribe – ruin occasioned by the white man's greed and the greed of the savage. It is a story of fetishes and many gods and the striving of each god's priests to entrench his own particular god more firmly than the others. […]
>
> There is so much of strange beauty in this book that one finds it difficult to attempt a description. One of the outstanding features of Mr. Beadle's style is his use of the simile. Writing of the native village, he says: "The village resembled a vast ant's nest disturbed, and hummed like swarming bees." And again he writes: "Then like the eyes of a hippopotamus above the water emerged the words of the Brass-Eater again." And again a village is "like a clutch of brown eggs nestling in the gold of grass country which is six sun's swift march from the village of Matanga." The eyes of the priests are likened to "a gorged snake." And an old crone, after a harangue with Tsabi, is "like a bundle of faggots rattling with wrath."
>
> One will find *The White Gambit* worth reading for its style alone and for the primitive beauty in it.

Reading between the lines, we can see that although the author was working with a potboiler plot his prose continued to refine itself, and this didn't fail to impress the reviewer.

A handful of Beadle's pulp fiction stories appeared in the 1940s, but after *The White Gambit* he no longer pursued any book-length projects in this genre.

***

Henry Miller's ground-breaking novel, *Tropic of Cancer* – destined to help redefine obscenity laws in America and around the world – was issued the following year by the courageous Jack Kahane and his Obelisk Press. A friend of Miller's named Eve Adams[192] – another expat living in Paris – was hawking copies of the book on Boulevard Montparnasse, right in front of Le Dôme and La Coupole: the grand brasseries across the street from La Rotonde.

It's tempting to imagine Beadle strolling along the boulevard, pausing to chat with Eve, and purchasing a copy of this forbidden fruit. Or perhaps he heard about the explosive novel in some other way; it was certainly drawing a lot of attention, especially in Montparnasse. Therefore one wonders if *Tropic of Cancer*'s explicit rendering of human sexuality offered Beadle an

[192] Née Chawa Zloczower (1881-1944), a Polish Jew and outspoken lesbian, who later changed her name to Eve Adams (a probable combination of "Adam and Eve"). In 1925 she published 125 copies of *Lesbian Love*, a collection of short stories and illustrations that portrays some of the gay women that she met in her travels. She was also a friend of the anarchist Emma Goldman. By 1919 J. Edgar Hoover and the U.S. Bureau of Investigation were keeping tabs on Eve. In 1927 an undercover cop entered her Greenwich Village tea room (known as Eve's Hangout). After the officer obtained a copy of the "indecent" *Lesbian Love*, Eve was booked on several charges, including "disorderly conduct." She was convicted of publishing an obscene book and of attempting to have sex with a policewoman. Thanks to the help of an unreliable witness, Eve spent eighteen months in jail and was then deported to Poland, at the end of 1927. By 1930 she resurfaced in Paris, where she sold "forbidden books" – such as *Tropic of Cancer* – in various cafés. During the German Occupation she was arrested in Nice, then detained at Drancy in December 1943. Eve Adams later died in Auschwitz. See Jonathan Katz, *The Daring Life and Dangerous Times of Eve Adams*, Chicago: Chicago Review Press, 2021.

incentive to go a step further with what would eventually become *Dark Refuge*. Published by Obelisk just four years later, in June 1938, it was his eighth and final novel, and one unlike any of the others.

It's possible that Beadle was still holding out in France as the dark clouds of war lowered over the Continent. But by 1939 he repatriated to England and was residing at 331 Homewood Road, St. Albans, Hertfordshire. This according to the 1939 England and Wales Register, located at the National Archives in London. We also have a far less orthodox source for Beadle's ever-shifting whereabouts. On 6 June 1939 he visited Aleister Crowley at the latter's residence at Morton House, in Chiswick. According to Crowley's notebook, this was the first of five visits that Beadle made to Morton House. Biographer Tobias Churton is the source for this information:

> Pulp writer of *Witch-Doctors* (1922) Charles Beadle – who'd socialized with Crowley in Paris 1920 – 1929 (and whom he'd met in America during the war) – arrived on the sixth, dining five times chez Crowley before a note of October 23 explained Beadle's purpose: 'Here to pick my brains regarding Montparno [Montparnasse – Crowley's old haunt].'[193]

As I mentioned earlier, Beadle was then collecting material for his chronicle about Modigliani and Montparnasse, which was published only two years later.

It's likely that Beadle repatriated to England because war with Germany seemed imminent. Three months after his visit to

[193] Tobias Churton, *Aleister Crowley in England: The Return of the Great Beast*, Rochester, VT: Inner Traditions, 2021, e-book version.

Crowley, Germany invaded Poland; and then, two days later, both France and England declared war on Germany.

In June 1941, during Beadle's fifty-ninth year, Faber and Faber published *Artist Quarter: Reminiscences of Montmartre and Montparnasse in the First Two Decades of the Twentieth Century.* Pseudonymously coauthored with Douglas Goldring (under the nom de plume "Charles Douglas"), for many years it was regarded as the urtext of Modigliani biography. Equally important for our purpose, some of the content in *Artist Quarter* serves to further flesh out the fictionalized events depicted in *Dark Refuge,* thus providing a final autobiographical treasure trove. Modigliani biographer Pierre Sichel qualifies the coauthorship as follows: "While Goldring was actually the author of the book, the Charles part of the pseudonym comes from Charles Beadle ... Beadle did much research for *Artist Quarter* and also supplied special material for the book. In some chapters, when 'I' is used, it is Beadle himself speaking from experience" (this is clearly the case).

Sichel adds that Goldring's wife, Malin, harbored "unflattering memories" of Beadle: "At the time *Artist Quarter* was written Beadle was down on his luck. The research materials he delivered were practically illegible. 'He requested money in advance almost every week by unstamped letters, before having sent any copy at all.' But Beadle's memories were rich."[194]

In late October 1943, while suffering from gastroenteritis pain that she believed was symptomatic of cancer, Beatrice Hastings killed herself by turning on the gas jets of her stove in Worthing, Sussex. Shortly afterward, Beadle and Goldring received a manuscript from her estate: a surrealist novella titled "Minnie

[194] Pierre Sichel, *Modigliani: A Biography of Amedeo Modigliani*, p. 71, 294.

Pinnikin," written by Hastings in French, which dramatizes her relationship with Modigliani.

According to Modigliani biographer Kenneth Wayne, William S. Lieberman (the curator of the Museum of Modern Art) was preparing for a 1951 exhibit of Modigliani's work "when he was put into contact with Goldring and Charles Beadle by the art historian Douglas Cooper," and "through them he obtained a copy of Minnie Pinnikin."[195] Wayne doesn't mention the year that Lieberman contacted the authors, but the range would probably be sometime in the mid-to-late 1940s.

This account provides us with one of the last pieces of evidence that Beadle was still alive during this period. The other clue to his existence occurs on 10 June 1947 (two years after the end of World War II), when Beadle's "Nameless Spy" appeared in *Short Stories* magazine. According to John Locke, it's a "contemporary tale set in French North Africa and refers to the Allied Forces. It's his last known published work."[196]

The Allies' North African campaign commenced on 10 June 1940 and lasted through 13 May 1943; so it's probable that the story was composed during or shortly after this period.

***

Beadle was born two decades before the end of the nineteenth century: a product of the Victorian Era and its psychic imprint. No doubt, he was educated in one of those terribly oppressive, narrow-minded English boarding schools, circa 1893, whose two key talismans were sexual repression and a blind belief in the dictates of the British Empire. When, at age eighteen, he

[195] Kenneth Wayne, *Modigliani and the Artists of Montparnasse*, p. 205.
[196] John Locke, "The World of Beadle," featured in Charles Beadle, *The Land of Ophir*, Elkhorn, CA, Off-Trail Publications, 2012, p. 2.

traveled to Africa (perhaps, in search of his missing sibling Henry), he ended up being employed in Cape Town by the British South African Police during a period in which Blacks were treated like chattel and forced to labor till they dropped. Both Belgium and Britain maintained some of the most repressive, horrific regimes in Africa; and the eighteen-year-old writer was not only witness to all that; he served, in some function – wittingly or unwittingly – to preserve the status quo.

But Beadle was also aware of the pitfalls of his homeland, and he wasn't afraid to critique it. As early as 1917, in his story "NQO," the narrator describes the protagonist "Bob Byron" as "One of the thousands turned out yearly by the British educational machine, grandiosely ignorant save of the verb 'to rule.'" A striking passage in Beadle's novel *Witch-Doctors* is remarkable for its lambasting of all forms of Empire. While analyzing the motivations of the character "Zu Pfeiffer" – that wicked German imperialist who attempts to conquer various African tribes in the most sadistic manner – the protagonist "Birnier" remarks:

> the driving power in his caste and tribe was love of power to an excess masked with portentous solemnity under the cloak of benefiting this people and the peoples of the world; forcing them to have broad streets and sanitary arrangements, compelling them to laugh, to sing, and to be happy whether they would or no: an urge which is the curse of the world, the impulse to interfere in other folk's affairs, to teach them, to make them to know the true God, the right way of living, the right way of doing everything from the rising of the first sun of consciousness to that happy crack

> of doom when our planet tries to enforce its orbit upon some other planet.[197]

Witch-Doctors was warmly received by the British, in part because they viewed such remarks as being critiques not of themselves but of the "Teutonic" people and the German Empire (Zu Pfeiffer's homeland). But one can easily see that although his critique begins with allusions to Germany, it culminates in an exhortation against all forms of Empire everywhere.

A modern reader will certainly find many objectionable notions in *Dark Refuge,* chief among them the narrator's embittered appraisal of women and his overt and covert racism. These are the sorts of things that cast a shadow over the narrative, limit its artistic scope, and blunt its attempt at universal appeal. Yet perhaps the key question is not "Why was a man born in England in 1881 a misogynist racist?" For I would posit that almost anyone born anywhere in the white world of that time would be deeply imbued with such biases; and both the men and women of that era were imprinted with a culture of machismo that led them to view the differences between the sexes in a manner that would be regarded by many today as being utterly primitive.

With this in mind, perhaps a more interesting question might concern things such as: What made this fellow – who was otherwise such a predictable product of his era – into such a gifted artist, and one who achieved a vision that was so far in advance of his time? What gave him the courage to abandon his homeland, reject so much of his culture, and wander through Africa for so many years, seeking the beatific wonders and horrific mysteries that he hoped to encounter there? What impelled him to cross the Atlantic in 1916 and attempt to gain a

[197] See *Witch-Doctors*, London: Jonathan Cape, 1922, p. 178.

foothold in America while he catapulted from New York to Baton Rouge to San Francisco, all the while absorbing the flora and fauna of yet another foreign land, the details of which would eventually find their way into his ever-expanding literary palette? What drove him to such splendid cultural focal points as the Butte Montmartre during the days of Picasso; or to the artist quarter of Montparnasse during the reign of Modigliani? How did he manage to escape the repressive sexuality of Victoria's England and attempt to promulgate a more liberated view at such an early date? And most important of all, how was he blessed, so late in life, with the ability to render a sentence with the pure, streamlined elegance of high art?

All this is meant not to excuse the author but to place him in a proper context.

***

The great mystery of Beadle's peripatetic literary journey revolves round the question of how a man who preoccupied himself with the creation of pulp fiction for so many years could turn around at the relatively late age of fifty-six and publish such a remarkable work of literature. Certainly, nowhere in his prior career do we have a foreshadowing of the author who would eventually pen this stunning paragraph, featuring the voice of an intoxicated Cecci / Modigliani as he experiences the oncoming rush of artificial paradise:

> I glare at her open mouth which seems as if it were never going to shut. I never knew her face was so ugly, yet distorted beautifully. The gold stopping of a tooth looks like a black hole containing slaughtered sailors. I wonder who they could

> have been, those sailors, and why they were buried there. I've always known she was cunning, Magda. They must be murdered lovers, for no one would think of looking for their corpses in a rotten tooth. But I am still watching the open mouth, fearful to see the rotting bodies, and I sigh with relief when the lips come together. Then a terrible fear seizes me that they may open again, and I shall be forced to gaze on the skeletons, and I hate to see skeletons because they remind you of death. I never did like death. I shudder to think what I have escaped. Evidently she intended to murder me, too, and bury my body in her tooth. How wise I was to decide to get rid of her in time. And the diabolical cunning! She must have got a poor innocent dentist to put a gold tombstone on their grave.

We don't know what, exactly, triggered this transformation. Something must have opened Beadle's eyes and allowed him to penetrate more deeply into the creative matrix of literature. But as outlined above, at least we have at our disposal a few literary footprints that, upon closer inspection, reveal some clues along the way.

Neil Pearson has also raised the point that while Beadle may have preferred to pursue a literary career, being a down-and-out writer for much of his life he was forced to instead focus on commercial fiction: "As a writer-for-hire, I think he would have loved to have written on the level of *Dark Refuge* – and beyond, if he could – if people had been paying him enough to do that. But this is a guy who seems, for most of his life, to have not been sure where the next meal – and certainly the next drink –

was going to be coming from." [198] Perhaps Beadle was confirming this notion when, in a letter penned to his niece Isabel, he writes: "I'm going back to try to write a short story wherein as usual I may not say the things I think."

***

It's appropriate that *Dark Refuge* begins with an incarnation of Ganesha, deity of beginnings. For through the use of an omniscient first-person narrative, we witness (and vicariously participate in) the protagonist's godlike ability to enter into the psyche of the tale's various characters (like a peephole into the soul). The effect is kaleidoscopic. Part of the variegated psychic reflections result from a multiplicity of eyes / "I"s: *myself-that-was* or *myself-that-had-been* now being contemplated by *myself-that-is*. (E.g., "Eagerly myself-that-is seized the controls of myself-that-was.")

Self-contemplation begins when the ego-complex turns its gaze upon itself. But this process has no inherent limits – nothing to stop a third "I" from watching the second "I" contemplate the first. And so on: like two mirrors facing each other, reflecting the reflection ad infinitum. The simile is especially apropos if we consider the multiplicity of "egos" that comprise a human life over the course of decades. With this in mind, the elasticity of time, and the protagonist's interweaving dance through its interstices, provides the perfect web upon which to gather a phantasmagoria of "I"s / eyes, all glittering under the watchful triune gaze of Ganesha. The effect thus produced – an accordion-like unfolding of myriad states of consciousness – is what happens when, for example, Bill watches himself ("that was") through Francine's eyes ("those-that-had-been") and the eyes of "myself-that-is." Multiple "I"s through

[198] Interview with Pearson, 24 July 2022.

multiple "eyes." (A literary Cubism?) And yet, even this is not sufficient enough explanation. For it isn't clear whether what one sees (with the help of the hashish god) is objectively real. Is it a dream, a vision, a prophecy, the result of telepathic resonance, or something else? All we are left with are the haunting words of the subconscious, who declares that sometimes we sublimate "and sometimes we don't.... sometimes we find other ways and means."

It's also highly unusual for a novel to feature so many characters (I count over sixty, including those mentioned briefly in passing) and so many fanciful, outlandish episodes: a veritable thousand-and-one nights. At the same time, the author captures the panoply of Paris as it rolls by during this fascinating historical period – the end of La Belle Époque and the ensuing opulence and excess of the Roaring Twenties (known in France as Les années folles) – and portrays it in such a unique hallucinatory manner.

How ironic that Charles Beadle, who descended from a long line of sea captains, now portrays himself as "Beel" in the fo'c'sle of a ship, but one turned inward and navigating through the thoughts and feelings of his immediate contemporaries.

Another peculiar detail in the Beadle saga is that although the author may still claim a small cult following that remains focused on his adventure fiction, his most important work, *Dark Refuge,* is almost completely forgotten. The few references to the novel that exist online predictably zero in on the drug use in the story, as if this particular element is the only thing of import in the tale. A comparison between *Dark Refuge* and *Tropic of Cancer* might be enlightening in this regard. For just as the latter is still considered by many to be merely a "dirty book," *Dark Refuge* seems to have accrued a singular reputation for being a "dope book." It's certainly rife with sundry tales of intoxication; but if

one looks beneath the surface it's also host to so much more than that, for the chronicle is woven in the style and manner of literary art.

One thing that makes it so compelling is the author's ability to empathically render the lives of so many protagonists, largely through a carefully crafted dialogue. And like any good novelist, he accomplishes this by portraying those innumerable details that define characters as they confront the challenges and preoccupations of daily life. A sterling example is found in Beadle's rendition of Cecci / Modigliani. Since the artist would later become such a celebrated cultural figure, the author might have chosen to depict his most dramatic moments of success and failure, presenting Modi's story as, say, Thaddeus Wittlin does in his fictionalized Modigliani "biography." In other words, focusing on the artist's key achievements and challenging defeats; the crucial encounters and iconic highlights that comprise a great man's life. But instead, Beadle elaborates upon the peculiarities that frame an ephemeral moment, with its quirky little euphorias and prickly little annoyances, all of which slowly reveals the essence of personality as the plotline continues to roll forward. Therefore, instead of rendering only the heroic, peak experiences of biography, the narrator delights and revels in the minutia that delineates so much of human life.

Just as a talented painter would attempt while applying a fine, pointed brush, when Beadle lingers over the physical details that are embodied by such figures the effect is indeed painterly. For example, summoning the image of "Izzy" / Max Jacob, he conjures this: "On the far side of a large square table sat the gnomelike Izzy, queerly resembling a monk in a cell at work upon an illuminated parchment. Before him was a medley of papers and a mess of wet ashes in a saucer. Pen in one hand and a cigarette in the other he stared with diamond bright eyes at his friend, a malicious smile upon his cup-rimmed mouth." As I

mention in a footnote, Max was known to use ash as a painting medium.

But the "everyday minutia" of a typical *Dark Refuge* character is markedly different from that of an ordinary, law-abiding citizen. Thievery, threat of arrest, and con artist scams that backfire; paranoia, confusion, and delusion triggered by hashish hallucination and cocaine intoxication; the creepy-crawly addictions of morphine and heroin that make day-to-day life center round obtaining the next fix without attracting the attention of *les flics*; the shifting emotional alliances that are born during those dope-riddled pansexual orgies, which result in petty squalls, bitter hatreds, or overidealized declarations of "love"; the maniacal pursuit of art, music, or mysticism in such a manner that these quests become as destructive as any serious drug addiction ... Such are the challenges that consume our heroes and antiheroes in their troubled, tumultuous quest for inner and outer "refuge." At times, one wonders if the complete shedding of taboos is really worth it. But then again, once one steps foot on such a path, it's difficult to turn back. While some manage to dabble with dangerous toxins and maintain their sanity and creative ardor, others are crushed as a result of leading such a lifestyle, and they die prematurely – often in a horrific manner.

What remains especially striking about the novel – beyond the drug addiction, the luxurious orgies, or the shocking activities of characters such as Theodosia and Volodia – is the narrator's ability to not only enter into the psyche of his comrades but to return with a deeper understanding and compassion. The self-confessed man of atrophied "sentimentalities" – victim of a bad marriage to an iced-over prude who was a product of Britain's repressive "stiff upper lip," with its tendency to squelch authentic emotion and abort any direct expression of feeling – has, at this late juncture in life, opened his heart just a crack.

What seeps in through that aperture is a wholly other world. How fortunate it is that we're allowed to participate in it, voyeurs to the master voyeur: Bill, Beel, or Beadle.

Rather than constructing the dramatic arc of a traditional novel in which the main protagonist would – through incremental stages – undergo radical change and graduate through conflict, resolution, and revelation into a major characterological shift, the author has fashioned a protagonist who remains more focused on chronicling the deeply shifting characters and quicksand fortunes of those around him (although he himself does undergo certain subtle changes). And some of these shifting sands of fortune result in rather tragic episodes and highly dramatic conclusions. For this reason, *Dark Refuge* is no mere happy-go-lucky jaunt through the ecstasy of drug-induced euphoria. Lives are destroyed; human beings end up at the very bottom of the heap; and men are imprisoned, beaten to a pulp, and left to die in repressive Parisian jail cells. Women contract untreatable venereal disease as a result of being somewhat less than discriminating when selecting partners during those drug-fueled orgies, and their bodies are left to rot or are "treated" with quack remedies (such as mercury ointments) that poison them even more profoundly.

Then there are addictions that have nothing to do with drugs but that are certainly just as destructive. Vee is a victim of wooly-eyed mysticism and of a black-and-white fundamentalism that disables her from appreciating the human kindness with which she's met; for she remains so judgmental and narcissistic in her rejection of anyone who fails to meet her rigid expectations. ("If only he could see the light!" she exclaims to herself, bemoaning Bill's lack of so-called spiritual enlightenment.) The penalty for such narrow-mindedness is isolation from humanity and separation from her authentic self,

resulting in a desolation as barren as a junkie's empty, needle-festooned hovel.[199] (There were other punishments as well, and perhaps just as tragic: Picasso prohibited Hastings from his studio after she laughed at a Rousseau.) Among Vee's final remarks in the novel is the fitting phrase: "I must find a refuge somewhere."

The sybaritic Theodosia is a soulless voluptuary possessed by a cold-blooded aestheticism: "Man's title to the rank of the superior animal is that he applies aesthetics in the approach to, and variety in, the act of love, and the duration of sensation augmented by the invention of alcohol and the discriminate use of drugs!" She also symbolizes an aspect of Bill's tortured soul, whose feeling-function has been eclipsed and then usurped by the pursuit of sensual pleasure. But Theodosia also embodies something far more dangerous. While the nihilistic forces of fascism were cresting during the interwar years, this Aryan goddess wonders why the scientific principles of breeding are not applied to human beings. And while interacting with guests such as Volodia, she appraises them much as a laboratory researcher might examine an animal locked in a cage.

The richly layered character known as Volodia is a victim of an obsessive addictive need to serve the Muse of music. (He also realizes that music produces a druglike reaction in others: "for music I have noticed, always has an exciting effect on women.") He sacrifices his life to art, but his dual addiction to both music and drugs leads only to incarceration and to a pitiful, horrific death. His music monomania reminds one of the soldier "John Andrews" in the novel *Three Soldiers* (1921) by Dos Passos. Like Volodia, Andrews is a musician (and a composer),

[199] Modigliani biographer Meryle Secrest says of Beatrice Hastings: "It is hard to believe anything from a woman capable of weaving such a moonbeam cocoon of fantasy around herself." Secrest, *Modigliani: A Life*, New York: Knopf, 2011, p. 245.

and his obsession to create a work of genius completely derails the rest of his life. He finally goes AWOL and is arrested by two members of the military police, who severely beat him and then toss him into jail. The ordinary, everyday wonders of life are obliterated by a mad, Icarian quest to serve an intangible Muse.

But with characters such as Andrews and Volodia, the blame cannot be laid upon the Muse; the danger is spawned by an improper mental attitude that warps the individual and distorts and narrows his vision. At one point, Volodia rhetorically asks: "Am I not one of the greatest violinists in Europe? Shouldn't I be the greatest if I were known?" But minus an engagement with the violin, he cannot imagine a life worth living. When, during a dope-inspired delusion, he believes that he's lost his right arm, he concludes: "My career is finished. I am done. Nothing is left but suicide." Later in the tale, after he returns to his senses (relatively speaking!), his singular preoccupation is to "play something that would move a frog to tears."

Only Volodia's bizarre fetish with the contemplation of sparkling diamonds will empower his talent, and he flatly states: "I would follow jewels to hell" – which is precisely what occurs. (Those brightly glittering stones are also a powerful symbol of the immature artist's dependence upon something external, rather than looking within for authentic inspiration and drive.) Volodia remains far more enamored by these precious gems than by the alluring figure of Theodosia, whom he describes as "tall and very beautiful, blond with blue, blue eyes." (Note how that second "blue" serves to make Beadle's sentence especially evocative.) A unique character in literature, Volodia is utterly twisted; but in certain ways he remains so naive that the reader sympathizes with his plight – while simultaneously gaping at his freakish abnormalities. It's also through the personage of Volodia that we approach the deepest, darkest levels of the underworld.

While the "real-life identity" of Volodia will probably remain enshrouded in mystery, the narrative contains a number of clues regarding the model for Theodosia. Though she may be a composite figure, her portrait bears a strong resemblance – physically and psychologically – to Natalie Clifford Barney (1876 – 1972), a wealthy blonde American lesbian known for her literary salons, which, beginning in January 1909, were held at her villa at 20, rue Jacob. Like Theodosia she was a proselytizer of nonmonogamous affairs. A long-term political conservative, throughout WWII she held pro-Fascist views (cf. Theodosia's notions about "breeding"). Her salons were legendary for their sexual open-mindedness and hosted guests of various persuasions, including homosexuals, bisexuals, and heterosexuals. Max Jacob, who frequently corresponded with Natalie, attended her salons in the 1920s and was also a recipient of her financial aid. In her biography on Dolly Wilde (*Truly Wilde*) author Joan Schenkar regards Barney's salon as "a place where lesbian assignations and appointments with academics could coexist in a kind of cheerful, cross-pollinating, cognitive dissonance." Her salon was also unique for its international flavor: something uncommon in pre-1920s Paris.

Theodosia's fascination with being an "androgyne" or "hermaphrodite" finds its parallel in Barney's novel, *The One Who is Legion,* which features a protagonist who commits suicide but who is then reincarnated as a hermaphrodite. When the twenty-five-year-old British writer Derek Patmore met Natalie Barney in the early 1930s (when Natalie was in her mid-forties), he described her as: "Still a very handsome woman, she had the natural authority of someone who has been known as beautiful, and her vivid blue eyes were unusually arresting. There was an imperiousness about her blond good looks that explained how she had conquered the intellectual world of Paris

... Watching Natalie Barney as she acted the charming and gracious hostess, I sensed the ruthlessness beneath the smooth surface of the clever, well-bred wealthy American woman who long ago had decided to conquer Europe."[200] Just as Beadle does in *Dark Refuge*, Patmore does a wonderful job of intermingling physical description with the inner, core elements of being so that the latter shine through the former. And the way that he describes Barney perfectly parallels Beadle's portrayal of Theodosia.

There are other clues that might lead us to believe that Beadle had Barney in mind when he constructed the character of Theodosia. When Volodia rides in her "huge, luxurious car," he notices that she "speaks several times to her companion in a language I don't know, English, I think." Once inside the gates of her "private hotel," he notices "The bath taps are not nickel. I peer closely. They are of solid silver! She must be very, very rich. An American, no doubt." In a conversation with one of her German guests, Theodosia admits to "a sexual prejudice. I cannot support actual penetration. And as a matter of fact such an act is a nearly physical impossibility, for my clitoris is so abnormally developed that I am almost the perfect hermaphrodite." She also advises him that "I'm always incognito from Friday" (when she hosts her weekly events) "to Tuesday morning."

Like Theodosia, Natalie Barney is a rich, cultivated, and imperious hostess who lives in a private townhouse (in French, a *hotel particulier*) and who rides around in a spacious, chauffeur-driven car: a Renault Cabriolet, the same luxury automobile owned by Marshal Ferdinand Foch, the Supreme Allied Commander of World War I. She also avoids sexual

[200] Derek Patmore, *Observer*, September 1971, as quoted in Suzanne Rodriguez, *Wild Heart, a Life: Natalie Clifford Barney's Journey from Victorian America to the Literary Salons of Paris*, e-book version.

penetration with men and identifies with being an hermaphrodite. (But unlike Theodosia, who frequently sleeps with her husband's boyfriends, Natalie seems to have been exclusively lesbian.) And she hosts her legendary international salon (note the presence of foreigners at Theodosia's house) every Friday night.

At first we're left with the impression that Theodosia may be American, but when Volodia embarks upon a conversation with an Austrian contralto seated at his table she informs him that Theodosia is "Madame la Baronne de Volnier, the wife of the ex-minister and daughter of Monsieur le Comte de Bézues."

> "Oh?" I say. "She must be very rich then?"
> "Oh – oh! one of the richest families in France."
> "Has she children?" I ask for something to say.
> "Oh no, pardie! She merely needed a distinguished husband and he needed a distinguished and rich wife."

What further complicates the matter is that after Bill emerges from his trance and reflects upon Volodia's experience with Theodosia, he informs us: "in this occult experience I had recognized her name – which I had often heard and read – that of a quondam wealthy dilettante and well-known poetess who had left society to bury herself in a Tibetan convent, according to report."

Although Natalie Barney was a "well-known poetess" of lesbian love (and one that could be considered as a "dilettante"), she would never have buried herself in a Tibetan convent! Was Beadle making an allusion to Alexandra David-Néel, the French explorer who was the first European woman to enter Lhasa, in 1924? But Alexandra wasn't known as a poet, and her some-

what homely looks would seem to preclude her being a model for Theodosia.

Another part of the Theodosia composite may have been derived from the colorful figure of Constance Crowninshield Coolidge (1892 – 1973): a wealthy heiress, Boston Brahmin, Parisian expatriate, and one-time lover of the drug-addled publisher Harry Crosby. Although Constance was a brunette, her beauty and slender hips neatly dovetail with Bill's feminine ideal. She was also known as "Europe's leading femme fatale."[201] During her first marriage – to the U.S. diplomat Ray Atherton, who was posted in China – Constance lived in a temple and earned the nickname "The Queen of Peking" due to her scandalous behavior there as a gambler; her unconventional manner of dress; and her numerous extramarital affairs. (According to Caresse Crosby, Constance earned this sobriquet "more for her ability to dazzle than to rule.") She later divorced and moved to Paris, where she was whisked around in her luxurious chauffeur-driven Hispano-Suiza. In October 1924 she married Count Pierre de Jumilhac, thereby becoming the Comtesse de Jumilhac. The Count has been described as being "impecunious," which would match the Austrian contralto's remark that Theodosia "merely needed a distinguished husband and he needed a distinguished and rich wife." The Count was also a drug addict who grew violent when snorting cocaine: one of the factors that led to their divorce in May 1929, which was widely reported in the media. Caresse Crosby's daughter Poleen Wheatland once remarked about Constance: "I'm fond of her, but she's one of the most selfish women I've ever known." Constance was also friends with writers such as Hart

[201] Andrea Lynn, *Shadow Lovers: The Last Affairs of H. G. Wells*, Routledge, 2001, p. 8. Thanks to Christopher Sawyer-Lauçanno for first drawing my attention to Constance Coolidge.

Crane, Ernest Hemingway, Robert Herrick, Somerset Maugham, and H. G. Wells (with whom she was romantically involved).

***

One cannot help but be impressed by the beauty of certain passages in which Beadle attempts to describe the drug experience from the inside out. First, we have Bill's opening salvo at the very beginning of *Dark Refuge*:

> Beneath the kimono fairy hands caressed my body from brow to soles. The menacing rumble of a train developed into a whistle which hurtled through the window with the volume of a wireless siren; dashed about the room beating the wings of a trapped albatross; as suddenly was not, as a moth scorched by a flame. Hosts of centipedes; ice clawed, were scampering along my veins dumping plummets of anguish in my brain. Again the albatross shrieked in agony; the din of invisible wings droned into a tremendous rumble – roaring, moaning, into distance. My nerves unknotted. The balm of hush soothed.
>
> Daring all, I opened my eyes. The walls had receded; the ceiling had risen, to the proportions of a temple.

The prose style eerily anticipates that of Bill Burroughs' *Naked Lunch* (1959) by about twenty-one years.

Beadle also accomplishes wonders by utilizing the vernacular expressions of various characters and their diverse manners of speech. For an intoxicated Izzy, "thought quickens like a motor when one steps on the gas." For Cecci, "God is crying harder

than ever, and I suck in his tears." Bill's erstwhile mistress Francine is focused upon the erotic delights that are fitfully awakened by such forbidden substances, which she describes in her own colloquial manner: one that's both charming and engaging.

> But it's quite true that hashish does make things seem more wonderful; even a caress appears to last for hours deliciously, and the funny part is that the sensation seems alive all by itself somehow, and – Oh! when you really make love – oh! you go on and go on and go on and just when its insupportable it fades away and you begin all over again until you feel you're going utterly insane …

And then we have Belle, initially portrayed at an early stage in her life, when she has yet to emerge from a naive, superficial, flighty sensibility. First, in one of the most erotic passages, she rapturously describes her delightful initiation into lesbian love:

> A queer delightful feeling is all over me coming from one point. Even my hair tingles. I want to scream. "I can't stand it! Oh, darling I can't stand it!" But I hold my breath. It is so delicious! The exquisite agony becomes unbearable, I try to push her head away, but fierce hands clutch my bottom. Then a groan is wrenched from my bursting lungs. I am so dizzy I don't know where I am. I can only moan in joy and relief. Dimly I see half-lidded eyes, a mass of hair and a wet mouth. I recognize Betty.
>
> "Oh, darling!" I breathe, "I didn't know there was anything so wonderful in all the world."

Again, a handful of sentences that would have condemned *Dark Refuge* as an "obscene" novel in Britain or the U.S., as well as threatening its author with imprisonment. The narrative continues:

> Betty laughs as she smoothes back her reddish-bobbed hair with a slender blue-veined hand and sits on the bedside.
>
> "Well, now, my delightful child, you're beginning to live," she says, lighting a cigarette. She looks down at me tenderly. "You'd better have a pick-me-up," she adds.
>
> She rises and goes to a table to mix cocktails. I still feel muzzy and exhausted. I watch her lithe body and long legs. She is lovely. She has quite a big brown mole just below the crease of her bum. I am still bewildered because I have never had such curious sensations. Somehow I feel lighter; much better than I did. I don't yet understand why. Still there are lots of things I don't understand – I mean I'd always thought that only a man and a woman could – well, I can't recall exactly what I did think.

At the insistent urging of the more dominant and worldly Betty, Belle swallows her first heroin tablet and – in a fit of stream-of-consciousness chatter – describes the unusual experiences that overtake her:

> As I just scramble into a dressing gown a wonderful sensation comes over me – as if I were drunk, but different – excited and wildly happy. I hear Eddie's voice speaking to the maid and dance into

> the sitting room as he enters. I kiss him madly. He looks slightly startled and glances across the room to where Betty is standing in the bedroom doorway, smiling. Her eyes are glittering, and the kimono is half open, revealing most of one white thigh.
>
> "Oh, Eddie, darling," I say, and my voice sounds queer, "this is a dear friend of mine I want you to know...

Then she becomes unwittingly intoxicated from one of Eddie's cigarettes, laced with either hashish or marijuana:

> Another and stranger sensation comes over me. Betty suddenly seems quite a way off, although she's just beside me, and Eddie appears handsomer than ever. I love to watch his slender white hands as he is shaking the shaker, although he does appear to be doing it so slowly. But I don't care as I am feeling happier than ever. Suddenly a fit of the giggles takes me, for Eddie looks so comic as he pours out the cocktails, and I laugh till I cry. Again the two exchange glances, but neither says a word. I am still gasping with laughter when I notice that the chink of the ice sounds like bells ringing, and a passing taxi makes a noise like a train.
>
> Betty is lying back watching Eddie, and her nostrils are quivering just as they did with me – before. He hands me a glass. I never knew a cocktail tasted so delicious. It trickles down my throat for a long time – lovely and cool, like a caress. Then Eddie sits beside me, and they talk,

> but I can't listen. Their voices appear so far off, and I'm too happy! Eddie's hand tickling my thigh is exquisite, and I feel woozy with delight. We all smoke another of Eddie's cigarettes and have another cocktail. In a mist vaguely I see Betty whispering to Eddie.

It's fitting that Belle reappears at the very end of the book, at a point in her life when her silly, hopeful, happy illusions have been smashed out of her being. And then, the same woman who gave Belle such libidinous joy at the novel's inception (shortly before introducing her to heroin) can no longer even remember Belle:

> It's such a long time since we met, isn't it? and life's so jolly swift, and such lots of people in it, aren't there? It's difficult to remember everybody, isn't it? Besides, I'm frightfully gone on a new couple I met lately, so I'm sure you'll understand. You tell me you've gone back on the stage again. Splendid! I'm certain you'll have a ripping success! although I can't quite recollect which one you are, but I'm sure you'll understand.
>
> Cheerio! Betty.

Upon reading this callous letter, Belle experiences a final collapse and personal defeat. Now, there's little left to buoy her shattered spirit. Hopelessly addicted, weary of life's sufferings, and physically crumbling under the ravaging progress of a fatal venereal disease, all that remains is her talent as a vocalist. But even her ability to perform is dependent upon receiving a properly timed shot of heroin into her needle-riddled thighs.

The story of Belle alone, as it is so artfully accomplished, could have been expanded into a full-length novelistic treatment. But in *Dark Refuge* it remains merely one of many intoxicatingly beautiful tiles in a vast mosaic of humanity.

Even some of the novel's more minor characters achieve a phosphorescent luminosity before they wither, decompose, or disappear from the plotline. Just before the police close in to arrest Georgette at Monte Carlo's chic Café de Paris, she sees Bill walking by and reaches out to him for assistance. Once he offers to pay the tab and the cops slither way, he uses the opportunity to pick Georgette's brains about their past acquaintances, while Georgette's only wish is that he'll pick her up and take her home.

In what is surely one of the most poignant cameos in *Dark Refuge,* we witness a flowing display of unrequited affection as it steadily effuses from Georgette to Bill while they linger in this sumptuous, Belle Époque-style setting, with the dialogue is punctuated by those charming turns of phrase – the chummy, rummy, oh darling, *oh, darling!* ejaculations – that are hallmarks of the interwar years. But we're also privy to Georgette's secret disappointment that she cannot flitch a handful of francs brimming from Bill's wallet (perhaps, while he's asleep in his bedroom), since he's not interested in seducing her or bringing her home.

The scene is reminiscent of an old Hollywood movie depicting an opulent ballroom or grand casino in the ebullient 1920s. But the scheming, rapacious con artists depicted in such vintage films are rarely motivated by the desires that drive Georgette, with morphine stashed in her pocketbook, the cops hot on her trail, and her mind preoccupied with the worry of how she'll obtain her next fix. (Only in Pre-Code Hollywood would we find such a scenario.) The glitter of the posh Café de Paris, with its bright lights, icy buckets of expensive champagne, and

sparkling crystal chandeliers serves to cast an even greater contrast to Georgette's dark, underworld persona: dealing dope and jabbing a needle into her tender flesh as she navigates her battered canoe through such nettlesome straits, a true outlier to "polite" society.

The scene also embodies a rather ironic, self-referential dimension. For one can easily imagine the author methodically grilling one of his acquaintances, hoping to obtain grist for the mill of his *Dark Refuge* epic (just as he did with Aleister Crowley, who complained that Beadle was dining with him merely to collect information about Montparnasse). Therefore, the passage may be portraying Beadle mining for details to later use in his novel – a snapshot that is then woven into the novel itself.

It also highlights how the author never shied away from self-portraits that were less than complimentary. (E.g., he depicts Georgette musing over Beel's impatience, his "sharp" manner of interrupting, and the "queer, cold English way he always had.")[202] And there are numerous other examples of authorial self-deprecation peppered throughout *Dark Refuge*. Yet, in seeming contradiction to Beadle's "atrophy of the sentimentalities," he procures the necessary magic to enable us to fall in love with so many of these characters.

***

The narrator of *Dark Refuge* is also a bit of an armchair psychologist, and he considers several formative factors as

[202] On page 110 of *The Esquimau of Montparnasse*, when the character "Frank" accuses the "Esquimau" protagonist (Beadle) of being "cold-blooded" and having "no feelings," the Esquimau replies: "You're wrong. I've got feelings all right, but I reflect first before I give 'em their heads." Perhaps that's why he's known as the Esquimau.

being fundamental in the process of human growth and development. One is what we bring into life from wherever it is that we come from. Another is how we're imprinted in early childhood, through environment and culture: what we're exposed to and how we react to it.[203] A third factor concerns our physical constitution (which the narrator inspects via an instrument panel inside the brains of his various subjects). But there's also a fourth factor: an individual's relationship to his or her own unconscious.

This is vividly portrayed during Bill's controversial encounter with the "dark man," whom he chances upon while strolling under a Parisian arcade. Eventually he realizes that the figure is a projection of his own shadowy psyche, which nicknames Bill "conny" – short for *consciousness* – while Bill refers to the dark man as "subby" or *subconscious*. Thanks to a dialogue between these two essential characters the underlying meaning of the novel's title becomes clear.

Keep in mind that Beadle and his ilk are conducting a mopping up operation against the last remaining outposts of the Victorian Era: a task first initiated by Friedrich Nietzsche and then continued later on by Freud, whose work the author continues to grapple with and to critique. The exploration of the unconscious – a reservoir of all that is hidden and neatly tucked away from the polite "upperworld" of consciousness – was also part and parcel of this noble anti-Victorian operation.

Related to all this is the fact that both "Bill" and the narrator of *Artist Quarter* seem to hold the view that certain drugs, when used in moderation, may enhance sensory experience and thus

[203] Beadle probably held this view for quite some time. In the opening paragraph of his story, "The Better Man," published in the March 1913 issue of *The London Magazine*, the narrator describes two young men who are "most brutish by instinct, by environment, and birth."

serve as tools for apperception, rather than serving merely to imprison or destroy us, as when used immoderately. But while they may alter experience and augment inspiration to a certain extent, Beadle says that they do not provide us with the means of achieving what we would not ordinarily be able to achieve as artists. In *Artist Quarter* he makes a point of disagreeing with André Salmon in this regard, as Salmon – himself a devoted hashish enthusiast – believed that Modigliani's use of the drug was the key factor that resulted in the artist's great accomplishment. Not so, avers Beadle:

> Here I feel I must join issue with Salmon,[204] in spite of my respect for the virtues of hashish. I think he has, to some extent, allowed his literary instincts to run away with him.... Loss of timidity, indeed, a certain bold assurance, are ... typical symptoms of hashish. But that one night, or a thousand nights' influence of the drug, turned a mediocre painter into a great one, I do not believe for a moment. True, Salmon admits that Modi possessed within him the powers of a great painter, but he insists that no trace of this appeared in his "pre-miracle" [pre-hashish] work. Hashish may give inspiration or, to be exact, stimulate it, but nothing will ever convince me that it can make

[204] A terribly unreliable biographer, Salmon was known to fabricate and exaggerate (being primarily concerned with spinning a good yarn rather than sticking to the facts), especially concerning the biography of Modigliani. According to Modi's model Lunia Czechowska, Salmon's unreliability was rooted to the fact that "Modi and Salmon detested each other." For this and for more on Salmon's falsehoods and distortions, see Secrest, *Modigliani*, pp. 9-10.

> up a deficiency of talent or transform mediocrity into genius.[205]

New information that has been brought to light – thanks to the astute biographer Meryle Secrest – allows us to evaluate Modi's drug use from a different angle. Secrest believes that the real reason he indulged in hashish, alcohol, and laudanum-based opium is related to his suffering from tuberculosis, which the artist hoped to keep a secret. "The received wisdom was that he drank himself to death. The reverse is the case; alcohol and drugs were the means by which he could somehow keep functioning, the necessary anesthetic, as well as hide the great secret that must be kept at all costs." Thus, the intoxicants helped to suppress the symptoms of tuberculosis, chief among them the tendency to cough and then spit up blood. During this period, antispasmodics administered in hospitals included both morphine and heroin. "Other remedies guaranteed to soothe the cough and stop the diarrhea included whiskey, brandy, and laudanum (opium dissolved in alcohol).... A cure for tuberculosis did not come until World War II." Citing the diary of Modigliani's mother, Eugénie Garsin (who referred to her son as "Dedo"), Secrest adds:

> Reading between the lines, she [Eugénie] provides the clue. Dedo did not want anyone to know – she used the verb "to flaunt, show off, make a point of" – the terrible shadow under which he was living. Only his closest friends knew he had tuberculosis, for the reason that, if such a fact had

[205] See *Artist Quarter*, pp. 96-97. In addition, as Secrest notes: "Modigliani seldom drew while taking hashish, preferring to recall his visions in sobriety with the aim of reproducing the heightened effect." Secrest, *Modigliani*, p. 116.

> been known, he would have been avoided, if not shunned by everyone. He *had* to pretend. Nothing had changed since the days when Chopin's and Keat's landlords had burned the furniture after they moved out. If anything, matters had grown worse because, in 1882, Robert Koch famously demonstrated that tuberculosis was a bacillus and easily transmissible. This medical discovery coincided with the fact that, by 1900, tuberculosis was the leading cause of death in France.

That the artist would be inclined to hide this malady certainly makes sense. To cite just one example, if Picasso had known the true nature of Modigliani's situation he would have completely avoided him; according to art historian John Richardson, Picasso was deathly afraid of contracting the illness and had stopped eating meat as a result. In order to preserve the secret, Secrest says, Modigliani assumed the persona of a drunken artist suffering from *la vie maudite*: a doomed, accursed life – rather than from a life-threatening chronic illness. In addition, "As spitting was considered tantamount to involuntary manslaughter, the urge to spit and cough had to be suppressed. Opium, usually taken in a preparation called laudanum, was the most effective antispasmodic and was legal, along with morphine and heroin. Failing these, alcohol was the remedy of choice. Cognac, brandy, and whiskey were preferred, but wine would do. The consumptive took a small sip here, another sip there, whenever he or she felt a cough coming ... It was primitive self-medication but effective." The taking of small intermittent sips also tallies with other biographical accounts of Modi sipping from a glass of cognac while painting a model in a studio provided by his art dealer, Zborowski.

Secrest attributes Modigliani's increasingly quixotic nature – "full of changing moods, and quick to take offense" – to the debilitating psychological effects of the illness. "One never knew when this seemingly lovable personality might become haughty or rude, spiteful, and even hostile. The fact is that such mood changes are to be expected and are common, if not universal, among tuberculosis victims."[206]

Thus, Cecci / Modigliani's" relationship to drugs is in a category all by itself.

Modigliani's most important model was his friend, confidant, and probable lover Lunia Czechowska: the subject of fourteen of his portraits. Her remarks about the artist not only buttress Secrest's view ("he only drank," said Lunia, "if tormented by a particular problem": a veiled allusion to his tuberculosis); Lunia also said something that dovetails precisely with the theme of Beadle's book:

"I am convinced that alcohol was not necessary to his genius but it was a refuge … a kind of anesthetic."[207]

***

According to the narrator of *Dark Refuge,* many of those who dabble with intoxicants do so in order to escape from the constriction of taboos:

> "Well, subby," I say, "so you like drinking too?"
> "Sometimes, conny," he retorts, impertinently, "that is the only way to obtain some relief from that pretentious prig of a conscious. I don't like to be continually tormented by your ridiculous taboos. Alcohol, or any drug, is a refuge; puts your

[206] Secrest, *Modigliani*, pp. 8, 64-65, 181-183, 189, 298.
[207] As quoted by Secrest, *Modigliani*, p. 243.

> taboos to sleep, and leaves me a little freedom to do what I want – or at least dream of it if I can't obtain."
>
> He chuckles.

And later on:

> "Conscious!" he guffaws. "You call your part of us the conscious, and you, conny, aren't even conscious that you're lying! You'd have just stalled, and waited for me to hatch out some absurd lies to appease what you term your principles which are merely an acquired set of taboos! O-oh! our hairy aunt!" he sighs prodigiously, "you really work us subconsciousnesses to a shadow! Positively," he adds sarcastically, "you shock me so that I need another drink!"

Lingering behind the urge to intoxicate the mind and distort the senses one often finds another motivation: one that might be regarded as idealistic in its core nature. An excerpt from a 1957 interview with Carl Jung serves to explicate the matter:

> American life is in a subtle way so one-sided and so uprooted that you must have something with which to compensate the real nature of man. You have to pacify your unconscious all along the line because it is in absolute uproar; so at the slightest provocation you have a big moral rebellion in America. Look at the rebellion of modern youth in America, the sexual rebellion, and all that. These rebellions occur because the real, natural man is just in open rebellion against the utterly inhuman

> form of American life. Americans are absolutely divorced from nature in a way, and that accounts for that drug abuse.[208]

Thus, a "one-sided" society may produce an unnatural desire for sedation in order to "pacify" the psyche. This is symptomatic of an unnatural culture: one that is denatured and thus dehumanized. But since the unconscious is in a state of "absolute uproar," certain drugs may also trigger a rebellion, leading to an eclipse of consciousness and to its usurpation by the unconscious.

From this point of view, drug use represents a primitive, unsophisticated attempt to break free of the shackles that led to such a repressive condition in the first place. And what Jung says about "American life" applies even more so to the use of intoxicants during and shortly after the Victorian Era.

When the societal norm becomes so one-sidedly repressive, an explosion is bound to occur, ushering in a change to the opposite condition. In the words of the narrator of *Witch-Doctors*: "natural emotions suppressed find an outlet in some form."[209] Many of those who indulged in drugs felt as if they could more easily cast caution to the wind, discard the restraining reins of an outmoded collective persona (and the taboos that went along with it), and follow the lead of an intoxicated psyche – with its urges ready to spill over. *Dark Refuge* records the human toll that this involves.

Despite the dangers involved, the need to explore a greater state of freedom; to embrace human sexuality and pioneer its

[208] Richard I. Evans, *Jung on Elementary Psychology: A Discussion between C. G. Jung and Richard I. Evans*. New York: Dutton, 1976, p. 148. From four one-hour discussions held between Jung and Evans on 5-8 August 1957.
[209] *Witch-Doctors*, p. 183.

limits; to reject the whalebone-lined corsets of a constricted "consciousness" and to instead explore forms of art, literature, dance, and music that many contemporaries regarded as diabolic and wicked were just some of the things that attempted to surface and break through, from the other side of being. The problem is not the ideal but the means of effecting it.

When the psyche is incapable of incarnating such ideals in a more sophisticated manner (as a result of being blocked by a narrow-minded mental attitude), sometimes they can only emerge in a more primitive (unconscious) and dangerous fashion. That, too, is a principal theme of *Dark Refuge*. Beadle touches on this when, during a hashish-inspired vision, the narrator engages in a dialogue with his "subconscious":

> "You're very interesting, subby dear," I flatter him. "Now tell me, a lot of people find a refuge in religion instead of alcohol or drugs. What do you poor birds do then?"
>
> "Well, conny dear," he replies, smiling pleased, "we sublimate – and sometimes we don't."
>
> "What d'you mean?"
>
> "Sometimes they chase the devil – that's me – by starvation to enfeeble the physical motor force, and also by minor drugs such as lime juice, camphor, and sometimes we find other ways and means."
>
> "What?" I demand curiously.
>
> "Oh," says he, giggling, "we persuade the conscious to fall in love with Jesus, or Mary, or any old saint will do, or even the idea of God, and continuous prayer may lead to a state of exaltation that frequently ends in a physical orgasm. There are cases who are so obsessed by sex that they

> become what you term 'mystics,' and rave in speech and prose about invisible spouses, even – rarely – write beautiful poesy to some phallic symbol, such as the Song of Solomon. But, of course," he adds judiciously, "all these methods are not very satisfactory, and I'm always very sorry for those subs who are certainly out of luck."

It's not uncommon for drug users to say that they're in control of the game and know how to maintain a proper moderation while others do not. Therefore, one wonders to what extent Beadle (the author and actual man, and not merely the narrator of *Dark Refuge*) was kidding himself regarding his extended and extensive use of hashish. One also wonders how his overall lifestyle (which included experiments with many other drugs) may have affected his health.[210] There were also those many years spent in Africa. It wasn't uncommon for Europeans to return from that continent with serious, debilitating health problems, especially during this period. In one of his stories published in the *International* in 1917, Beadle remarks upon this very problem, when the narrator of "NQO" says that many were forced to return to England "doomed by a fever-ruined health." Thanks to Beadle's essay "Diseases of East Central Africa," published in the "Ask *Adventure*" forum on 18 September 1918, we know that he contracted at least one disease: "the only thing I collected was malaria and not much of that."

I raise this issue in the course of wondering if, by the time he was composing *Dark Refuge,* Beadle feared that his life was nearing its end. If this was indeed the case, it might help to

[210] On page 97 of *Artist Quarter*, he casually mentions in passing: "I have, at one time or another, experimented with every kind of dope indulged in by artists in Montmartre and Montparnasse."

explain another overarching theme: the narrator's looking back upon his life while peering into the hearts and minds of those closest to him, then contemplating all this with not only a newfound sense of awareness but also with a tinge of regret as he considers, as we say, "what might have been."

These are just a few of the impressions that I'm left with after reading *Dark Refuge* for a second time. It's my sincere hope that a new audience may be found for this noteworthy confession, despite whatever flaws one finds in the author or his novel. My gut tells me that there's something extraordinary and exciting happening here: that it's a work readers will feel compelled to return to, such is its artistic and imaginative depth.

There's another central figure in *Dark Refuge* that I've only briefly touched upon, and that is the city of Paris itself. It stands there as a solid presence and continually beckons us, with both its ineffable mystery and its attendant horrors, as dangerously alluring as ever.

– Rob Couteau

Postscript

On several occasions when talking with William Burroughs, he would often mention an esoteric book he had read at some point in his life. Some were familiar to me; most weren't, as many were pulp fiction and I had never been a reader of that particular sub-genre. But since Burroughs had found these writers worthwhile, I would occasionally try to track down a title Burroughs had mentioned but rarely had any luck. (These were pre-Internet days; googling was done by browsing shelves in bookstores.) And so, with the exception of a few books such as Rex Weldon's *Curse of Cain,* I generally came up empty-handed.

To my knowledge, William never mentioned Charles Beadle. He could have come across the book in Paris, as Obelisk editions could still be had by rifling through the wagon-green stalls of the bouquinistes even into the 60s. But had he read *Dark Refuge,* I think he would have likely cited it. The emphasis on heterosexual sex wouldn't have appealed to him much but the hallucinatory, disjunctive narrative would have caught his attention. And he would have definitely related to this statement: "I was dwelling in a state where time is a curve. Delusion and reality had become so interwoven that there was difficulty to distinguish one from the other. No doubt, I reflected gravely, I had hit one of those famous kinks in time."

I bring in Burroughs because in the minds of many he was simply a chronicler of drug use. The same could be said of Beadle. And while drugs certainly play important roles in their fiction, what makes their writing exceptional is not the subject matter – books about drug use are not all that uncommon from

De Quincy on – but the way both writers utilize the drug experience to construct fractured narratives to reveal the drug-induced displacement of time and space. And that is new. And fascinating.

Indeed, Beadle's book reads so well because he gets utterly inside the experiences he relates, shows us what is happening from an interior point of view. His unique narrative device of creating individual monologues that also function intertextually as objective description, allows us an unusual opportunity to encounter the principal personae through their thoughts, dialogue with others, and their space and place within the often-lyrical renderings of situation and scene. Here, for instance, in a cathartic interlude, we see Vee in her milieu, in all her contradictions, her heart on her sleeve:

> Tears well in my eyes. I am conscious that something quickens in my veins and I loathe it. Bill is still virile, I can feel too, and – Oh, my face is a net of wrinkles! He has a few, too, but that doesn't matter with a man. Oh, damn him! Why did he come? Oh, how I wish he'd go. Oh, damn him, oh, God damn him! All this will upset my training and I shan't be able to concentrate for weeks. Oh, perhaps never again. I shall go away. I'll go back to England and start that paper. I've enough capital saved up now. I must find a refuge somewhere.
>
> As I turn away to hide my eyes I catch a glimpse of him in a mirror. He is shaking his head with a whimsical smile. Oh, curse him! Oh, I could kill him. Coming here to laugh at me! Why, why did I let him speak to me? But I turn and say icily:
>
> "I'd rather you went, Bill, please."

> "Well, Vee," says he, rising, "I'm awfully glad to have seen you again, but I'm just as sorry that my accidental visit seems to have annoyed you so."
>
> I give him my hand, mechanically. I can't speak. He looks at me queerly and goes. I bang the door shut, and throw myself on the bed, sobbing, sobbing....

So much takes place here. Vee's character is plumbed, accentuated first by her maudlin soliloquy, then by descriptive detail (the mirror, the shaking head), next by two lines of conversation, which then reaches a climax of inner revelation in an outward manner (sobbing). This is a complex modality, compressed into less than a page. Other passages of equal intensity and expressiveness abound. In the hands of a lesser writer, this scene (and so many others) could be trite, clichéd. But Beadle's careful word choice, relentless focus on the portrayal of small details that create a larger whole, and his ability to show simultaneously situation and the emotions elicited are riveting.

Beadle is the real deal. And Rob Couteau is the real deal too. Without his desire to rescue *Dark Refuge* from oblivion, we would all have missed out on a tremendous modernist novel that should rank among other classics such as *Tropic of Cancer, Nightwood, Nadja, Ulysses, To the Lighthouse,* and, of course, *Naked Lunch*. And thanks to his extensive annotations and deep research, we have both the novel and the context that created it. I am admiring and grateful.

– Christopher Sawyer-Lauçanno

Illustrations

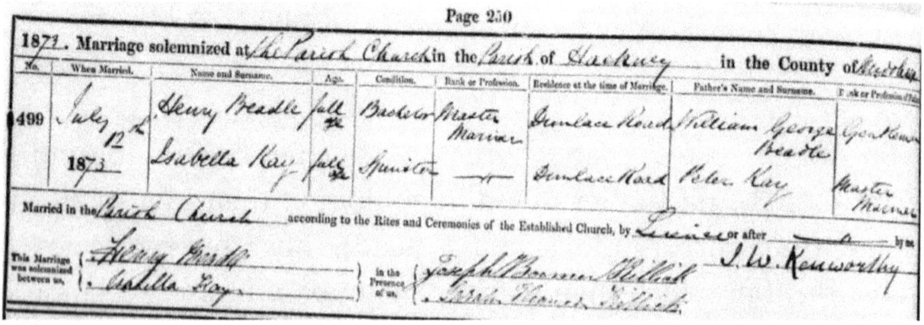

Page 250

1873. Marriage solemnized at the Parish Church in the Parish of Hackney in the County of Middlesex

No.	When Married.	Name and Surname.	Age.	Condition.	Rank or Profession.	Residence at the time of Marriage.	Father's Name and Surname.	Rank or Profession of Father.
499	July 12th 1873	Henry Beadle	full age	Bachelor	Master Mariner	Dunlace Road	William George Beadle	Gentleman
		Isabella Kay	full age	Spinster	—	Dunlace Road	Peter Kay	Master Mariner

Married in the Parish Church according to the Rites and Ceremonies of the Established Church, by Licence or after — by me, J. W. Kenworthy

This Marriage was solemnized between us, Henry Beadle, Isabella Kay; in the Presence of us, Joseph H. Bowman Pollick, Sarah Bowman Pollick

12 July 1873: Marriage of Henry Beadle and Isabella Kay at St. John's, Hackney, London. Both Henry and Isabella's father, Peter Kay, were master mariners; while Henry's father, William, is listed as a "gentleman."

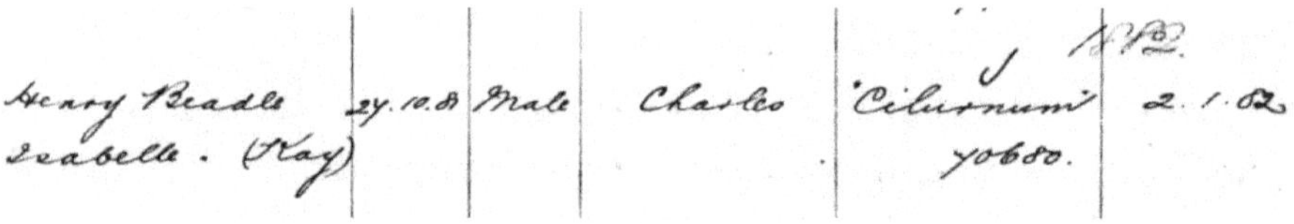

Henry Beadle Isabella (Kay)	27.10.81	Male	Charles	"Cilurnum" 70680.	1882 2.1.82

27 October 1881: Record of Beadle's birth aboard the SS *Cilurnum*, from "UK Registers of Births, Marriages and Deaths at Sea, 1844-1890." Other documents, such as his draft registration card, indicate he was born the day before, on 26 October 1881.

(Above:) The brothers Henry, Charles, and William Beadle. (Below:) Various portraits of Beadle from a family photo album. Courtesy of Beadle's great-niece Patricia and her daughter Liz.

Inscribed: "Your [affectionate] nephew Charlie."

Circa fall 1900 – 1901. Beadle in Mashonaland, South Africa. From the archive of Patricia and Liz.

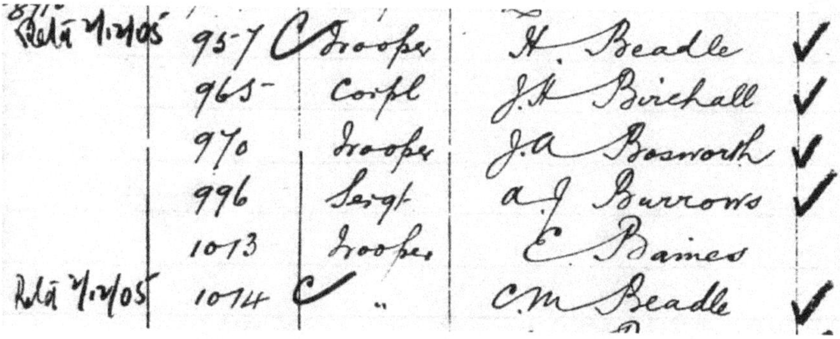

Rcd 7.12.05	957	C Trooper	H. Beadle	✓
	965	Corpl	J.H. Birchall	✓
	970	Trooper	J.A. Bosworth	✓
	996	Sergt	A.J. Burrows	✓
	1013	Trooper	E. Barnes	
Rcd 7.12.05	1014	C ✓ "	C.M. Beadle	✓

During this period Beadle received various decorations and service awards. A “Roll of individuals entitled to the South Africa Medal and Clasps, April 1901” includes Trooper Charles “Marmaduke” Beadle, who served in the National (Waldon’s) Scouts and Orange River Colony Volunteers, Nesbitt´s Horse, Regiment Number 1014. He may have fictionalized his middle name in order to enlist a second time.

Undated photo of Henry Beadle (1844 – 1906), father of Charles. Courtesy of Patricia and Liz.

Another photo of Henry Beadle, courtesy of Patricia and Liz.

Photo of Charles Beadle featured in *The Wide World Magazine*, May 1907.

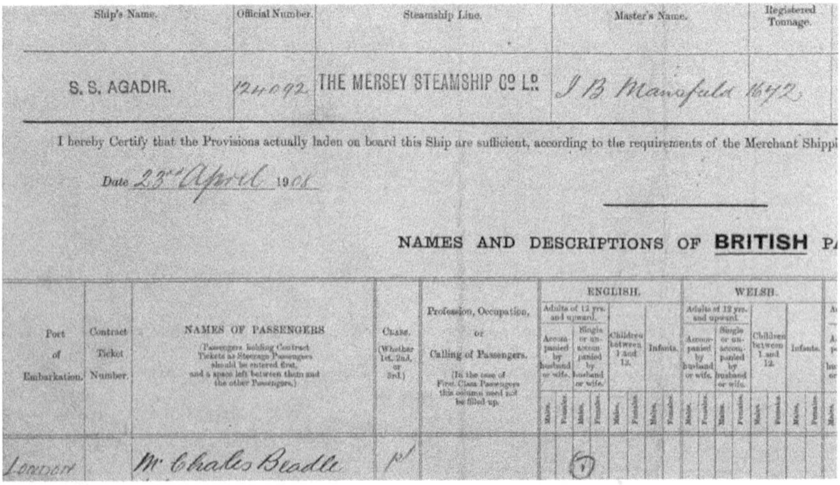

Ship's Name.	Official Number.	Steamship Line.	Master's Name.	Registered Tonnage.
S. S. AGADIR.	124092	THE MERSEY STEAMSHIP Co Ld.	J B Mansfield	1642

I hereby Certify that the Provisions actually laden on board this Ship are sufficient, according to the requirements of the Merchant Shippi

Date 23rd April 1908

NAMES AND DESCRIPTIONS OF BRITISH P

Port of Embarkation.	Contract Ticket Number.	NAMES OF PASSENGERS (Passengers holding Contract Tickets as Steerage Passengers should be entered first, and a space left between them and the other Passengers.)	Class. (Whether 1st, 2nd, or 3rd.)	Profession, Occupation, or Calling of Passengers. (In the case of First Class Passengers this column need not be filled up.)	ENGLISH. Adults of 12 yrs. and upward. Accompanied by husband or wife. Male / Female	Single or unaccompanied by husband or wife. Male / Female	Children between 1 and 12. Male / Female	Infants. Male / Female	WELSH. Adults of 12 yrs. and upward. Accompanied by husband or wife. Male / Female	Single or unaccompanied by husband or wife. Male / Female	Children between 1 and 12. Male / Female	Infants. Male / Female
London		Mr Charles Beadle	1st			1						

Passenger list of the SS *Agadir*, 23 April 1908, with Beadle on his way to Morocco, where he would interview Sultan Mulai-El-Hafid.

Beadle disguised as a dancing girl or, alternately, a holy man, during his June 1908 expedition to Fez, published in the photo essay "A Talk with the New Sultan of Morocco," *The Pall Mall Magazine*, October 1908.

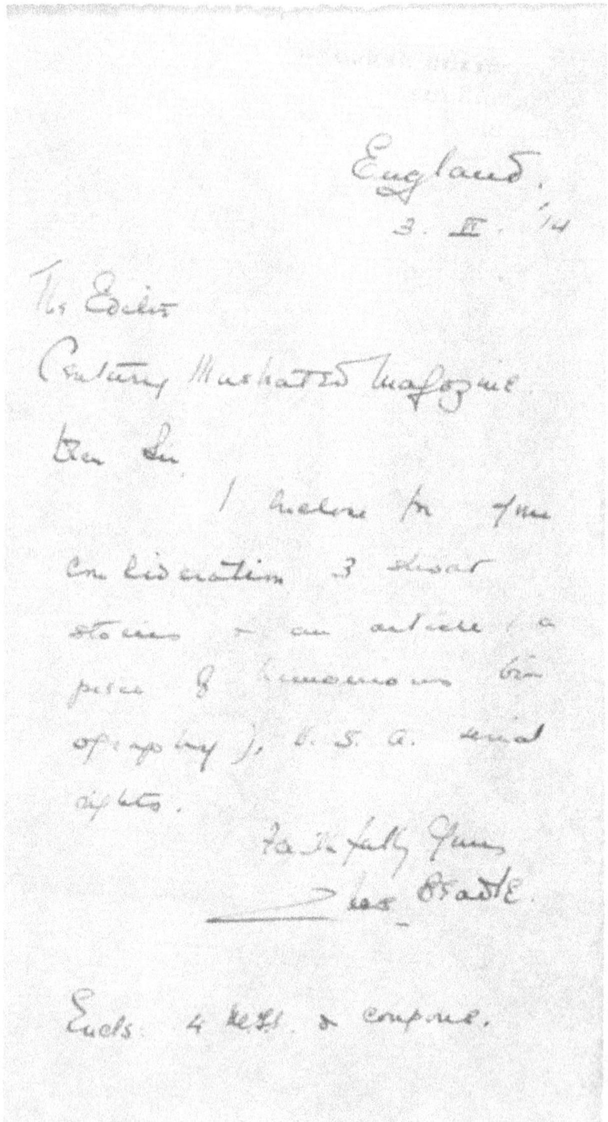

England.
3. VI. '14

The Editor
Century Illustrated Magazine.

Dear Sir,

I enclose for your consideration 3 short stories & an article (a piece of humourous biography) for U.S.A. serial rights.

Faithfully Yours
Chas. Beadle.

Encls. 4 MSS. & coupons.

3 June 1914: A letter to the editor of *Century Illustrated*: "England 3 VI 1914 The Editor Century Magazine Dear Sir, I enclose for your consideration 3 short stories & an article (a piece of humourous biography) for USA serial rights. Faithfully Yours Charles Beadle Encl. 4 Ms. & coupons." Courtesy of the New York Public Library, Century Company records, Series I. General Correspondence 1870 – 1930.

MAIRIE DE CANNES
Alpes-Maritimes

Ville de Cannes

Acte de décès - Copie Intégrale

N° 603
Hornsby
Sylvia Grace Elley

Le treize Septembre mil neuf cent quinze à dix-neuf heures trente, Sylvia Grace Elley Hornsby, née à Londres (Angleterre) le vingt-huit Octobre mil huit cent quatre-vingt-onze, sans profession, fille de Edmond William et de Teresa Isabelle Hornsby, épouse de Charles Beadle, domiciliée [illegible] est décédée à Cannes, Hôtel Beau Rivage.
Dressé le quatorze Septembre, mil neuf cent quinze, à quinze heures du ..., sur la déclaration de Joseph Vallier, cinquante deux ans, comptable et de Antoine Aragon, soixante quatre ans, tous deux domiciliés à Cannes, qui, lecture faite, ont signé avec Nous Marcellin Bella, chevalier de la Légion d'Honneur, Adjoint au Maire de Cannes, Officier de l'état civil par délégation.

Copie délivrée selon procédé informatisé.
A Cannes, le 28 juin 2022

Pour le Maire,
L'officier de l'état civil par délégation

Copy of Sylvia Hornsby's death certificate, retrieved by Céline Cardon on 30 June 2022. The French vital statistics bureau had misspelled her surname (it appears in their index as "Homsby"), making its retrieval a particularly tricky task. From this document we learn that Sylvia died at the Hotel Beau Rivage (now known as the Hotel Majestic). This was during a period in which the villas and hotels of Cannes were used as hospitals, especially for the soldiers of WWI. So, she essentially died "in hospital" on 15 September 1915.

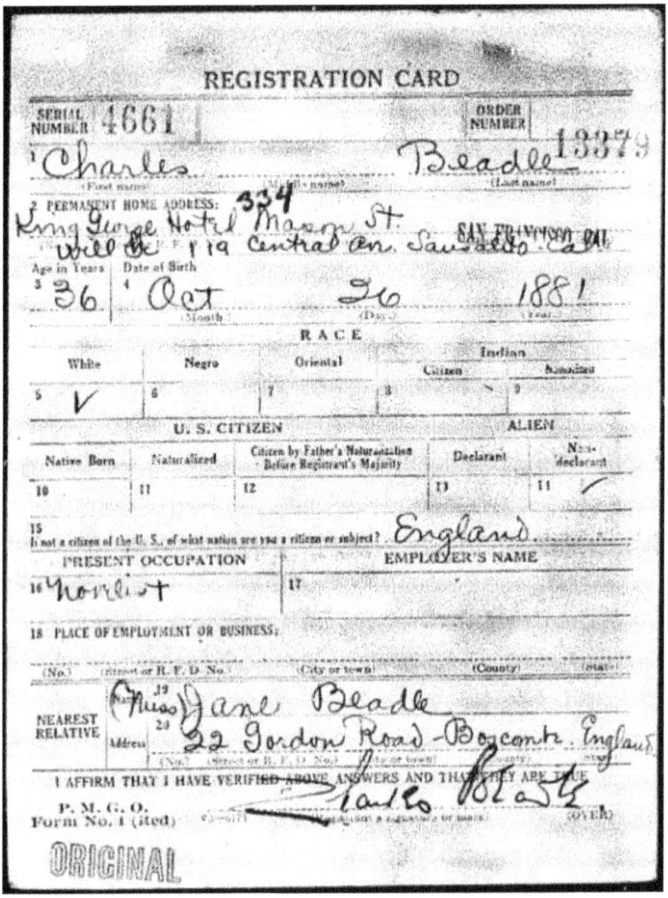

REGISTRATION CARD

SERIAL NUMBER 4661 | ORDER NUMBER 13379

1 Charles Beadle
(First name) (Middle name) (Last name)

2 PERMANENT HOME ADDRESS: 334
King George Hotel Mason St. SAN FRANCISCO CAL
will be 119 Central Av. Sausalito Cal

Age in Years: 3 36 | Date of Birth: 4 Oct 26 1881
(Month) (Day) (Year)

RACE

White	Negro	Oriental	Indian: Citizen	Indian: Noncitizen
5 ✓	6	7	8	9

U. S. CITIZEN: Native Born	U. S. CITIZEN: Naturalized	U. S. CITIZEN: Citizen by Father's Naturalization Before Registrant's Majority	ALIEN: Declarant	ALIEN: Non-declarant
10	11	12	13	14 ✓

15 If not a citizen of the U. S., of what nation are you a citizen or subject? England

PRESENT OCCUPATION	EMPLOYER'S NAME
16 Novelist	17

18 PLACE OF EMPLOYMENT OR BUSINESS:
(No.) (Street or R. F. D. No.) (City or town) (County) (State)

NEAREST RELATIVE: Name 19 (Miss) Jane Beadle
Address 20 22 Gordon Road - Boscombe. England
(No.) (Street or R. F. D. No.) (City or town) (County) (State)

I AFFIRM THAT I HAVE VERIFIED ABOVE ANSWERS AND THAT THEY ARE TRUE
Charles Beadle
(Registrant's signature or mark)

P. M. G. O.
Form No. 1 (Red) (OVER)

ORIGINAL

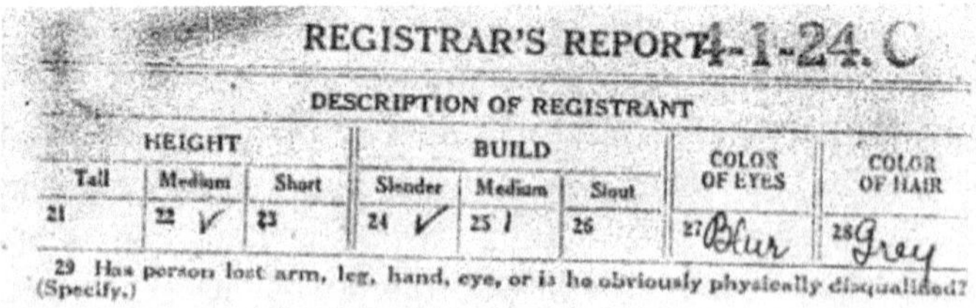

REGISTRAR'S REPORT 4-1-24. C

DESCRIPTION OF REGISTRANT

HEIGHT: Tall	HEIGHT: Medium	HEIGHT: Short	BUILD: Slender	BUILD: Medium	BUILD: Stout	COLOR OF EYES	COLOR OF HAIR
21	22 ✓	23	24 ✓	25 /	26	27 Blue	28 Grey

29 Has person lost arm, leg, hand, eye, or is he obviously physically disqualified? (Specify.)

12 September 1918: A month short of his thirty-eighth birthday, Beadle registers for the military draft in San Francisco, just before relocating to Sausalito. Under the heading "Description of Registrant" it notes that he is of medium height with a slender build, blue eyes, and gray hair. His occupation is "Novelist." He lists his daughter (then living in Boscombe, Bournemouth, England) as his "nearest relative."

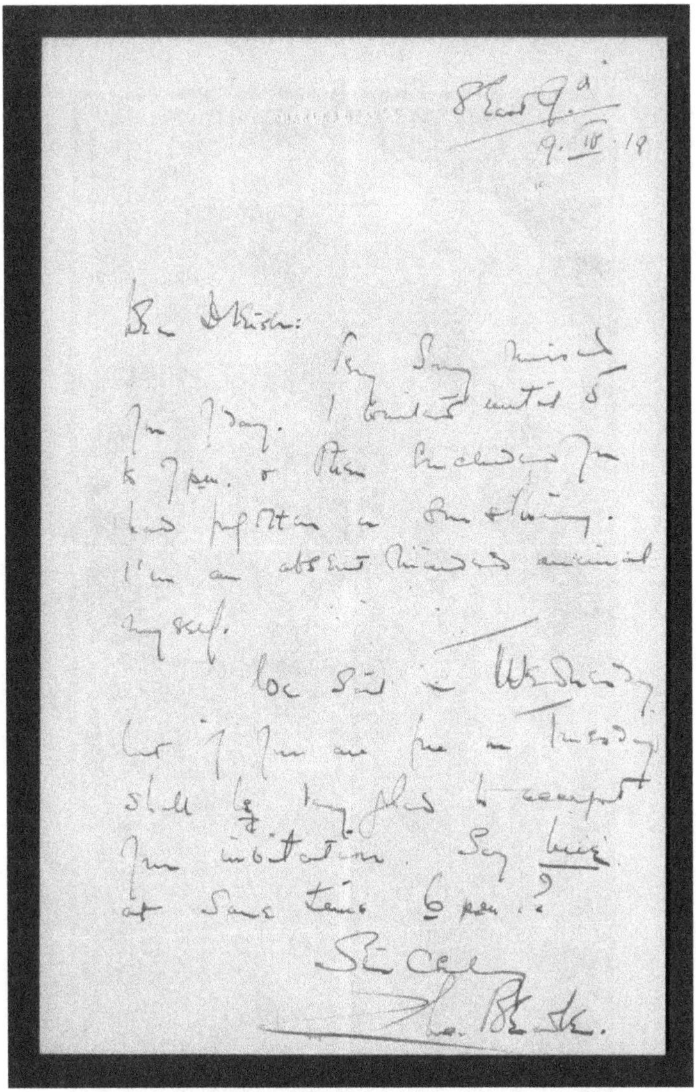

19 October 1919: A letter to the celebrated author Theodore Dreiser: "8 East 9th, 19.10.19 Dear Dreiser: Very sorry missed you y'day. I waited until 5 to 7 p.m. and then concluded you had forgotten or something. I'm an absent minded animal myself. We said on Wednesday but if you are free on Tuesday shall be very glad to accept your invitation. Say <u>here</u> at same time <u>6</u> <u>p.m.</u>? Sincerely Chas. Beadle." Beadle's flat was located between University Place and Broadway, three blocks north of Washington Square Park. Dreiser lived at 165 West 10th, a half mile west of Beadle. (Courtesy of the University of Pennsylvania, Kislak Center for Special Collections.)

Publicity shot of the author featured in the *Sioux City Journal* on 18 May 1930, accompanying a review of *Expatriates at Large*.

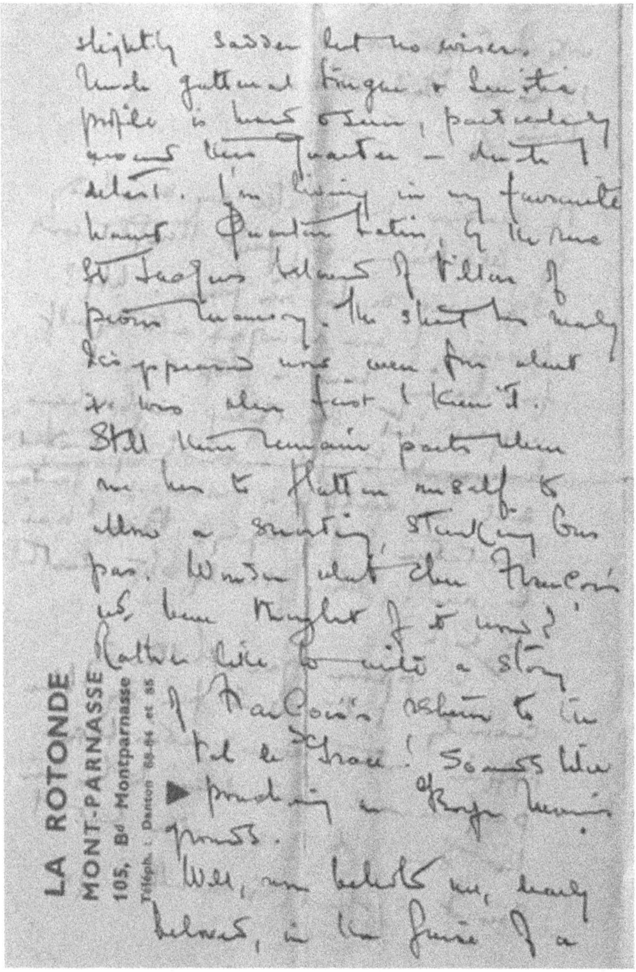
slightly sadder but no wiser. Much guttural tongue & Semitic profile in evidence, particularly around this quarter — dare I admit. I'm living in my favourite haunt Quartier Latin, by the rue St Jacques whence of Villon of grim memory. The street has nearly disappeared now even from what it was when first I knew it. Still there remain parts where one has to flatten oneself to allow a swaying, staggering bus pass. Wonder what the François would have thought of it now? Rather like to write a story of François's return to the Tel de Grace! Sounds like something in Kafka's process.
Well, one beholds me, nearly beloved, in the guise of a

LA ROTONDE
MONT-PARNASSE
105, Bd Montparnasse
Téléph. : Danton 68-64 et 65

Second page of an undated letter composed by Beadle and sent to his niece Isabel, with the return address of "Hôtel des Capucines, 13, rue des Feuillantines, Paris." The letter is written on stationery from the Café de la Rotonde, which was located only several blocks away from the Hôtel des Capucines. Courtesy archive of Patricia and Liz.

When and where born	Name, if any	Sex	Name and surname of father	Name, surname and maiden surname of mother	Occupation of father	Signature, description and residence of informant
Seventh August 1946. 9 Saxonbury Road U.D.	Elizabeth Owen	Girl	Igor Bely	Jane Owen Bely formerly Beadle at 14 Dean Park Road Bournemouth U.D.	Chemical Engineer of 29 Rue Assalit, Nice France.	Jane Owen Bely Mother 14 Dean Park Road. Bournemouth.

7 August 1946: birth of Elizabeth Owen Bely, daughter of Jane Beadle and Igor Bely, at 9 Saxonbury Road, about four miles east of Jane's residence at 14 Dean Park Road, Bournemouth, England. Igor is identified as a "Chemical engineer of 29, rue Assalit, Nice, France."

Le vingt trois août mil neuf cent soixante deux,
trois heures trente minute
est décédé en son domicile 99 avenue
Cyrille Besset
Elisabeth, Owen BELY
née à Bournemouth (Grande Bretagne)
le sept août mil neuf cent
quarante six, sans profession
fille de Igor Bely quarante
six ans Traducteur et de
Jane BEADLE son épouse
Interprète domiciliée à Nice
20 rue Parmentier Célibataire
Dressé le vingt cinq août mil neuf cent soixante deux,
Dix heures, sur la déclaration de le père de la
défunte

qui, lecture faite a été invité à prendre directement connaissance de l'acte
et à le signer avec Nous
Auguste VEROLA, Chevalier de la Légion d'Honneur
Adjoint au Maire de Nice, Officier de l'Etat Civil par délégation

Elizabeth Bely died at the age of sixteen on 23 August 1962 at her home at 99, avenue Cyrille Besset, Nice. Her death certificate identifies her as the daughter of Igor Bely, "translator," and his wife Jane Beadle, "interpreter." Jane's address is listed as 20, rue Parmentier, Nice.

VILLE DE NICE

ACTE DE DECES
COPIE INTEGRALE

N° 005012 / 2002 Jane BEADLE

Le vingt six novembre deux mil deux à une heure treize minutes, est***** décédée avenue des Roses "Rimiez", Jane BEADLE, née à Saint-Tropez (Var) le 8 juillet 1915, en retraite, domiciliée à Nice (Alpes-Maritimes) 8,** avenue Georges Clémenceau, fille de Charles BEADLE, et de Sylvia Grace** Ellen HOMSBY, décédés ; veuve de Igor BELY.**************************** Dressé le 28 novembre 2002 à 9 heures 28 minutes sur la déclaration de** COPPOLANI Tony, 39 ans, Chef de Bureau à Nice (06), 3 rue Alexandre***** Mari, qui, lecture faite et invité à lire l'acte, a signé avec Nous,**** Andrée GUILLAUMIN, fonctionnaire de la Mairie de Nice, Officier de****** l'Etat-Civil par délégation du Maire.**********************************

Nice,
le 7 juin 2022,
Pour copie conforme,
L'Officier de l'Etat Civil délégué,

Aurélie FAREY

Jane Beadle's death record, retrieved by Céline Cardon on 13 June 2022. Note that the surname of Jane's mother is misspelled and appears as "Homsby" instead of Hornsby. Jane lived at 8, avenue George Clémenceau, but at the time of her death on 26 November 2002 she was at the Avenue des Roses, in the Rimiez quarter of Nice. This quarter hosts the Hôpital Les Sources, a geriatric hospital. The record includes the name of Jane's husband, Igor Bely (1916 – 1978).

Timeline

12 July 1873. Marriage of Henry Beadle (b. January 1844, in either Romford or Barking, Essex, England) and Isabella Kay (b. 23 May 1849 in Liverpool) at St. John's, the parish church in West Hackney, London. According to the marriage certificate both Henry Beadle and Isabella's father, Peter Kay, were master mariners, while Henry's father, William, was a "gentleman." The newlyweds lived on Dunlace Road.

12 July 1876. Birth of Max Jacob.

27 January 1879. Birth of Beatrice Hastings (née Emily Alice Haigh).

25 October 1881. Birth of Picasso.

26 or 27 October 1881. Birth of Charles Beadle at sea, aboard the SS *Cilurnum* (a Merchant Marine vessel), to Isabella and Henry Beadle (the ship's captain). Charles is the youngest of four children (Henry, born in 1874, is the oldest, followed by William and then Catherine, who died after less than nine months). The family resides in West Hackney, London, where Charles is raised.

[Age 2] 2 July 1884. Death of mother from "consumption" (i.e., tuberculosis) at sea while aboard the *Cilurnum*.

[Age 2] 12 July 1884. Birth of Amedeo Modigliani.

[Age 3] 22 October 1885. Destruction of the SS *Cilurnum*. A court rules that "the explosion and the subsequent loss of the said ship was due to the fire generated by spontaneous combustion in the coal which she had on board, and that the master, officers, and crew used all proper measures ... to save the vessel." Source: "Merchant Shipping Acts, 1854 to 1876."

[Age 9] 5 April 1891. The English census shows that the family is still residing at 80 Benthal Road, West Hackney.

[Age 9] July 1890. Death of maternal grandmother Catherine Owens, who helped to raise Charles while his father was at sea. Perhaps as a tribute of his affection for her, Charles will later give his daughter Jane the middle name of "Owen" (and Jane will give her daughter Elizabeth the same middle name).

[Age 18] Abt. 1899: Employed by the British South African Police in Cape Town. (Source: Autobiographical sketch in "The Camp-Fire" column, *Adventure*, 3 July 1918.) Beadle's great-niece Patricia wrote to Neil Pearson: "We thought [Charles] might have gone to Africa in search of his eldest brother, Henry, who disappeared in Rhodesia having gone out to Africa 'with Cecil Rhodes.'" (Rhodes was a British imperialist, mining magnate, and Prime Minister of the Cape Colony from 1890 to 1896.) "[Charles] had an odd upbringing." When I spoke with Patricia on 6 October 2022 and asked what she meant by this last remark, she said Beadle's father Henry and his second wife, Sarah Killick, "were frequently away at sea on long voyages, so we think the children were cared for by Henry's sister Sarah Beadle and by Catherine Owens, Charles' grandmother, who lived with them. Catherine was wealthy and blind. He was also raised

with the children of his father's other wife. Charles and his brother joined the South African Police on the same day, to fight in the Boer War. London was rife with recruiting posters back then. Henry later went missing. He was possibly killed in the war, although there's no military record of his death. I also heard that Henry may have died in a bicycle accident."

[Age 18-21] Abt. 1899 – 1902: Transvaal, South Africa. Second Boer War, British South African Police. Serving in Morley's Scouts, Stock and Recovery Department. (Source: *Adventure*, 3 July 1918.) During this period Beadle receives various service awards.

[Age 18] September 1900. At age sixteen, Modigliani contracts pleurisy, which develops into tuberculosis.

[Age 18] Fall 1900. Mashonaland, South Africa. Guest of an Englishman named Mason, who owns a large farm. Beadle is nearly killed by a lioness during a hunt that was organized on his behalf. Source: "My Narrow Escape From a Lioness." *The Brooklyn Daily Eagle* (*Junior Eagle*), 7 August 1910.

[Age 21] Abt. 1902. Employed by Transvaal Customs as Assistant Compound Manager, Witwatersrand Native Labor Association. Source: *Adventure*, 3 July 1918.

[Age 22] August 1904. Travels along the Zambezi River, Chikoti, Zambia. His Zambian expedition is later chronicled in "Our Trip Down the Zambezi," *The Wide World Magazine*, May 1907. (See below.)

[Age 22] 1904. Departs from Africa and briefly visits Paris.

[Age 23] December 1905. Employed at Government House, Fort Portal, Uganda. "Engaged in recruiting and registering fresh porters" for an expedition into the Congo. (Fort Portal: aka Kabarole; formerly of the Toro Kingdom). Source: Beadle's essay "Two Close Calls." *The Captain: A Magazine for Boys and "old Boys,"* June 1910.

[Age 23] 5 January 1906. Embarks from Fort Portal and enters the Congo. Attacked by a buffalo and almost killed by a herd of stampeding elephants.

[Age 24] Abt. January 1906. Modigliani leaves Italy and arrives in Paris.

[Age 24] 19 Mar 1906. Death of father, Henry Beadle, in Buenos Aires. According to Beadle's great-niece, Charles inherited a substantial amount of money, including assets that would have gone to his brother Henry, who had disappeared. This allows Charles to finance his African expeditions. Source: conversation with Patricia, 6 November 2022.

[Age 24] Abt. 1906. London, England. Elected as a Fellow of the Royal Geographical Society (FRGS).

[Age 25] February 1907. Northumberland Avenue, London. Elected to the Royal Colonial Institute. Source: *Journal of the Royal Colonial Institute,* February 1907, p. 138.

[Age 25] May 1907. Publishes "Our Trip Down the Zambezi" in *The Wide World Magazine*. Illustrated with photos mostly taken by the author, it also features one of Beadle wearing a pith helmet.

[Age 26] June – July 1907. Picasso paints *Les Demoiselles d'Avignon*. Shortly afterward Modigliani visits his studio and sees the painting. In the first volume of *A Life of Picasso* (1991), John Richardson calls it a work that "established a new pictorial syntax" and "the first unequivocally twentieth-century masterpiece, a principal detonator of the modern movement, the cornerstone of twentieth century art."

[Age 26] 1908 – abt. 1911. Residing in Morocco.

[Age 26] Abt. February 1908. Travels to Borneo. Source: diary of Roger Pocock, housed at the Bruce Peel Collection, University of Alberta.

[Age 26] 23 April 1908. Embarks from the Port of London aboard the SS *Agadir*, heading for Morocco.

[Age 26] 4 May 1908. Arrives in El Jadida, Morocco (originally known in Berber as Mazighen), a port city located on the Atlantic coast).

[Age 26] 19 May 1908. Embarks for Tangiers.

[Age 26] 9 June 1908. Arrives in Larache, Morocco.

[Age 26] 14 June 1908. Arrives in Meknes, a city in north-central Morocco, and shortly afterward enters Tangiers.

[Age 26] 19 August 1908. In Morocco during the Battle of Marrakesh, a decisive encounter that occurred between the opposing sultans, which resulted in the forces of Mulay

Hafid defeating the army of Abd El Aziz. Beadle later portrays this conflict in his novel, *The City of Shadows*.

[Age 27] October 1908. Publishes "A Talk with the New Sultan of Morocco," *Pall Mall Magazine*. Illustrated with photos mostly taken by the author; includes a portrait of Beadle disguised as a dancing girl.

[Age 28] Circa 1909. Morocco. Begins to write fiction. Source: Beadle's contribution to the forum, "Contemporary Writers and Their Work," published in *The Editor: The Journal of Information for Literary Workers*, 25 February 1920. In this discussion of his writing process, Beadle says: "I began when I was 28 or 29." Age twenty-eight would have been 1909; two years later he published his first full-length novel, *The City of Shadows*.

[Age 28] January 1909. Natalie Clifford Barney moves from Neuilly to 20, rue Jacob, Paris, where she hosts her famous salon for the next sixty years.

[Age 28] 2 September 1910. Death of "Le Douanier" Rousseau.

[Age 29] October 1910. The first issue of *Adventure* magazine (dated November 1910) appears on the newsstands.

[Age 29] 1911. Resides in Hampstead, England.

[Age 29] abt. March 1911. Publication of *The City of Shadows: A Romance of Morocco* (London: Everett and Co.).

[Age 29] July 1911. Café La Rotonde opens at 105, Boulevard Montparnasse. This setting is prominently featured in

Beadle's novels *The Esquimau of Montparnasse* and *Dark Refuge*. Source: Luc Bihl-Willette, *Des tavernes aux bistrots: Une histoire des cafés*, Paris: L'Age d'Homme, 1997, p. 174.

[Age 30] 23 September 1912. Picasso leaves Montmartre and rents a studio in Montparnasse at 242, boulevard Raspail: a ten-minute walk from the Rotonde.

[Age 31] October 1912. Publication of *A White Man's Burden* (London: Stephen Swift and Co.).

[Age 32] 1914. Elected Fellow of the Royal Geographical Society.

[Age 32] 14 March 1914. British Consulate General, Paris, France. Marries Sylvia Grace Ellen Hornsby (1891 – 1915), daughter of Edmund William Hornsby (1861 – 1908) and Teresa Isabel Ashwell (1866 – 1940). The couple was then residing at 4, rue de la Grande Chaumière, just a few doors away from the famous Académie de la Grande Chaumière (located at 14, rue de la Grande Chaumière), where Modigliani, Gauguin, and many other artists drew from the model. Source: Certified copy of marriage certificate in possession of Beadle's great-niece Patricia, who also recalls having a Picasso print in the house "for which Sylvia probably modeled."

[Age 32] 28 July 1914. Austria-Hungary declares war on Serbia. On 1 August 1914 Germany declares war against France, Belgium, and Russia.

[Age 33] January 1915. Absinthe banned in France by presidential decree.

[Age 33] 8 Jul 1915. Birth of daughter Jane Owen Beadle (1915 – 2002) in Cannes.

[Age 33] 20 August 2015. Letter from former President Theodore Roosevelt Jr. to Charles Beadle, thanking him for sending a copy of his book.

[Age 33] September 1915. Residing at the Villa Robinson, St. Tropez. (Source: Last Will and Testament of Sylvia Beadle.) That same month *A Passionate Pilgrimage* is published by Heath, Cranton, and Ouseley in London.

[Age 33] 13 September 1915. Death of wife, Sylvia Beadle, in Cannes. According to her death certificate she died at the Hotel Beau Rivage (now known as the Hotel Majestic) during a period when the villas and hotels of Cannes were used as hospitals, especially for the soldiers of WWI.

[Age 34] 1915. Residing at Place du Tertre, Paris.

[Age 34] c. 1915. Modigliani creates a pencil drawing of Charles Beadle in Beadle's flat at Place du Tertre. (The portrait is described in detail in Beadle's Modigliani biography, *Artist Quarter*.) The sketch is stolen from Beadle but resurfaces in the Perls Galleries in New York, in 1951, and, decades later, at an auction held by Christie's in 2007. Titled "Le jeune Pelèrin" (The Young Pilgrim), the Christie's provenance record makes no mention of Beadle's prior ownership and fails to identify him as the subject of the drawing. (A photo of the drawing is available online.)

[Age 34] 13 November 1915. D. H. Lawrence's novel, *The Rainbow*, is banned in Britain; censors burn over 1000 copies.

[Age 35] 30 October 1916. Embarks from Cadiz, Spain, and travels to New York. On the ship's manifest Beadle lists Beatrice Hastings as his "closest friend living in country of departure," noting her address at 13, rue Norvins, Paris.

[Age 35] 14 November 1916. Arrives in New York City.

[Age 36] March 1918. Outbreak of Great Influenza Pandemic. First documented case occurs in Kansas. By the end of the pandemic in 1920, about 500 million will become infected worldwide, resulting in fifty million to one-hundred million deaths, with 675,000 deaths in the U.S.

[Age 36] 18 May 1918. Publishes "The Christ-man," the first of twenty-six stories that will eventually appear in *Adventure*.

[Age 36] Aug 1918. Residing in or traveling through Grand Isle, Jefferson, Louisiana. Source: announcement in *Adventure*, 18 August 1918.

[Age 36] 12 September 1918. Draft registration in San Francisco. The card indicates that Beadle was then living at the King George Hotel on 334 Mason Street and that he would soon be moving to 119 Central Avenue, in nearby Sausalito. Under "Description of Registrant" it notes that he's of medium height with a slender build, blue eyes, and gray hair. His occupation is listed as "Novelist."

[Age 37] (October?) 1918. Residing in Sausalito, CA.

[Age 37] 11 November 1918. End of World War I.

[Age 37] 15 March 1919. Publishes "Witch-Doctors" as a four-part serial in *Adventure* (March 15 to May 1, 1919). Later published as a book by Jonathan Cape (UK) and Houghton Mifflin (USA) in 1922.

[Age 37] 19 October 1919. Corresponds with novelist Theodore Dreiser while residing at 8 East 9th Street, in Manhattan. Source: University of Pennsylvania, Kislak Center for Special Collections, Rare Books and Manuscripts.

[Age 38] November 1919. Residing at 7, place de Tertre, Paris. Source: notice in *Adventure,* 3 December 1919, p. 188.

[Age 38] 8 January 1920. Spotted in Paris by the occultist Aleister Crowley: "I ran around Paris, and walked into Lapérouse for lunch to find Beadle and Willy!" ("Willy" was the Pulitzer Prize-winning journalist Walter Duranty.) Source: Aleister Crowley, *The Magical Record of the Beast 666. The Diaries of Aleister Crowley, 1914 – 1920* (London: Duckworth, 1972), p. 90.

[Age 38] 17 January 1920. Volstead Act goes into effect, prohibiting the manufacture and sale of alcohol in the U.S. The Prohibition Era continues until 1933.

[Age 38] 24 January 1920. Death of Modigliani.

[Age 38] 25 January 1920. Death of Modigliani's companion, Jeanne Hébuterne.

[Age 38] 3 March 1920. Residing at 7, place de Tertre, Paris. Source: *Adventure*'s "Ask Adventure" column ("A Free Question and Answer Service Bureau on Information on

Outdoor Life and Activities Everywhere and Upon the Various Commodities Required Therein"), p. 188. Beadle's entry reads: "Covering geography, hunting, equipment, trading, climate, mining, transport, customs, living conditions, witchcraft, opportunities for adventure and sport."

[Age 38] 3 August 1920. Residing in Westminster, London. Source: announcement in *Adventure*, August 3, 1920: "Care Society of Authors and Composers, Central Buildings, Tothill St., Westminster, London, England"; repeated in the 18 October 1920 and 16 March 1921 issues.

[Age 39] 21 February 1921. After *The Little Review* features excerpts of James Joyce's *Ulysses* in its 1920 issue, the magazine is successfully prosecuted for obscenity, effectively banning *Ulysses* from publication in the United States.

[Age 39] April 1921. Residing in Paris. Source: copy of a letter written by Beadle and featured in the 3 May 1921 issue of *Adventure*, pp. 174-175.

[Age 39] 1921. Death of Modigliani's lover Simone Thiroux, from tuberculosis.

[Age 39] 1921. Picasso portrays Max Jacob as a monk in his two oil paintings of the *Three Musicians*.

[Age 40] 2 Feb 1922. Sylvia Beach publishes Joyce's *Ulysses* in Paris.

[Age 40] June 1922. After being serialized in *Adventure* magazine, *Witch-Doctors* is issued as a book by Jonathan Cape.

[Age 40] 20 June 1922. A note in *Adventure* lists Beadle's location as Île de Lerne: a small island off the northwest coast of France in the Gulf of Morbihan.

[Age 44] 1925. Embarks from New York City and arrives in Paris.

[Age 45] April 1927. Publication of *The Blue Rib: A Romance of the Riviera* (London: Philip Allan and Co.).

[Age 45] August 1927. Residing in the vicinity of Nice. Source: letter to his niece Isabel.

[Age 46] 1928. D. H. Lawrence's *Lady Chatterley's Lover* is privately published in Florence. The novel is subsequently declared "obscene" and banned in Britain (until 2 November 1960) and in the United States (until 21 July 1959).

[Age 47] Fall 1928. Publication of *The Esquimau of Montparnasse* (London: John Hamilton), a satire about Parisian expatriates.

[Age 48] 29 October 1929. The stock market crash ushers in the Great Depression.

[Age 48] February / March 1930. *The Esquimau of Montparnasse* is republished as *Expatriates at Large* (New York: Macauley).

[Age 48] 18 May 1930. The *Sioux City Journal* features a photo of Beadle standing in profile in its review of *The Esquimau of*

Montparnasse, under the title: "Paris Quartier Latin Sans Romantic Gloss."

[Age 49] Circa 1931. Teaching English as a second language at the International School, 1, avenue St-Hilaire, Grasse, Côte d'Azur, France. Source: letter to his niece Isabel.

[Age 49] 19 February 1931. Residing in the vicinity of Nice. Source: letter to Isabel.

[Age 51] May 1933. Palais-Royal Press publishes *The White Gambit* in Paris.

[Age 52] 5 December 1933. End of Prohibition in America.

[Age 52] 1 September 1934. Jack Kahane's Obelisk Press publishes Henry Miller's *Tropic of Cancer*.

[Age 56] June 1938. Kahane publishes Beadle's *Dark Refuge*.

[Age 57] 1939. Repatriates to England and resides at 331 Homewood Road, St. Albans, Hertfordshire. Source: 1939 England and Wales Register. The National Archives; Kew, London; 1939 Register; Reference: RG 101/1668I.

[Age 57] 6 June 1939. Visits Aleister Crowley in Chiswick.

[Age 57] 2 September 1939. Jack Kahane dies from heart failure.

[Age 57] 3 September 1939. Two days after Germany invades Poland, both France and England declare war on Germany.

[Age 59] June 1941. Faber and Faber publishes *Artist Quarter,* pseudonymously coauthored with Douglas Goldring.

[Age 62] October 30 or 31, 1943. Death of Beatrice Hastings, who commits suicide in Worthing, Sussex. Shortly afterward Beadle and Goldring receive a manuscript from her estate: a surrealist novella titled "Minnie Pinnikin," written by Hastings in French, which dramatizes her relationship with Modigliani. According to Modigliani biographer Kenneth Wayne, the curator of the Museum of Modern Art, William Lieberman, was preparing for a 1951 exhibit of Modigliani's work "when he was put into contact with Goldring and Charles Beadle by the art historian Douglas Cooper," and "through them he obtained a copy of Minnie Pinnikin." Source: Kenneth Wayne, *Modigliani and the Artists of Montparnasse,* New York: Harry S. Abrams, 2002, p. 205.

[Age 62] 24 February 1944. The Gestapo arrest Max Jacob.

[Age 62] 5 March 1944. Jacob dies at the Drancy internment camp, two days before being shipped to Auschwitz.

[Age 63] 2 September 1945. End of World War II.

[Age 64] 7 August 1946. Birth of Elizabeth Owen Bely, daughter of Jane Owen Beadle and Igor Bely, in Bournemouth, England.

[Age 65] 10 June 1947. "Nameless Spy" appears in *Short Stories.*

Charles Beadle Publications

Literary and pulp fiction novels:

— *The City of Shadows: A Romance of Morocco*. London: Everett and Co., 1911.

— *A White Man's Burden*. London: Stephen Swift and Co., 1912.

— *A Passionate Pilgrimage*. London: Heath, Cranton and Ouseley: 1915.

— *Witch-Doctors*. London: Jonathan Cape, 1922. Boston: Houghton Mifflin, 1922.

— *The Blue Rib: A Romance of the Riviera*. London: Philip Allan and Co., 1927.

— *The Esquimau of Montparnasse*. London: John Hamilton, 1928. Later republished as *Expatriates at Large*. New York: Macauley Company, 1930.

— *The White Gambit*. Paris: Palais-Royal Press, 1933.

— *Dark Refuge*. Paris, Obelisk Press, 1938.

Nonfiction:

— *Artist Quarter: Reminiscences of Montmartre and Montparnasse in the First Two Decades of the Twentieth Century* (with Douglas Goldring). London: Faber and Faber, 1941. Published under the pseudonym "Charles Douglas." Later republished as *Artist Quarter: Modigliani, Montmartre and Montparnasse*. London: Pallas Athene Arts, 2018.

Short works of fiction and nonfiction in journals and periodicals:

— "Our Trip Down the Zambezi" (nonfiction). *The Wide World Magazine: An Illustrated Monthly of True Narrative, Adventure, Travel, Customs and Sport,* May 1907.

— "A Talk with the New Sultan of Morocco" (nonfiction). *Pall Mall Magazine,* October 1908.

— "What Has Happened to Muley Hafid" (nonfiction). *The Sphere,* 3 July 1909.

— "Two Close Calls" (nonfiction). *The Captain: A Magazine for Boys and "old Boys,"* June 1910.

— "My Narrow Escape From a Lioness." *The Brooklyn Daily Eagle,* "Junior Eagle" section (nonfiction), 7 August 1910.

— "In the Heart of the Kopje. A Story of the Mashonaland Rebellion." *The Wide World Magazine* (nonfiction), June 1912.

— "The Triumph of Tony." *Windsor Magazine,* July 1912.

— "The Better Man." *The London Magazine,* March 1913.

— "Romance for Sylvia." *Cassell's Magazine of Fiction,* March 1913.

— "A Decade of Christmas Dinners." *The Badminton Magazine of Sports and Pastimes* (nonfiction), December 1914.

— "A Pinch of Fever." *The Badminton Magazine,* June 1915.

— "An African Love Song." *The International,* October 1917. This piece appears to be a translation into English of a traditional African poem. (The same issue of the *International* features a lead story by Aleister titled "Cocaine.")

— "NQO," *The International.* December 1917.

— "The Palm Tree and the Window." *The International.* March 1918. (In the February issue of *The International,* under the feature "Jugging the March Hare," Editor Aleister Crowley remarked about this forthcoming tale: "Mr. Charles Beadle brought out his Eastern comedy, "The Palm Tree and the Window.")

— "A Doctor of Men. *The International.* April 1918. (In the March issue, under the title "April Showers of Amusement," Crowley writes: "Charles Beadle contributes a delightful sketch of life in the Latin Quarter of Paris with its curious mixture of religious fervor and debauchery."

— "The Christ-man." *Adventure,* 18 May 1918.

— "The Autocrat." *Everybody's,* June 1918.

— "The Idol of 'It.'" *Adventure,* 3 July 1918.

— "John O'Damn." *Adventure,* 3 August 1918.

— "The Double Scoop." *Adventure,* 18 August 1918.

— "The Cave." *Adventure,* 3 October 1918.

— "The Winged Avenger." *Adventure,* 18 October 1918.

— "The Black Lure." *Adventure,* 18 November 1918.

— A story in *The International*. December 1918. (In the November issue, in a feature titled "The Editor Boosts the Next Number, Aleister Crowley writes: "A story of African magic by Charles Beadle is really better than any of Kipling's African tales. That's going some, but it is true."

— "*Rabbit: Philosopher*" (novelette). *Adventure,* 18 January 1919.

— "Witch-Doctors" (novella). *Adventure,* 18 March 1919 (part one); 3 April 1919 (part two); 18 April 1919 (part three); 3 May 1919 (part four).

— "Uncle." *Ainslee's,* April 1919.

— "The Breaker of Idols." *Ainslee's,* May 1919.

— "Red Infidel" (novelette). *Adventure,* 18 May 1919.

— "Through Rabat's Eyes." *Argosy,* 2, 16, 19 August 1919.

— "The Tree of Life" (novella). *Adventure,* 3 August 1919.

— "The White Frog." *Adventure,* 18 August 1919.

— "Through Rabat's Eyes" (3-part serial). *Argosy,* 2, 9, 16 August 1919.

— "Captain Tristtam's Miracle." *Adventure,* 18 October 1919.

— "The Inner Hero." *Romance,* November 1919.

— "The Brothers." *Romance,* December 1919.

— "The Woman Courageous." *Ainslee's,* January 1920.

— "The Alabaster Goddess." *Adventure,* 3 January 1920.

— "Technique." *The Blue Magazine*), February 1920.

— "The Spell." *Adventure,* 18 February 1920.

— Untitled. *The Editor: The Journal of Information for Literary Workers* (nonfiction contribution to the forum "Contemporary Writers and Their Work." A discussion of Beadle's writing process), 25 February 1920.

— "An African Love Song." *Coterie* No. 4, 1920. (Reprinted from *The International,* October 1917.) The *Coterie* journal, a quarterly of art, prose, and poetry, boasted an impressive editorial board, including Conrad Aiken, T. S. Eliot, Richard Aldington, and Aldous Huxley. This particular issue features a poem by Douglas Goldring, who would later coauthor the book *Artist Quarter* with Beadle. It also hosts

work by several of these contributing editors, poetry by Amy Lowell, and drawings by Zadkine and André Derain.

— "The Singing Monkey" (novella). *Adventure*, 3 March 1920.

— "The Picture." *The Blue Magazine*, June 1920.

— "The King's Sword." *Adventure*, 3 August 1920.

— "The McIntosh" (novella). *Adventure*, 30 October 1920.

— "The Bowl of Alabaster." *Adventure*, 18 September 1920. (A sequel to "Alabaster Goddess.")

— "The City of Baal." *Adventure*, 18 January 1921.

— "Buried Gods," (novella). *Adventure*, 3 September 1921.

— "The Land of Ophir" (3-part serial). *Adventure*, 10, 20, 30 March 1922.

— "Gifts of Diamonds." *Adventure*, 20 June 1922.

— "The Lost Cure" (novella). *Adventure*, 30 January 1923.

— "Sparklers and the Rascals" (novella). *Top-Notch Magazine*, 1 March 1923.

— "The Ghost of Fat Lung." *Argosy Allstory Weekly*, 4 August 1923.

— "Toll of the Jungle." *Tip Top Stories of Adventure and Mystery*, January 1924.

— "The Alabaster Goddess." *The Regent Magazine,* June 1924. (Reprinted from Adventure, 3 January 1920 or 1921.)

— "The Philanthropist" (novella). *Short Stories.* 10 June 1924.

— "White Medicine." *Short Stories,* 10 August 1924.

— "The Blond Spiders" (novella). *Adventure,* 20 December 1924.

— "The Wild Man." *Short Stories,* 25 February 1925.

— "White Magic." *The Frontier,* March 1925.

— "Romance," *Adventure,* 20 April 1925.

— "The Mark of the Leopard." *Short Stories,* 10 May 1926.

— "Hashish," "Voyage," and "Small Body." Bob Brown. *Readies for Bob Brown's Machine.* (Cagnes-sur-Mer: Roving Eye Press, 1931), p. 105.

— "Black Velvet." *This Quarter.* March 1932.

— "The Idol." *Short Stories,* 10 October 1933.

— "Mr. Burnjack's Crime." *The 20-Story Magazine,* January 1935.

— "Magic Head." *Short Stories,* 25 October 1938.

— "The King of Many Voices." *Short Stories,* 10 November 1939.

— "The Explorer's Graveyard." *Short Stories,* 25 April 1941.

— "The Baboon's Paw." *Short Stories,* 10 December 1945.

— "Ant Island." *Short Stories,* 10 October 1946.

— "Lost Heritage." *Short Stories,* 25 December 1946.

— "Nameless Spy." *Short Stories,* 10 June 1947.

Posthumously reprinted stories and collections:

— *The City of Baal*. Introduction by John Locke. Castroville, CA: Off-Trail Publications, 2007.

— *The Land of Ophir*. Introduction by John Locke. Castroville, CA: Off-Trail Publications, 2012.

— *The Blond Spiders* (e-book). Good Press, 2020.

— *The Double Scoop* (e-book). DigiCat, 2022.

Commentary in *Adventure*'s "The Camp-Fire" column:

— 3 July 1918. A detailed five-paragraph autobiographical sketch, from which we can draw various threads from Beadle's early life, including childhood trips into Asia and various titles of employment later in Africa. (The letter was composed circa May 1918. See John Locke's "Introduction" to *The City of Baal,* p. 13.)

— 20 January 1918. A commentary on the walled cities of Zululand (with a passing reference to Sir Richard Burton).

— 3 October 1920. Describes the events that inspired "The McIntosh."

— 18 January 1921. Some remarks about "The City of Baal."

— 20 June 1922. Provides biographical background to "Gifts of Diamonds."

Commentary in *Adventure*'s "Ask Adventure" column:

— "Diseases of East Central Africa." 18 September 1918.

— "The Rhodesian Mounted Police." 18 September 1919.

Letter to *Romance* magazine's "Meeting-Place" forum:

— January 1920. Beadle remarks that "Personally I have a theory that a writer should only use material which he has more or less actually lived. Anyway, I work on that principle." And he adds: "That is all writing is (to me); a mania to tell other folk what I see in my walks abroad."

Reviews of Beadle's Novels

The City of Shadows (1911):

— *The Times* (London).

— *Manchester Courier*.

— *Daily Mirror* (London).

— *Westminster Gazette* (London), 11 March 1911, p. 1.

— *Croydon Chronicle and East Surrey* (London), 18 March 1911, p. 20.

— *Globe* (London), 7 April 1911, p. 6.

— *The Academy and Literature* (London), 6 May 1911, p. 555.

A White Man's Burden (1912):

— *The Athenaeum: Journal of Literature, Science, the Fine Arts, Music and the Drama* (London), 26 October 1912, p. 477.

— *The Scotsman* County (Midlothian, Scotland), 4 November 1912, p. 2.

A Passionate Pilgrimage (1915):

— *Freeman's Journal* (Dublin), 2 October 1915, p. 8.

— "Echoes from Everywhere: What Men and Women are Talking of." *Liverpool Echo*, 11 November 1915, p. 4. (A list of quotations from various books, including three from *A Passionate Pilgrimage*.)

<u>*Witch-Doctors* (1922):</u>

— *The Scotsman* (Midlothian, Scotland), 13 July 1922, p. 2.

— *The Times* (London), 28 July 1922, p. 13.

— *Punch* (London), 16 August, 1922, p. 168.

— "An American God." *Westminster Gazette* (London), 29 August 1922, p. 12.

— *The Province* (Vancouver), 30 August 1922, p. 6.

— *The Kingston Whig-Standard* (Kingston, Ontario), 2 September 1922, p. 4.

— *Calgary Herald* (Calgary, Alberta), 2 September 1922, p. 2.

— *The Topeka State Journal* (Topeka, Kansas), 9 September 1922, p. 8.

— *The News Journal* (Wilmington, Delaware), 9 September 1922, p. 8.

— *The Kansas City Star* (Kansas City, Missouri), 9 September 1922, p. 6.

— *Evening Public Ledger* (Philadelphia), 12 September 1922, p. 18.

— *Liverpool Post and Mercury*, 13 September 1922, p. 9.

— *New York Herald*, 17 September 1922, p. 19.

— *Buffalo Morning Express and Illustrated Buffalo Express* (Buffalo, New York), 17 September 1922, section 7, p. 4.

— "Fiction Snapshots," *New York Times Book Review and Magazine*, 17 September 1922, p. 7.

— *Buffalo Courier* (Buffalo, New York), 24 September 1922, p. 15.

— *New York Tribune*, 24 September 1922, section 5, p. 7.

— "Charles Beadle Tells Something about Himself." *Deseret News* (Salt Lake City), 30 September 1922, section 5, p. 3.

— *Detroit Free Press*, 15 October 1922, p. 12.

— *Daily Arkansas Gazette* (Little Rock, Arkansas), 15 October 1922, p. 4.

— *Hartford Courant*, 15 October 1922, p. 13.

— *Democrat and Chronicle Rochester* (Rochester, New York), 15 October 1922, unpaginated, section B.

— "The Witch Doctors." *Oakland Tribune* 15 October 1922, section S, p. 8.

— *The Chattanooga News*, 28 October 1922, p. 8.

— *Omaha Daily Bee*, 5 November 1922, p. 8.

— *The Buffalo Times*, 26 November 1922, p. 45.

The Blue Rib: A Romance of the Riviera (1927):

— *Aberdeen Press and Journal*, 21 April 1927, p. 3.

— *Montrose Standard* (Angus, Scotland), 22 April 1927, p. 6.

— *Birmingham Post* (West Midlands, England).

— *The Observer* (London), 15 May 1927, p. 8.

— *Sheffield Daily Telegraph* (Yorkshire, England), 11 June 1927, p. 10.

The Esquimau of Montparnasse (1928):

— *Sheffield Independent* (Yorkshire, England), 12 November 1928, p. 3.

— *Birmingham Daily Gazette* (Warwickshire), 22 November 1928, p. 3.

— *Northern Whig* (Antrim, Northern Ireland), 24 November 1928, p. 11.

Expatriates at Large (1930):

— *Argus-Leader* (Sioux Falls, South Dakota), 9 March 1930, p. 14.

— *Saturday Review of Literature,* April 1930).

— *Buffalo Evening News* (Buffalo, New York), 19 April 1930, p. 4.

— *Kansas City Star,* 19 April 1930, p. 8.

— *San Francisco Examiner,* 20 April 1930, p. 10 E.

— *Boston Globe,* 26 April 1930, p. 13.

— *Sioux City Journal* (Sioux City, Iowa), 18 May 1930, unpaginated. Features a photo of Beadle standing in profile.

— *The Minneapolis Star,* 3 June 1930, p. 15.

— *Birmingham News,* 8 June 1930, p. 4.

— *The Gazette* (Cedar Rapids, Iowa), 22 June 1930, p. 5 A.

— *New York Times Saturday Review of Books and Art,* 22 June 1930, p. 9.

— *St. Louis Post-Dispatch* (St. Louis, Missouri), 2 July 1930, p. 3 C.

— *Atlanta Constitution,* 3 August 1930, p. 8.

— *Detroit Free Press,* 17 August 1930, part four, p. 4.

— *Los Angeles Evening Post-Record,* 19 August 1930, p. 2.

— *Brooklyn Daily Eagle,* 10 September 1930, p. 18.

— *Book Review Digest*, 1931, volume 26, p. 62.

The White Gambit (1933):

— *The Daily Times-News* (Burlington, North Carolina), 10 June 1933, p. 2.

Artist Quarter: Reminiscences of Montmartre and Montparnasse in the First Two Decades of the Twentieth Century (1941):

— *The Observer* (London), 13 July 1941, p. 3.

— *Birmingham Post* (Birmingham, West Midlands, England), 22 July 1941, p. 2.

— *News Chronicle* (London), 1941.

— *Western Mail* (Cardiff, South Glamorgan, Wales), 5 August 1941, p. 2.

— *Time and Tide* magazine (London), 1941.

— *The Gazette* (Montreal), 29 November 1941, p. 21.

Bibliography

Alexandre, Paul. *The Unknown Modigliani: Drawings from the Collection of Paul Noël Alexandre*. New York: Harry N. Abrams, 1993.

Beadle, Charles. *A White Man's Burden*. London: Stephen Swift and Co., 1912.
— *The Esquimau of Montparnasse*. London: John Hamilton, 1928. Republished as *Expatriates at Large*. New York: Macauley Company, 1930.
— *Witch-Doctors*. London: Jonathan Cape, 1922. Boston: Houghton Mifflin, 1922.

Beadle, Charles. John Locke, ed. *The City of Baal*. Castroville, CA: Off-Trail Publications, 2007.
— *The Land of Ophir*. Elkhorn, CA: Off-Trail Publications, 2012.

Churton, Tobias. *Aleister Crowley in England*. Rochester, VT: Inner Traditions, 2022.

Diamond, Michael. *'Lesser Breeds': Racial Attitudes in Popular British Culture, 1890 – 1940*. New York: Wimbledon, 2006.

Douglas, Charles (aka: Charles Beadle and Douglas Goldring). *Artist Quarter: Modigliani, Montmartre and Montparnasse*. London: Pallas Athene Arts, 2018. (Originally published in London by Faber and Faber, 1941.)

Evans, Richard I. *Jung on Elementary Psychology: A Discussion between C. G. Jung and Richard I. Evans*. New York: Dutton, 1976.

Fifield, William. *Modigliani: The Biography*. New York: William Morrow and Company, 1976.

Ford, Hugh. *Published in Paris: A Literary Chronicle of Paris in the 1920's and 1930's*. New York: Collier Books, 1988.

Girodias, Maurice. *The Frog Prince*. New York: Crown, 1980.

Gray, Stephen. *Beatrice Hastings: A Literary Life*. Johannesburg: Viking / Penguin Books, 2004.

Hamnett, Nina. *Laughing Torso*. New York: Ray Long and Richard R. Smith, 1932.

Johnson, Benjamin; Erika Jo Brown, eds. *Beatrice Hastings*. Warrensburg, MO: Pleiades Press, 2016.

Modigliani, Jean. *Modigliani: Man and Myth*. New York: The Orion Press, 1958.

Pearson, Neil. *Obelisk: A History of Jack Kahane and the Obelisk Press*. Liverpool: Liverpool University Press, 2008.

Rodriguez, Suzanne. *Wild Heart, a Life: Natalie Clifford Barney's Journey from Victorian America to the Literary Salons of Paris*. New York: HarperCollins, 2002.

Saper, Craig J. and Eric B. White, eds. *Readies for Bob Brown's Machine: A Critical Facsimile Edition*. Edinburgh: Edinburgh University Press, 2020.

Secrest, Meryle. *Modigliani: A Life*. New York: Knopf, 2011.

Sichel, Pierre. *Modigliani: A Biography of Amedeo Modigliani*. New York: Dutton, 1967.

Warren, Rosanna. *Max Jacob. A Life in Art and Letters*. New York: W.W. Norton Company, 2020.

Washington, Peter. *Madame Blavatsky's Baboon: A History of the Mystics, Mediums, and Misfits Who Brought Spiritualism to America*. New York: Schocken Books, 1995.

Wayne, Kenneth. *Modigliani and the Artists of Montparnasse*. New York: Harry S. Abrams, 2002.

Appendix: Additional Materials

"Two Close Calls," The Captain: A Magazine for Boys and "old Boys," June 1910

I LEFT Toro (Fort Portal), my diary tells me, on the early morning of the fifth day of the New Year, 1906. I had been held up at this Government station for some three weeks, engaged in recruiting and registering fresh porters before crossing the border into the Congo. The Waganda men whom I had brought with me from Entebbe refused point-blank to entertain any idea of entering the country of the Bulamatadi, listening with ready ears to exaggerated tales of the horrors and distances. The Wunyoro, too, were averse to volunteering except at exorbitant rates, usually contenting themselves with doggedly shaking their heads and pretending not to know where such a country was. In many cases they were not lying, as few of them knew aught of any country outside their own districts; the country of the Bulamatadi, the Sudan, and Ulayi (Europe) being all vaguely classified together. At length, by means of judicious baksheesh to Kasagama, the "King," and the Kati-Kiro (prime minister), who would insist upon sitting on my bed in my tent whilst negotiating, succeeded in gathering a bunch of "volunteers." Then came the registering with the Government, at which chance they developed all manner of diseases and divers fantastic reasons why they should be excused.

At last tents were down, and the long line of the "Safari" streamed out past the small Indian bazaar towards the Crater camp, where it is usual to halt; but, considering that this place was in unhealthy proximity to Toro and my men's homes, I

pushed them on to the escarpment, a good twelve miles.

Late in the afternoon, I sat upon a convenient rock to enjoy one of the most magnificent sunsets to be seen the wide world over.

By noon next day we reached the Semliki River, and pitched camp upon the opposite bank. Ferrying the loads across occupied the rest of the day. 1 took my rifle and went off to shoot Pookoo – Uganda cob – and a few crocodiles. There was a good deal of buffalo about, so the natives told me; mostly in the foothills and to the southwest. They spoke true words, I discovered.

At two next morning I awoke the camp, and by dint of much blackguarding and calling of names, we got on the move by three. There was no moon, so I had lanterns carried at the head and tail and in the middle of the caravan. We swung along across the plain quite gaily for an hour and a half and were well amongst park bush and cactus. I glanced at my wristwatch, with a thought of calling a halt for the usual spell, when I heard a sudden commotion at the head of the line and noticed the headlight flying across an open space at right angles to the line of march. The middle light went out amid a chorus of yells, and I heard the thump of loads going down and the rustling of flying figures in the grass on both sides of me. The light near me also disappeared, while its bearer fled with an inarticulate yell. At the same moment I heard the sound of furious galloping. I dropped to the ground to get the objects against the skyline. Trees, bushes, and the flying head of a man were silhouetted against the stars; then a grayish mass with a glint of eyes appeared.

It was a charging buffalo!

For a moment I hesitated whether to shoot, fearing to hit any of the men in the darkness. The animal was almost on top of me when I fired hurriedly from the hip and fled away at right

angles, as with a snort the beast thundered past behind me. Running through the grass I kicked something soft, which grunted, as I fell head foremost into a bush. I scrambled out, scratched and torn, and sat still watching and listening. The cause of my fall was one of the porters in hiding. I whispered "Obani?" He mumbled something in Lunyoro which I could not understand.

Shouting was still going on some distance up the trail. The buffalo had apparently disappeared, but I knew of old that the animal in question has an inveterate habit of waiting quietly behind a bush and then suddenly charging, usually with disastrous effect to the unwary. Some bushes crackled near[by]. I jumped and peered, but could see nothing. I knew from the thud and snort after firing that I had wounded him, and wished that I had not been so hasty, as otherwise Mr. Buffalo might have gone peacefully on his way, while he would now be probably hanging about minus some blood and very angry.

The men kept shouting to one another at intervals. I heard Kagswa, my headman, asking where I was. I replied, and inquired where the buffalo was, but he did not know and said it was not safe to move in the dark. I asked him where *he* was. He replied, "Up a tree." As I laughed I heard a shriek close by, a snort and pad of hoofs, then a renewed outburst of shouts and inquiries. I felt very uncomfortable, every moment expecting the buffalo to wind me and charge.

I started out to crawl towards the nearest large tree. I dared not stand erect. I climbed up the tree and made myself as comfortable as possible. I could not see any signs of the buffalo; in the next tree was the dark shape of another porter. I tried to see the time, but could not. I shouted to Kagswa, and gradually picked up the voices of several others. A dismal voice came from away on my left. It was the cook; whilst telling his tale of woe his voice ceased abruptly in a stifled yell. The noise of pots

and pans clashing sounded. I shouted to the cook again, but could get no answer, and wondered if the beast had got him.

Hanging on to the tree, my limbs got stiff, but it did not seem healthy to wander about in the dark; moreover, I could do no good. I seemed to have been there hours, listening eagerly to an occasional shout of the carriers and the usual voices of the forest, when a faint flush began to appear in the east.

Gradually trees and things grew out of the gloom; in twenty minutes it was broad daylight. I laughed as I took stock of my immediate surroundings. Seven trees were fully occupied with human tenants, three or four in each tree; on the ground, huddled in impossible attitudes and peering about like scared apes, were five more men, one of whom was the cook, unhurt. Round and about, amongst the grass, were bales and boxes.

I climbed out of my perch, and inquired for the buffalo. Nobody knew exactly, but everyone was certain that he was not far away. Then rose a chorus of lament and fearful hairbreadth escapes. One man swore the buffalo had trodden upon him; another had been tossed; yet another declared that the beast had walked up, eyes glaring, and *smelt* him! By degrees the men began to drift in from all quarters of the compass, in various stages of blue funk. I walked round, keeping a wary eye open, I must confess, chaffing those who still clung to points of vantage.

After a while I began to grow confident that the beast had departed. I examined his spoor and searched for traces of blood, intending to follow him up, warily, and try my best to bag him. Under Kagswa's superintendence the men were collecting the discarded loads, and I started off with M'tandwa, my gun bearer, when suddenly a hubbub, preceded by a bloodcurdling yell, arose, and the men hurriedly began to select available trees.

I hesitated for a moment, threatened M'tandwa with unutterable penalties if he bolted with my reserve gun, and advanced

cautiously towards the sound of the first yell. We had passed through the next small glade when a man in a tree gesticulated, pointing beyond him. I gave a final glance at my gun breech and, motioning to the gun bearer to keep close in behind me, crept forward. Another man in a tree directed me, and, turning through a patch of bush, half expecting to be rushed at close quarters, I peered through the foliage. The man above got excited, and commenced to chatter. I turned to quiet him, when the rapid "s-s-s!" and pointing finger of M'tandwa drew my attention.

As I looked, I caught sight of the top of the buffalo's head over a clump of bush.

The idiot in the tree broke out again. Like lightning the buffalo whipped round through the intervening bush and, head down and eyes shining wickedly, charged. He had been standing at about forty paces.

I heard the sharp intake of breath of my gun bearer behind me as I brought my gun to my shoulder and felt for a firm stand. I half lowered the rifle, preferring to wait until the beast was clear of the bushes and their shadows. The rising sun behind me shone straight in his wicked eyes as he plunged across the open, lit up the points of my sights, and when within fifteen paces nearer than I had intended, I fired full above the eyes, just under the ruffle of his crest, and leapt aside. keeping my eyes upon him, I shouted for my second gun. There was no need. He crumpled up, shot through the brain, although the impetus of his charge carried him just beyond where I had stood to fire. M'tandwa stood well, putting the fresh gun in my outstretched hand as I watched the last convulsive twitches.

Soon there was much whooping and chanting as the natives gathered round the fallen beast. My cook was early on the scene, keen upon securing the tidbits for me – and himself. I had coffee made and proceeded to breakfast on fresh kidneys, whilst

the bearers sliced up the meat amongst them. Kagswa reported five loads missing. The delinquents were named and dispatched, with a headman, to find them on pain of forfeiting their share of meat plus the usual penalties. They found them.

II.

It was nine o'clock before the caravan got under way again, and only by the use of much breath, chaffing, bullying, and jeering did I succeed in persuading them to reach the village on the top of the Congo plateau. On the next hill to the east was the site of one of Stanley's famous camps, overlooking Lake Albert.

Many of Emin Pasha's old soldiers had settled down in this region; one of them was a titular chief of this village. I arrived there about four in the afternoon. It had been a stiff uphill climb in the broiling noonday sun all the way from the place of the buffalo episode.

During the rest of the afternoon the carriers arrived in twos and threes. For the last half mile the track wound round and up the side of a hill nearly as steep as the escarpment on the Uganda side, and I was deeply thankful to loll in the shade of a deserted mission house just outside the village stockade.

Some minutes elapsed ere the chief appeared, during which a considerable commotion ensued inside the village. At length he showed up, bearing a bowl of fresh milk, for which I blessed him, in kind as well as words. He had at first thought that I was a Belgian; later he diffidently explained that my approach had been noticed and that he had been busy sending off his flocks and herds to a safe health resort in the hills, but now it was all right. He didn't seem to like the Belgians somehow. He had just begun to explain that there was another white man there, when a voice said:

"Hullo! it's an Englishman!" and a tanned, stalwart figure,

clad in shirt and khaki slacks, advanced and shook hands.

We dined together sumptuously on buffalo steaks, and chatted far into the night, after the manner of the exile. He was engaged in trading and elephant shooting, and invited me to join in a hunt on the morrow. I accepted with alacrity. Kagswa was summoned and instructed to tell the men that we would not march in the morning. Kagswa delightedly bawled the news to the gorging savages spread in numerous rings around their respective fires.

About two in the morning we lay down to snatch a brief sleep. At four-thirty Kagswa awakened us, bringing coffee and biscuits, and, together with our friend the chief and three of his men, we left camp, and struck downhill to the west. A steady tramp of nearly an hour, mainly through dense forest – the fringe of the famous Ituri forests – and we came hot upon the spoor of our quarry. Several times as we marched we heard the crash of bushes and saplings, indicating their proximity. It was close upon sunrise when, from the top of a small hill, covered with eight-foot elephant grass, we saw vistas of herds and herds of elephants. The greatest danger in such a stiff country is when the herds, other than the one under consideration, take into their vast noodles to stampede. Several and distinct herds of elephants rushing excitedly about, in different directions, through stuff which is only as grass to them but like a Hampton Court maze to a human being, has sufficient potential sensations to titillate the most jaded of palates. An African elephant is as blind as a bat and as deaf as a post, figuratively speaking; so the obvious safety zone is not necessarily distance, but up wind.

To obtain this strategic position we maneuvered successfully, as regards our own particular herd; but the others interfered. Numerous avenues had been made by the passage of the brutes, the elephant grass standing like a wall on either side, criss-

crossed in every direction. We walked openly – that is, upright – in single file, and our guides led us to within two hundred yards of the selected herd. After a whispered consultation we crept forward cautiously, with M'tandwa and the chief in attendance, through a small belt of dense forest.

From the edge we could see about ten elephants, one quite close and apart from the others. All were standing up to their knees in swamp. Some, filling their trunks, spouted the water over their own broad backs; others tore off bunches of twigs; all were making a vast amount of noise, snorting and squelching about amid the crackling of young timber.

M'tandwa, who had left our side, suddenly reappeared to the right, signaling. We followed up a track, crouching. "Hiya," said the native, indicating the lonely one, "obaya sana" (She no good). "The King of elephants is quite close. Come!" We followed, plunging back into the forest. Presently there came a sibilant "s-s-s."

Peering through the interstices, we saw the heads and shoulders of several elephants. Lying flat in the grass we wriggled closer, dragging our guns along the ground. Another forty paces, and M'tandwa stopped, finger on lips, and slowly stood up under cover of a bush. Presently he signaled dumbly to my friend and Kagswa to go to the left, motioning myself to follow him. I did so. Then came another wriggle for sixty paces at right angles ere M'tandwa halted, peeped through the top of the grass, and grinned, opening wide his hands to indicate huge tusks.

I had placed wads in the muzzles of the rifles to protect them during the crawl through the swamp. I withdrew them and looked to the breeches of both. I was soaked to the skin, very muddy and scratched all over. Rising cautiously, I located the elephant indicated by M'tandwa. He was standing motionless, his huge tusks gleaming, about sixty paces away, and three-

quarters on; I dropped down and crawled around a little to improve my position.

I wondered how the others were progressing. I dared not delay my shot for fear he might move or go away. Drawing a very careful site on almost the rim of his huge ear, and low down, I fired. I heard the dull thud of the impact. Simultaneously another shot rang out not far away, and then came shrill trumpetings and a crashing of saplings and bushes. My beast had disappeared, apparently swallowed up by the earth.

I started forward to explore when M'tandwa, his face a dirty ash color, caught my arm.

"Listen! Said he, indicating the rear of our position. I did so; and suddenly became conscious that the trumpeting and crashing had increased to a pandemonium which came from all around us. *All the elephants in the valley had stampeded in different directions, and we were in the center!*

I did not know what to do and felt myself go icy cold.

"Upesi! Miti! Upesi!" (Quick! The trees!) cried M'tandwa. We ran back, slipping and stumbling in the elephant tracks, to the nearest trees. Halfway there, the screaming and the crashing increased in volume right ahead of us. Then out of the gloom of the forest charged a herd of elephants, trunks up, shrieking in blind fright, young trees and bushes bowing down before them like an asparagus bed before a lawn roller. It was worse than useless to fire; one might as well have attempted to stop an avalanche. M'tandwa yelled, flung down my spare rifle and fled to the right. I hesitated; then followed suit in the opposite direction.

No sooner had I commenced to run, or flounder, than I lost my nerve completely. I believe I yelled, too, in my agony of fright. The whole universe seemed full of leviathans intent upon stamping me to death. I imagined the black stinking ooze being forced into my mouth and ears. I saw myself after, a mere

indistinct jumble of mud, blood and grass. I fell several times in the huge footprints. I lost the perspective of things; I seemed to have been racing for miles and miles; I became horribly conscious that one of my leggings was undone; then the vast, thundering army behind seemed to loom over me, and I shrieked with terror.

A sudden stumble; a vision of black-brown hides, trees, sky; a splash, and cold water closed over my head. I had fallen into a pool or elephant wallow. I crawled out, gasping, and lay in a tumbled, panting heap half out of the pool of mud and water, trembling with fright and shock, whilst the crashing of bushes all about me sounded like thunder in my ears.

At length the hubbub subsided. I lay where I was, too scared to move. My nerves had completely gone for the time being. I literally jumped at every sound. After a while I started to shout, and at length was answered by Kagswa.

The elephant I had fired at lay dead some distance away. My friend and Kagswa had had ample time to climb into a large tree, from the branches of which they shot two more. As for M'tandwa – alas! the elephants who missed the master did not miss the man.

Commentary in *Adventure*'s "Camp-Fire" column, 20 January 1918

HERE is some more about the walled cities of Zululand, from Charles Beadle of our writers' brigade who, as you will note, has wandered from the States to Paris:

Paris, France.

Dear Camp-Fire:

W. E. Keever's article on the walled cities of Zululand is particularly interesting to me as I happen to have been in the Niekerk Zimbabwe district – (Inyanga – The Spell: Motokos – The White Frog) and he gives me much information which I did not know. The currently accepted theory there – among whites of course – is that it is the work of the Phoenician or else of Arabic origin built or taught by Arab slave raiders from the north.

AS I have seen them and camped among 'em, they covered several acres at a time as if they were the ruins of a small town: triangles and squares of *stone* walls usually about a foot or two high – said conformation suggesting that some crazy giant had been teaching Euclid and illustrating the propositions for the benefit of his pupils. On the tops, too, of kopjes – usually granite and boulder-strewn – were what had been decidedly fortifications: walls remaining breast high with vents for arrows – equally useful for rifles. Upon the side of hills were terraces built up by stone suggesting the terraced vine hills of Greece. On the back of the Inyanga station on a rough kopje was quite an extensive old fortification which we adapted and rebuilt as a fort. "Old workings" of gold mines are all over Rhodesia from Tuli (Big Zimbabwe) in the south to the Ruania River in the North and, as the Britannica says, are now operated with profit.

PERSONALLY I cannot swallow the idea that

ever the Bantu progressed as far as building these structures or mining as illustrated there. I have almost a conviction that Solomon or some of the Pharaohs sent their people right down through Uganda, etc., to Rhodesia by *land* and not fleets by sea. Certainly in comparatively modern times Arabs from as far north as the White Nile came down through or round Abyssinia as far south as this, slave raiding as they did upon the other side of Africa, Dongola and Barotseland. I think it is quite conceivable that, say, Solomon's parties would establish distant camps as the Romans did where they would teach their native slaves to build houses as they knew them; for certainly they would remain there some time after such a trip, say, from Egypt.

NOW there is no trace that I have ever heard of the Bantu constructing anything like such permanent dwellings. The Baganda were renowned upon discovery – first I think by Burton although I am not sure. Or was it Baker Pasha? – for the fact that they, a Bantu race, made more or less real roads, broad, and with bridges across swamps etc. If such an advanced race of the Bantu existed, where has it disappeared to? And why? Africa is fairly well explored now. There cannot remain a sufficiently large area unknown as to provide a safe hiding-place for this super-Bantu tribe – and report of such doings and things would spread for many hundreds of miles. I cannot even imagine a plausible theory to account for their having been wiped out. The men who made those ancient dwellings must have been equally advanced in the

arts of war.

Another point: the setting of the sites surrounded with fortified kopjes gives quite the sense of men living in an occupied territory. The baptismal records of the Dominicans mentioned by Mr. Keever do not, I think, dispose of the theory of a ruling or a different race for the "powerful king" might well have been a titular king – the Sultan of Morocco at the present moment is Mulai Ali Mohammed (I *think*, for they change so darned quick out there!) but the French are the rulers all the same.

However I wonder whether someone else can put forward a more plausible theory.

– Chas. Beadle.

From the "Ask *Adventure*," 18 September 1918

"Diseases of East Central Africa"

Question: – "I have knocked about considerably in various countries and it has long been my desire to visit the "dark continent." I have roughed it a great deal, am a good shot, etc., etc.

(1) "What are health conditions around and between Lakes Tanganyika and Victoria? That is, is it a healthy region?

(2) From an African point of view is it heavily forested?

(3) Is game more or less abundant there than in other parts of the interior? Especially large game, *i.e.*, of cat and herb-eating species?

(4) Can one live off the country outside medicinal and other necessities not furnished by nature?" – W.E.C., Belmore, Ohio.

Answer, by Mr. Beadle: – (1) Health conditions between Lakes Tanganyika and Victoria are fairly bad. Malaria, spirillum, blackwater, and sleeping sickness are the principal diseases. In case you are not familiar with these I will explain briefly, taking it for granted that you know what malaria is.

Spirulam is given to man by the bite of a tick and produces a fever very like malaria, but quinine has no effect; it lasts some time and knocks you out, leaving the patient usually very weak, but never have I heard of it being fatal.

Blackwater is violent inflammation of the kidneys (it is a matter of dispute whether blackwater is the result of excessive malaria or not) resulting in the urination of blood (hence the name). Very often fatal as the patient dies of heart failure. Medicines are calomel and purge thoroughly (stop quinine), and as much champagne and brandy as the patient will take with the object of keeping up the heart's action, on which everything depends. If you get blackwater once and get over it my advice is to clear out of the country.

Sleeping sickness is given by the bite of the tsetse fly (rather like a horsefly with the wings crossed). First produces a slight fever, headaches, etc., and perhaps vomiting, afterward affects the nervous system with the result that patient becomes restless, irritable and indifferent by turns until finally he lapses into a coma – sleep – attendant with anemia and a general wasting away. There is no cure yet discovered. The percentage of these flies with the germ in them ready for business is reckoned to be about two per cent.

But still don't run away with the idea that the country is fatal. I've lived there and the only thing I collected was malaria and not much of that.

(2) From a general African point of view it is fairly wooded. That is[,] compared to the Congo forests the forest there is slight and variable. There are uplands with open rolling country and scrub.

(3) Game (large) is fairly abundant but varies greatly. Stretches without game at all and in other parts extremely thick – of both sorts.

(4) No, you cannot reckon on living off the country. Chickens, eggs, and sometimes goats and milk are obtainable at villages by trading – if the natives happen to be friendly and they usually are if you know the way to go about it. Game is too erratic to rely upon. One week you may have enough to feed a caravan to gorging and the next not enough for a dog, and as for said villages there are large tracts uninhabited. Sometimes you can get sweet potatoes, but rarely in my experience. And Nature's supply of food for man, white men particularly, is conspicuous by its absence in most of Africa.

From "Ask *Adventure*," 3 November 1918

"Travel in Upper Congo"

THIS inquirer puts thirteen questions to our expert with regards to people and things in that region of Africa made famous by Stanley and Livingstone. Here's hoping the number of his queries won't hoodoo his expedition:

Question: – "I am a young man interested in taking a trip to the Upper Congo in Africa, and would like the following information –

"1. – What are the opportunities for adventure?

"2. – How are the customs and living conditions?

"3. – What are the chances for big-game hunting?

"4. – What kind of an outfit should be taken?

"5. – Are there any working opportunities?

"6. – What kind of languages must one have at command?

"7. – Is witchcraft in practice yet in Africa?

"8. – Where could I get a map of Africa?

"9. – How much is the fare from New York?

"10. – Which is the best way to go from New York?

"11. – What are the methods and materials of Summer and Winter subsistence?

"12. – What is the best remedy for poison-snake bites?

"13. – Could outfits be bought in Africa?" – William F. Feser, Brooklyn, New York.

Answer, by Mr. Beadle: –

1. – Every chance for adventure with animals and man, crocodiles and flies.

2. – I take it you mean white man's customs. Practically only Belgian officials in the country (who are composed of nearly every nationality in Europe). You carry your own chow, canned goods; live on them, chickens and eggs (when you can) and game (when you can). There are no stores in Upper Congo as all trading is governmental.

3. – One of the finest elephant countries in Africa; also large game of all descriptions. But all game is preserved. You have to get a special license for elephant. As far as I recollect the license is about the same as on the British side: two hundred and fifty dollars for two male elephants, which carries with it about two of every species of buck.

4. – See Answer 13.

5. – Practically none. Both jobs on the Kilo mines and all others are given (or were) from Brussels.

6. – French absolutely necessary; if staying in country have to learn Kiswahili, otherwise you will always be at the mercy of a highly paid interpreter.

7. – Yes. Not to the extent that it was in districts that are under immediate white supervision; but there are vast tracts that are not.

8. – New York Public Library; to buy one go to Brentano's and ask for section maps of Upper Congo. The French are the best.

9. – Impossible to say as all steamship prices are altered now. But remember that after reaching the mouth of the Congo you have half a thousand miles by river-boat to Stanleyville or some other jumping-off place and then another half a thousand through the forests. To get to the Upper Congo that way I should say roughly would swallow most of the small change out of five hundred dollars. If you went round to the east coast, up the Uganda Railway and across Uganda the trip would be easier but not less expensive.

10. – Again impossible to say in present conditions. If possible go to the Canaries and get a Holt or Elder-Dempster boat down the coast. Rest of the trip answered in 9.

11. – There is no Winter or Summer in tropics as we know them here. Two rainy seasons, but temperature much alike all the year 'round. Rest answered in 2.

12. – I don't know of any sure remedy. Sometimes alcohol will pull a man through; chief endeavor is to keep him awake at all costs.

13 (and 4). – Rot-proof tent, camp-bed and bar, medicine-chest, helmet or Tirai hat, usual tropic whites and khaki hunting-clothes, battery of light and heavy rifle, revolver are the chief points. On east, north, and south coasts you can buy outfits, and I suppose on the west, although I cannot say for

sure as I have never been there. Ask Mr. Miller, Section 22 of "Ask Adventure" if you intend to go.

Hope this is useful to you although I'm afraid that it isn't very encouraging.

From "Ask *Adventure*," 18 September 1919

"The Rhodesian Mounted Police"

HERE'S a good service for those who've had a taste of war, and like it, as so many of the fellows do:

> *Question:* – "I should like to get some information concerning the Rhodesian Mounted Police, especially concerning the work they do. I should also like to obtain the titles of any books written about them. If this letter is published in *Adventure* please withhold my name." –, 33rd Inf., Gatun, C.Z.

Answer, by Mr. Beadle: – The Rhodesian Mounted Police are the British South African Police with headquarters at Buluwayo and Salisbury, South Rhodesia. They are military police; mounted but usually on foot by reason of the horse sickness. Mostly stationed at posts on the *veld,* where they patrol among the natives and assist in collecting hut tax, etc.; arrest cattle thieves, odd murderers, etc. Those in towns do patrol through town and

reservations (forestry, farms, etc.). Some stations are fairly healthy; others rotten with malaria. Pay: troopers, five shillings per diem. Commissions through ranks; except for O.C.'s, usually seconded for service from the regulars. At one time used regularly to be provided with rebellions; but this practice has become unfashionable of late years.

I am speaking of the police in my day – about 1900. Since the Boer War they have probably – I have not heard so – been incorporated with the South African Constabulary (Transvaal and Orange Free State – that is, Orange River Colony now). Baden–Powell wrote a book on them in the early days, but have no means of looking up title here. For information apply to Secretary, the British South African Chartered Company, London Wall, London, G.B.

Hope this is of service. If other details are required, write me. But I have no up-to-date information.

Letter to *Romance* magazine, January 1920

CHARLES BEADLE, who wrote "The Inner Hero" for our November issue, also writes this greeting from Paris:

> ALLAH yahdik O Romance! as the Arabs would say. However, that's another side of my life than the milieu of "The Inner Hero." Personally I have a theory that a writer should only use material

which he has more or less actually lived. Anyway, I work on that principle. I was born at sea somewhere in mid-Atlantic and my people have been seafaring on both sides for some generations back; two grandfathers were North Sea Whalers – which doesn't in the least prove that I know anything about it you will probably say! Well, the tang of the sea seems good to me and I will defy any storm on any ship on any sea to make me seasick. The most exhilarating spectacle in the Universe to me is a storm at sea – preferably in mid-Atlantic – my native heath! Naturally I met with sailors and firemen of all sorts in my kidhood, but the principal material for this story was gained during an abortive attempt to become a marine engineer; about twelve months in the "shops" which persuaded me, incorrectly enough, that there was no romance in greasy pistons, valves and what not and set me wandering in Africa for a decade. I'm afraid that this confession won't convince anyone that I really lived that life; that I have done more than walk through a portion of it as it were. But then the whole point depends on what one can see in that walk, the possession of the "seeing eye" as Conrad has it. After all, baldly speaking, that is all writing is (to me); a mania to tell other folk what I see in my walks abroad. As Arnold Bennett, I think, pointed out once, the primitive novelist is the man who insists upon telling all his pals, often, to boredom, about the astonishing dog fight he has seen in the street.

Charles Beadle.

Beadle's contribution to the forum "Contemporary Writers and Their Work," *The Editor: The Journal of Information for Literary Workers* (NJ: Ridgewood), 25 February 1920

To recall the conception of the idea of "The Inner Hero" (*Romance* for November)* is difficult. It is one of a series of sailor and fireman stories conceived some years ago, and with the exception of two others abandoned. I think that I may express myself better if I speak generally rather than particularly, for as I have said, I can scarcely recall the genesis and parturition of this story, although it was born actually in New York. Usually I decide upon what class of mankind and in what environment I am going to ponder in search of an idea – too often, I regret to say, influenced by what I imagine will stand a sporting chance of selling: sometimes they sell; sometimes they don't; there are other gorgeous moments when intoxicated by a check – and rarer ones when I don't give a damn whether the heavens fall or the price of coal goes up – that I defy the gods by writing what I damn well please; they do not sell … except, in justice I must admit, with a few exceptions. Well, to continue; having decided upon a character or characters, usually based upon some person I have bumped against – maybe for for merely ten minutes – I seek a natural environment and his probable circumstances, male and female, I set them, as it were upon a stage in my mind. Then when they have become "real" I obtain an illusion that they are and merely sit down and record what they "insist" upon doing. I say "insist" because frequently when I, playing god, choose a nice comfortable and orthodox end for them they refuse to obey me, and as I have sunk into merely the position of reporter, the result is usually lamentable as far as editors and my bank account are concerned.

This account of writing "The Inner Hero" may not be accounted of much use to would-be writers (there is no

inference in the phrase for I am merely a would-be writer; I merely mention the fact because association brings to my mind cheap sneers which have been perpetrated), but if you will permit me to say, said account may teach more than a dozen "How to write short stories" instructions. That is to say that one can write or one cannot write and no amount of instructions will teach a man or woman. Again, that is to say that I do not mean anything about divine afflatus. To me as I see it – if you will again permit me to lapse into the "ideal world" – there is a métier for everyone. One man can make chairs perfectly or nearly so; another design bridges and engines; another make money – the least of all! The trouble is that there are so many chair makers trying to write short stories and many story writers trying to make chairs. Am I a chair maker or a story writer? Damned if I know! I'm trying to find out. Personally, as I am vain, I think that I could make chairs; but I don't think that the third chair would interest me much.

Well, experiences as a writer: I began when I was 28 or 29. I was stuck in the center of Morocco, isolated, and finding a library abandoned by – well, no names, no pack drill! – I read to pass the time, novels, and became so bored with them that I swore that if I could not write a better yarn than those in particular I would eat my hat and other clothes! Since then I have been trying to avoid eating my hat, etc. Personally, I don't think that I am called upon to do so. I began a novel there and finished it in London when I returned – broke; and being broke took it into my head that I would be a writer or bust! Every publisher in London turned it down; Public won't stand for it, etc. A friendly critic said to me, "Stick your tongue in your cheek, old man, and write something to please 'em!" I did. First publisher to whom it was offered gave special terms. My hoary aunt, I actually made money! Not much, but real money! That book is selling in cheap edition. I sat down again to write

"something that would please 'em!" Then occurred the process to which I have already referred. My "creations" would not obey their god (how very human). They would insist upon making a tragedy of it. After the fourteenth publisher I took to sending it round in couples. Two publishers, young, made an offer simultaneously. I accepted the better offer. My publisher on the day of publication eloped to Morocco with his typist and incidentally the firm's funds – and a few months afterwards the other fellow was in gaol for embezzlement. Fate "got me going and coming," as they say!

On further reflection, recalling the process of story making seems more difficult than ever. What I have already said is fundamentally true. I may add that the character, the atmosphere or the "meaning" of the story attracts me. The great thing that I am incapable of understanding is "plot." Personally, plot does not interest me in the least. It is merely the hobby horse on which to hang the clothes, but I do not feel that I need a hobby horse.

That's all there is to it. A cinema has need of a plot. Writing has not (I didn't say literature; I don't like the word and I am not a literateur. I am a writer. What's the matter with the word anyway?). The cinema – as it is now – cannot utilize the cadence of words, the nuances, the motivating psychology – except in very primitive form. (Uproar! Good!)†

As one editor was kind enough to say to me: We don't care a damn about atmosphere writing, psychology; we want a plot!

Bien!

A publisher who played the young girl with the petals, He loves me! He loves me not! business remarked upon the "faulty construction" of a manuscript. "What," said I, "do you mean by construction?" After vague explanations I saw a great light. "A-ah!" I cried, "plot you mean! "Oh, well," said he, "that's what the lowbrows call it!"

Well, the snow is here and no coal is nigh, but life's rather ridiculous, isn't it?

---

* Beadle's story, "The Inner Hero," published in *Romance* magazine, November 1919.
† Beadle is referring to the placards or "subtitles" used in silent films from the mid-1890s to the late 1920s.

Commentary in *Adventure*'s "Camp-Fire," 3 October 1920

SOMETHING from Charles Beadle about the facts back of his novelette ["The McIntosh"] in this issue:

Paris, France.

> This yarn was suggested by a real episode perpetrated by a bunch of the British South African Police who came down to Beira on leave, got in a mix-up and actually put the police in their own jail and then played Old Harry with the town. The torturing stunt is not in the least exaggerated, nor the possibilities on the Beira railway. It's great, that rail. Coming down from Beira, our train pulled up in the open veldt. Got out to see what was up. A Scotch engineer and the Irish conductor had worked up a dispute *en route* and, with the passengers forming a ring, fought it out. Then we continued peaceably. Another time someone spotted a lion. We stopped the train and

everybody joined in the hunt – for some hours, for we didn't get him after all.—Charles Beadle.

Commentary in *Adventure*'s "Camp-Fire," 18 January 1921

A WORD from Charles Beadle about his novelette in this issue ["The City of Baal"]. Also something of interest in connection with one of his former stories in our magazine:

Paris, France.

The source of the story is obvious to anyone who happens to recollect the short Camp-Fire discussion about Phoenician ruins in Rhodesia. I had had the nucleus of the idea in my head for some while but that kind of stirred it up, fertilized it as it were.

By the way, came across an item today that weirdly enough corroborates the possibility of the Alabaster Goddess and the Bowl of Alabaster. It is a report of an expedition which has just been completed through the very corner near the Gamballagalla or Ruenzori range of mountains. I quote:

"From Kigezi the expedition set out for Banyoro ... but instead of retracing its steps struck out a new route moving westward ... turned northward and followed the line of these lakes and Albert Lake. Some of the scenery in this little known

country … was found to be beautiful beyond description, comprising crater lakes surrounded by tropical vegetation of wonderful luxuriance. *The people, cut off from the world live happily in ignorance of their fellows a few miles distant.* In this African Arcadia … met the Bakunta, the descendants of a few Baganda who many years ago killed a prince in battle and fled their country to escape the avengers of blood." – *Man.* June, 1920, The Mackie Ethnological Expedition to Central Africa.

– Charles Beadle.

Commentary in *Adventure*'s "Camp-Fire," 20 June 1922

SOMETHING from Charles Beadle concerning the facts back of his complete novelette ["Gifts of Diamonds"] in this issue:

Île de Lerne, France.

The mechanism of this yarn – not the story – was suggested by Poe's "MS Found in a Bottle." I wanted to develop that and work out other methods of getting over a communication from a man or men tied up in a hopeless knot which was bound to lead to the final dive.

THE inner yarns on which the plot, if you like, is founded are historical, the strangulation of the priests by the Monomatapa, a chief who did reign

over an empire as told in the story. The center of his kingdom was in ancient times in the Mazoc valley, Southern Rhodesia, and his lineal descendant is now called Mudojumbo and he lives on the Urania. I've met him in Police days and he it was who was responsible for nearly all the Mashona Rebellions.

The dogs Kopman and Oompie I had on an exploring trip with me. When passing the Zambesi I had to leave one behind because of the fly and regulations, and when I returned, I found the beast madder than ever, stuck on an island in the middle of the river because the Boer with whom I had left him was scared to death of him. Also the *Wheeler* in this story is drawn from the life of a man once on safari with me, the incident of Oompie following Kopman outside and the threat to shoot me and afterward the fantastic challenge to a duel at a hundred yards with elephant guns! Yet that chap was one of the best – in civilization. Afterward, off safari, we were great pals, but never again as a partner on the trail, thanks! –

Charles Beadle.

Letter from Isabel Beadle to her uncle Charles

Dear Uncle,

I must say I was very much surprised to get your news, for as you know I was not aware that I had a cousin in France. Someday I hope to meet her, although I send all my wishes for her happy marriage. I can neither come over to France nor act as a member of the *Conseil de famille*, nor do I feel confident to act in that capacity in any way, knowing nothing whatever of the circumstances of all the parties involved. I feel anyway that you and you only as her father can judge whether [illegible] can bring her happiness.

Your affectionate niece,
Isabel Beadle

Letter from Charles Beadle to his niece Isabel

c/o Barclays Bank
Promenade des Anglais
Nice

? August 1927

My Dear Girl,

You don't seem to realize that I'm very, very old, and in consequence nothing surprises me. Your blots and smudges are a delight but […] little uncle is not. Don't like relatives. Never did. Haven't seen or heard of any for 20 years and now you bob up! Well, don't. I'll accept you as human animals – perhaps intelligent, perhaps not […]

What's all this snobbery about crests? I know a pretty good coal merchant who has a few million whose sole ambition is to sell trucks of coal who also is Charles Beadle and comes from Barking.

About your sketches – send me some. *But* Balham doesn't sound good. Reminiscent of esses and an accent. Hope neither of you have the latter? Re: book covers, nothing doing ([…] for your sweet benefit). That's all my publishers' job. I'll give you an introduction perhaps, but that'll be about as much use as a match in hell. (Are you permitted to say hell? This is important.)

How old are you two now? [Referring to Isabel's sister Barbara.] I can't add up – not even a bill, much less pay it. Are you the new generation? Tell me. Why go in for Art in teaching? Why not some other form of slavery? Marriage for instance. I hear Lady Astor wants to pension wives at 60. Rotten. Go to the States. Then you can divorce your husband after 6 months and

have a pension for the rest of your life. Oh boy I wish I were a gal.

As for news as I told you I don't know any relatives respected (none have any money as far as I know) or otherwise … I'm a savage. Savages may not look at their mother-in-laws and the Esquimaux bury alive their old people when they become a nuisance. Excellent. That's why I won't recognize you as relatives. Send me your sketches and tell me all about yourselves.

CB

Letter from Charles Beadle to his niece Isabel

Thanks sweet lass for a great disappointment! I was rejoicing after my fashion as Dowson might say* at being considered an imposter posing as the great writer Charles Beadle! Have had a copy of C-of-S [*City of Shadows*] weeks ago from a friend in London, but cinema people won't bite. I have been and am exceedingly busy, trying to do several things at once. So I have little or no head for writing letters. Excellently sweet of you to "admire" C-of-S, but personally I think it's just rotten. I've never yet written anything worth a damn that [...] brought me sixpence. The best things are seldom if ever published. Commerce and art! No, Sirrah, to quote the great bore Dr. Johnson. One of these days when I'm [...] I'll publish or at any rate have printed [...] Mss. which amuse me and promise to [...] you a copy, but when that great day for the human race will be "lies in the tomb of eternity" as Marie Corelli or Michael Arlen [...] have written –

an extremely awkward condition as among many other professions I am no midwife.

Be sweet and gracious and write me expecting no reward and send me your photos.

Love, if I may make so bold as the pirate said, to both of you.

CB

---

* Ernest Christopher Dowson (1867 – 1900), English poet associated with the Decadent movement, principally remembered for three lines culled from his poems: "I have been faithful ... in my fashion," "Gone with the wind" (both from "Non Sum Qualis eram Bonae Sub Regno Cynarae"), and "Days of wine and roses" (from "Vitae Summa Brevis").

CPSIA information can be obtained
at www.ICGtesting.com
Printed in the USA
BVHW040229060323
659697BV00006B/57

9 781736 004937